NATURAL HISTORY OF INFECTIOUS DISEASE

VACCINIA VIRUS

NATURAL HISTORY OF INFECTIOUS DISEASE

BY

SIR MACFARLANE BURNET

O.M., M.D., F.R.S., *Nobel Laureate*

Director of the Walter and Eliza Hall Institute
Melbourne

THIRD EDITION

CAMBRIDGE
AT THE UNIVERSITY PRESS
1962

PUBLISHED BY
THE SYNDICS OF THE CAMBRIDGE UNIVERSITY PRESS

Bentley House, 200 Euston Road, London, N.W.1
American Branch: 32 East 57th Street, New York 22, N.Y.

First Edition	1940
Second Edition	1953
Reprinted	1959
Third Edition	1962

First published under the title:
Biological Aspects of Infectious Disease

Printed in the United States of America

CONTENTS

PART IV

THE NATURAL HISTORY OF INFECTIOUS DISEASE

PART V

SOME IMPORTANT INFECTIOUS DISEASES

PART VI

EPILOGUE

FIGURES

PREFACE TO THE THIRD EDITION

Since this book was first written nearly twenty-five years ago, the whole outlook on infectious disease has changed remarkably. At that time the possibility of almost complete control of infectious disease was fully recognized but the process of realizing that control had only just started to accelerate into the modern phase. We were in the midst of a period of exciting biological discoveries and just ahead were the even more important discoveries of the antibiotics and the synthetic insecticides.

Today these discoveries have been effectively applied and at times one feels that to write about infectious disease is almost to write of something that has passed into history. There are still problems, however, and we can never forget that the apparent impotence of infectious disease over most of the world depends wholly on the maintenance of the structure of civilization and the intelligent and continuing application of the discoveries of the past.

Since the publication of the second edition in 1953 there have been notable advances in many fields. The viruses of trachoma and of the common cold have been isolated, vaccines against polio have been proved effective and in 1957 a new pandemic of influenza threw light on the vastly more lethal pandemic of 1918.

Immunology has changed its accent and with the emergence of selection theories of antibody production, at least as much interest is being devoted to cellular aspects as to antibody.

By far the most striking development, however, is the precipitate fall in death rates from infection. In most advanced countries deaths from tuberculosis fell by 1957 to ten or twenty per cent of what they were in 1946, thanks essentially to chemotherapy. Malaria is rapidly coming under control and even its elimination from the globe is being spoken of. As a result the threat of overpopulation, especially in Asia, has become the most important social and political problem of our times.

I have tried to incorporate the new material without increasing the size of the book and most of the chapters have been extensively rewritten.

F. M. BURNET

Melbourne
January 1962

ACKNOWLEDGEMENTS

I am indebted to Messrs I. M. Dawson and A. S. Macfarlane, of the National Institute for Medical Research, London, for permission to reproduce the electron micrograph of vaccinia virus, and to Dr J. H. L. Cumpston for allowing me to use data from his histories of infectious disease in Australia for the construction of Table I and Figs. 4 and 6 (in part). Fig. 7 is reproduced from the *Proceedings of the Royal Australasian College of Physicians*.

Part I

BIOLOGICAL CONSIDERATIONS

CHAPTER I

THE ECOLOGICAL POINT OF VIEW

Infectious disease is, and always has been, part of the everyday experience of life. In every generation men of affairs have had to cope as best they could with the practical problems it presents, while priests, philosophers, and, later, scientists have had perhaps the harder task of interpreting the significance of such disease in accordance with the intellectual outlook of their time. Over most of the historical period, the human attitude to epidemics and the other aspects of infectious disease was a curious mixture of erroneous theory with a good deal of useful common sense. On the practical side, we must remember that the contagiousness of some of the more easily recognized diseases like plague and leprosy was well understood in the Middle Ages, and logically planned measures to prevent or minimize epidemics were attempted. The institution of quarantine for travellers from infected regions by the Venetians in 1403 may be instanced, while a general recognition of the association of disease with civic filth and personal uncleanliness goes back to classical times.

Theoretical ideas took some fantastic forms, but after the time of Hippocrates there was nearly always evident a desire to replace the too simple explanation of disease as divine vengeance for wrongdoing by some more immediate cause. Infection seemed obviously to pass from person to person in the air, and it was a natural association of ideas to think of the spread of infection as analogous to the diffusion into the air of unpleasant smells from septic wounds or dead bodies. From the earliest times, putrefaction, especially of unburied human corpses, was regarded as likely to breed disease. In the early nineteenth century, bad drains, that is, smelly drains, were universally blamed for typhoid fever and diphtheria. Even as late as 1890, well-informed epidemiologists considered that epidemics of plague, influenza or yellow fever might be initiated by the diffusion of gaseous material from poisons in the soil, usually of putrefactive origin. They knew that a further generation of infective material in the bodies of those initially infected must occur and be responsible for spread of the epidemic, but they looked for the initiating cause of the epidemic in peculiarities of soil and weather.

With the coming of Pasteur and Koch, the mystery of infectious disease seemed to be swept away for ever. 'Fluxes, agues, botches and boils', not to mention the major pestilences, were all due to the attack of bacteria or similar microorganisms on the body. The new science of bacteriology provided a great impetus to the process of cleaning up the conditions of human existence which had begun, in England at least, a few decades earlier. A rational basis was now available for the demands for pure water supply, sewerage schemes, pure food and milk regulations, prevention of overcrowding, and so forth. Medical and particularly surgical techniques were revolutionized by antiseptic and aseptic methods. Typhoid fever disappeared, and infantile mortality rapidly declined, surgeons freed from the fear of sepsis flourished, and a few economically vital areas of the tropics were cleared of yellow fever and malaria. All these triumphs, and they were triumphs, received the publicity they deserved. Medical research, and especially bacteriological research, became an eminently worthy occupation.

By the end of the Second World War it was possible to say that almost all the major practical problems of dealing with infectious disease had been solved. The success of penicillin in the treatment of wound infection during the War had initiated a new phase of the revolution in treatment that the sulphonamides had begun in 1935. Since 1946 there has been a steady, almost embarrassing flow of new antibiotics and other antibacterial drugs, including especially several active against organisms untouched by penicillin, such as the tubercle bacillus. Despite much indiscriminate use and occasional calamities, the overall influence of the new drugs on infectious disease was wholly beneficial. In 1961 it is hardly an exaggeration to say that no previously healthy child or adult need die of any bacterial or protozoal infection if he can reach an adequately equipped hospital before the infection has irreparably damaged his tissues. New insecticides and new methods of using them have made it feasible to eradicate most of the insect-borne diseases even in relatively undeveloped countries. Malaria was banished perhaps for ever from continental United States in 1950 and typhus fever, thanks to a combination of preventive vaccination and improved measures against louse infestation, played no significant part in the War.

In many ways one can think of the middle of the twentieth century as the end of one of the most important social revolutions in history, the virtual elimination of infectious disease as a significant factor in social life. If we could be assured of peace we could feel confident that over progressively greater regions of the earth we should see a swift reduction in mortality, and the relegation of infectious disease to the relatively trivial illnesses which are all that most families in advanced communities know from direct experience.

Along with this development of practical measures of preventing and curing infectious disease, there has gone a steadily increasing interest in the intrinsic characteristics of the micro-organisms responsible for disease. In the early stages of laboratory research on infectious disease, most bacteriologists had been trained as medical men and their main interests were on the isolation of bacteria as causes of disease, on the development of diagnostic tests and curative sera, and on the experimental production of disease in the animals of the laboratory. Then as biochemistry developed, men with chemical training began to realize how convenient bacteria were for the study of many of the fundamental chemical problems of living substance. From the 1930's onward bacterial physiology which, in fact, is almost wholly biochemistry, has been a favourite topic for research. Then in the post-war years and especially after Lederberg and Tatum's discovery that bacteria could hybridize, bacterial genetics suddenly emerged as the most active

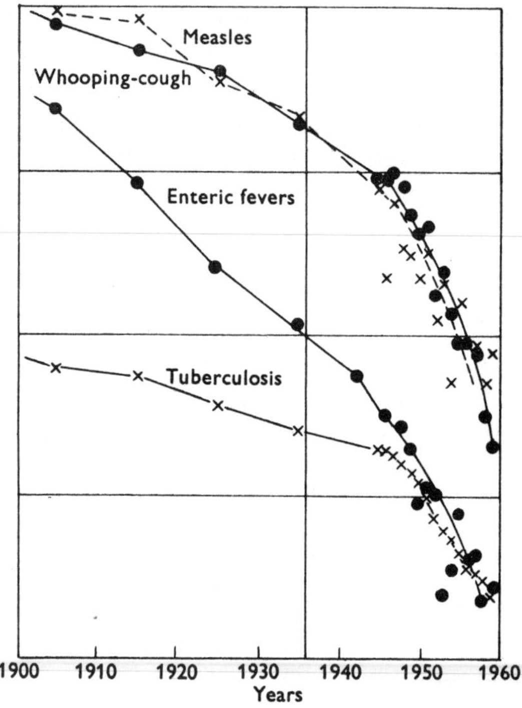

Fig. 1. To show the trend of mortality from some infectious diseases in England and Wales during the twentieth century. Relative death-rates are shown for measles, whooping cough, enteric fevers and tuberculosis. The absolute scales differ but all are shown logarithmically, the horizontal lines indicating a tenfold difference. Between 1936, when the first edition of this book was being written, and 1960, there has been almost one hundredfold diminution in the deaths from whooping cough and measles.

and illuminating aspect of laboratory research on bacteria. In 1960, medically orientated bacteriologists were mainly concerned with the study of virus disease using tissue culture methods, while most new work on bacteria involved the co-operation of biochemists and geneticists.

It is symptomatic of biological science at present that the Nobel prizes for Medicine in 1958 and 1959 went to men interested in the interaction of genetics and biochemistry as manifested in the study of microorganisms in the laboratory.

Perhaps it is a pity that the modern trend in academic circles is to neglect the microorganism as it exists in the outside world, in order to concentrate on the 'domesticated' microbes that can be so conveniently handled in the chemist's flasks and test tubes. Nevertheless the other biological sciences have by no means been neglected and, although workers in such fields are fewer in number, there are still many who are interested in what may be called the ecological aspects of infectious disease. In a broad way one can divide the biological sciences into two groups. There are those that are concerned with the structure and functioning of the living organism and of its component parts, anatomy, physiology, cytology, biochemistry and so on. On the other hand, there are those sciences which deal with the interaction of organisms with their environment and especially with other organisms whether of their own or different species in that environment. Ecology is a broad term covering such an approach to the problems of animals, plants and microorganisms, and in the human sphere we can include the social sciences under the same heading. Today there are at least two ways of studying bacterial ecology. In any studies on the genetics and biochemistry of a bacterial culture it is always necessary to have an understanding of how the millions of individual bacteria in the experimental cultures influence each other and survive or die under changing conditions. Less readily studied but more humanly important is that phase of microbial ecology that we call epidemiology, where we are concerned with those factors in the environment which influence the prevalence of disease. In many respects the two approaches, from the laboratory and the field, are complementary and taken together they provide the best introduction to an understanding of the broad features of infectious disease.

Since the eighteenth century, at least, there have always been educated men of some leisure with a natural interest in the activities of animals and plants. Many of these amateur naturalists, from Izaak Walton and Gilbert White onward, have written about the way animals make a living. The habits of birds in feeding, courting and nesting have attracted the interests of many. Others have spent years unravelling the life history of insects, especially the miniature civilizations of the ants, bees and termites. In more recent years, this essentially amateur type of observer has been supplemented by the professional biologist, whose more systematic investigations in the field once known as nature study have raised its dignity to the science of ecology. As the form of the word suggests, ecology is the study of the economics of living organisms. Animal ecology deals with the activity of animals as individuals and as species, their mode of feeding and of reproduction, the environmental conditions necessary for their well-being, and the enemies with which they have to contend. The combined action of such factors determines how numerous a species will be at any particular time and place. Sometimes inconspicuous changes in the environment of a species may produce extreme changes in its numbers, and in practice most ecological investigations are undertaken to elucidate the excessive abundance or undue scarcity of some economically important animal. Like most, perhaps all sciences, ecology has developed in response to practical human needs. On the one hand, there are countless pests which, when their numbers are excessive, cause great economic loss from damage to growing crops, domestic animals or stored food products. On the other hand, there are the economically important wild animals, the fur-bearing rodents and carnivores of subarctic regions, the edible fish of the North Sea, the whales of the Antarctic, and so on, where the problem is to avoid undue scarcity or extinction of the species. If the pests are to be controlled or the valuable species saved from extermination, every detail of their life histories, their physical environments, and of the numbers and habits of their enemies may be necessary. It is the task of the trained ecologist to provide this knowledge and to show how it can be applied to the desired end.

Every animal species reproduces its kind at a far greater rate than would be necessary to maintain its numbers if death occurred only as a result of old age or accident. In nature, of course, limiting factors are always present, and the maintenance of the numbers of a species can be regarded as the result of conflict between two opposing forces, the 'population pressure' of the species, the constant production of more young than can hope to survive, and the equally constant destruction of individuals by physical calamities, frosts, floods and the like, predatory and parasitic animal enemies and infectious disease. Except for some large, slowly breeding animals, the reproductive potentialities of most species are so great that it needs only a surprisingly short time for a vast increase in numbers to occur following some change in the environment unusually favourable to the species concerned. In most practical problems, this capacity for rapid multiplication can be taken for granted, and attention need be focused only on the two principal factors which diminish or limit the numbers of any species—the available food supply and the activity of enemies. The animal enemies of a species include those which capture and devour their prey (predators) and those smaller forms which live in or on the tissues of their host (parasites); and not infrequently there are enemies whose harmful activities are intermediate between those of predator and parasite —the blood-sucking insects and vampire bats for example. All these activities of enemies, however, have the same object, to obtain food for their own requirements from the tissues of their victims. Put concisely, the two essentials for survival are that an animal should find enough to eat and avoid being eaten itself. Food thus becomes the central problem of ecology.

Every animal needs for its nutrition some form of protein

which can be used to build up its tissues, and carbohydrate or fat to provide energy for its activities. In the body the chemical form of these substances can be modified, but the essential 'building stones', amino-acids and simple carbohydrates, must be obtained from without. Only the green plant can synthesize these substances from inorganic materials, and all animals are primarily dependent on plants for their nutrition. Probably more than half the species of animals and the vast majority of individuals feed directly on plants or their products. There is an infinite variety in the methods of such feeding. The single-celled protozoa engulf minute green algae, fish and molluscs browse on seaweed, insects and humming birds seek honey in flowers; there are eaters of seeds and fruit, leaves, bark and roots; insect larvae and termites tunnel through wood, using it as food in the process, and there are multitudes of insects which exist by sucking the juices of plants. A few species of animal, protozoa and certain corals, have dispensed with the necessity of devouring plant material by incorporating small green algae in their tissues and utilizing the food material synthesized by these primitive plants.

All these plant-feeding animals by their digestive processes break down the plant substances to simpler molecules, and discarding waste materials build these up into their own proteins and fats. In doing so they provide for other creatures a more concentrated and more readily utilized store of food. Nearly every animal is liable to become the prey of some predatory carnivore, and with the exception of the largest carnivores, this holds irrespective of whether the animal itself feeds on plants or on other animals. For every animal species one can trace back its food supply through one or more stages to the ultimate source in plant tissues. To take an unusually complicated example, a shark feeds on large fish which in most cases capture smaller fish. These probably find their main food supply in small crustaceans which feed on the protozoa of the surface waters. The protozoa live on microscopic green algae, the unicellular plant organisms which are the final source of food for most marine animals. Such a sequence of organisms, each feeding on the one beneath it, is referred to as a food-chain. Amongst land animals the food-chains are usually composed of fewer links than amongst the larger marine forms. A lion feeds on plant tissues at only one remove, since large herbivorous mammals are its usual prey. A longer chain leads from the small, but very numerous insects, aphis, plant lice, scale insects and so on, which suck plant juices. These are preyed on by the larvae of ladybird beetles, which may provide food for birds either directly or after being eaten by spiders. Owls and hawks, by feeding on the smaller birds, complete the chain.

In all the series we have mentioned so far, the animal which eats is larger than that eaten. At the end of each food-chain we find the larger carnivores, eagle and owl, wolf and lion, killer whale and shark, along with a few herbivores like the elephant, which, by their size or for some other reason, are immune from attack. Such animals have no visible enemies in nature, but they are just as exposed to the attacks of parasites as smaller types. The tiger may be the lord of the jungle, but its lungs may be riddled with parasitic worms.

The parasitic mode of life is essentially similar to that of the predatory carnivores. It is just another method of obtaining food from the tissues of living animals, and it is sometimes not easy to decide whether a given form is or is not a parasite. In general, a parasite may be defined as an organism smaller and less highly differentiated than its host, which lives on the skin or within the tissues or body cavities and gains its nourishment at the expense of the host's living substance. Although at present we are concerned with the means by which animals gain their food, we can class all the internal parasites together. The microorganisms of disease, just as much as parasitic worms, are using the tissues of their host simply as a source of the food they require for growth and multiplication.

As an example of the way in which this complex interaction of species feeding on and forming the prey of other organisms is reflected in the varying numbers of the species concerned, we may describe one of the first and most striking successes of applied ecology. Soon after orange growing had become an important industry in California, serious losses began to occur through the spread of a scale insect. The trees were covered with little white cushions built up by the insects as a protective covering beneath which they sucked the sap of the orange trees. It was soon found that the pest was not a native American insect, but an importation from Australia. There it normally lives on the native acacias, and when it spreads to orange trees does no particular damage. The difference between the behaviour of the insect in Australia and in California was not due to climate, but to the fact that in its native home the cushion scale insect is the chief food supply of a ladybird. The two insects automatically control each other's numbers. If the scale insect is particularly plentiful, the ladybird larvae find an abundant food supply and the beetles in their turn become more plentiful. An excessive number of ladybirds will so diminish the population of scale insects that there will be insufficient food for the next generation, and therefore fewer ladybirds. On the whole, a balance will be reached with such a population of each species that the destruction by enemies is approximately equal to the increase in numbers allowed by the available food supplies.

In California there were no carnivorous insects adapted like the Australian ladybird to feed on and reduce the numbers of scale insects to a normal level. The logical way to remedy the excessive multiplication of the pest was to introduce its most important natural enemy into the orange groves. This was done in 1889, and once the difficulties of breeding a sufficient supply of the little beetles had been overcome, the experiment was a triumphant success. The cushion scale was reduced in importance to a relatively trivial pest.

In this example we have a contrast between the behaviour of an organism, the scale insect, in its natural environment and in a new environment, which in essentials may be taken as the type of a large number of practical ecological problems. In Australia, the scale insect, like the other indigenous plants and animals, had been free to evolve and adapt itself to a relatively constant environment for millions of years. In the long period before extensive European settlement, the mutual action of all the species, animal and plant, had determined what numbers of individuals of each species would allow an approximately balanced and stable condition to be maintained. The interaction between scale insect and ladybird is only one of countless similar adjustments between all groups of species whose food-seeking activities influenced one another's numbers.

The process by which an approximately constant population of living organisms is developed has been studied in more detail by botanists than by animal ecologists, but the broad principles are the same for both great classes of living organisms. The final constant condition of the vegetation in any particular region is called by plant ecologists the 'climax' state. It is not infrequent for the normal vegetation of an area to be completely destroyed either by human activity or as a result of some natural catastrophe, fire, flood or volcanic eruption. If after the destruction the land is left to natural processes, a regular series of changes can be recognized in the return of plant life to the area. The island of Krakatoa in the East Indies provides the most striking example. In 1883 it was apparently completely sterilized of every living organism by intense volcanic activity. Within sixty years it had again become covered with dense tropical forest. First of all the lifeless volcanic ash was colonized by air-borne spores of bacteria, primitive plants, mosses and ferns, then in succession appeared grasses and shrubs from sea-borne seeds. Twenty-three years after the eruption, a forest of coconut palms, fig trees and others had developed along the shore and was gradually spreading inland. In another half-century, excluding further catastrophes, Krakatoa will be completely covered with tropical rain-forest. This succession of different types of vegetation is seen in all such denuded areas left to uncontrolled natural processes. In every case the succession goes on to a final state characteristic of the region, and determined mainly by the climate and nature of the soil. This final 'climax' may be tropical rain-forest, grass-covered prairie, pine forest or some other type of plant community, but once reached, it remains essentially constant, and is likely to change only as a result of long-period climatic changes or human activity.

Along with such changes in the plant life, a related series of changes in the animal population will occur, and with the establishment of the climax state of vegetation animal species will adjust themselves to an uneasy equilibrium. This mutual adjustment is an immensely complicated process, for all the food-chains concerned are naturally interwoven, and for every species there will be fluctuations in numbers from time to time, but on the whole, in a constant environment a reasonable approach to a stable balance will be maintained. As long as the number of individuals does not fall below a certain minimum, the lower the population density of a species, the greater the opportunity it has to multiply. There is a greater food supply available for each individual: general predatory enemies may consume much the same proportions, but there is less opportunity for enemies such as parasites and carnivores of restricted prey to thrive at their expense. Conversely, when the numbers increase, food supplies are limited, and there is increased opportunity for the activity of all those specialized parasites and predators that are more or less strictly confined to the species in question. So, from each side, there is an automatic tendency to the development of a balanced condition of affairs for every species. It is an uneasy balance, more often swinging widely above and below the equilibrium point than remaining nearly stable, and liable to be forced to a totally different equilibrium by the introduction of some new organism into the environment.

Australia provides some particularly striking instances of such changes, probably because the whole continent was practically isolated from the rest of the world for the long geological period from the Eocene until the European settlement. Plants which are relatively unimportant pests in their native habitats have only too often spread excessively after their introduction into Australia and become dominant forms in certain areas. The prickly pear cactus is the best known, but in the south the blackberry will become the dominant vegetation of fertile valleys unless kept continuously in check by human action, and thistles have spread intensely over the plains country. Amongst animals, the rabbit, hare and fox have almost completely replaced the native mammalian fauna in the south-eastern region. Only the arboreal opossums have managed to maintain their numbers.

Australia in its turn has provided pests for other countries, mostly insects. We have mentioned the cottony cushion scale of acacias and orange trees already. A leaf-hopper from Queensland at one period almost destroyed the sugar industry in Hawaii until suitable parasitic wasps from Australia were introduced to control its numbers. There are dozens of similar examples to be found in the literature on the spread and control of economically important pests, and there must be an infinite number of similar adjustments going on amongst organisms not important enough to man to call for detailed research.

This development of an approximately balanced condition between contending species is as characteristic of the relation between host and parasites as of any other such interaction, but there are certain special characteristics of the parasite-host relation which need to be considered. Most parasites are restricted to one host species, or at most to a small number of related species, and the main problem that a parasitic species has to solve if it is to survive is to manage the transfer of its offspring from one individual host to another. All sorts of methods have been developed: the production of enormous numbers of offspring is usual, and many larval forms find an intermediate host in some other animal whose movements or activities will help the transfer to fresh, final hosts. It will be clear, however, that no matter by what method a parasite passes from host to host, an increased density of the susceptible population will facilitate its spread from infected to uninfected individuals. Suppose we have ten fowls in a large enclosure, one of them infected with coccidia, a protozoal parasite of the bowel which is spread by contamination of food with infected droppings. It will probably be a long time before another bird becomes infected, and when it does, only a small number of parasites will be taken in and the fowl will probably escape with a mild infection. But if 500 fowls are placed in the same enclosure, again with one infected individual amongst them, there will be a fifty times greater chance that another bird will be infected within a short period. As soon as a few become infected and start excreting the parasite, the process will spread with accelerating speed until all are infected. Further, they will be constantly subject to re-infection, and liable to more severe symptoms and a higher mortality. This is precisely what is found to happen in poultry-farm experience if precautions against coccidial infection are not taken.

As a more natural example of the mutual influence of population density and parasitic activity, we may say something about the plagues of small rodents which occur periodically. The lemming swarms of Scandinavia are the classical examples, but in Australia we are more familiar with mouse plagues. In certain years the introduced domestic mouse multiplies enormously. The mice swarm in crops and haystacks, and literal bucketfuls can be caught in a single night. Hawks, owls and cats flourish at their expense, and birds like ibises change their normal diet to one of mice, but all these enemies have little effect in reducing the numbers. As a rule the plague ends rather suddenly. A few dead mice are found on the ground and the numbers dwindle rapidly to, or below, normal. Infectious disease has been at work, and when the population reaches a certain density, rapid and concentrated transfer of parasites, bacterial and otherwise, takes place. Not many opportunities have arisen for bacteriologists to determine what are the actual microorganisms responsible for these epidemics which bring mouse plagues in Australia to an end. We can be sure that the type of parasite will vary from one occasion to another. In 1940 I examined mice from the wheat areas of Northern Victoria where a mouse plague had been in progress for some months. All the mice were diseased with a fungal affection of the skin of the face, and large abscess-like swellings on the limbs due to an unusual type of bacterium (*Streptobacillus moniliformis*). On another occasion a mouse plague in Queensland was associated with widespread human cases of a form of typhus fever, and it is reasonable to think that it was an infection of this sort amongst the mice which terminated the period of over-population.

Such a reduction in numbers by the activity of parasites (including the microorganisms of disease) when animal populations become abnormally large is only another manifestation of the principle that for every organism there is a certain density of population which makes best for survival of the species.

How far is this ecological viewpoint applicable to man? For centuries he has been securely at the right end of a whole multitude of food-chains. But, like other mammals, he has persistently multiplied beyond the limits of subsistence, and in the absence of man-eating carnivores, other checks on population growth have developed. Simple starvation may sometimes have been important, but more often shortage of food supply has had indirect effects in forced migrations, internal and external war, diminished fertility and excessive infantile mortality. All of these have helped to effect the needed reduction in numbers. Even more important has been the influence of famine in predisposing to increased prevalence and increased intensity of infectious disease. War and famine have probably always taken their toll of human life more through the intermediary of the microbe than by starvation and the sword. And even in those rare phases in history when peace accompanied prosperity, infectious disease has played its part. Right up to the nineteenth century infectious disease was the most important agent in preventing human over-population, and in a few parts of the world it still remains so. With its progressive elimination from all the major centres of human population, infantile and childhood deaths are falling steeply and the greatest political problem of the second half of the twentieth century is now taking shape.

It needs only the most limited knowledge of human history to see that the whole process of civilization has been largely one of aggregation of greater and greater numbers of human beings into limited areas. Cities are essential to civilization, and until well into the nineteenth century, all cities were the spawning grounds of infectious disease. How could it be other-wise? For centuries all the precautions we now know to be necessary to prevent the spread of bacteria and animal para-sites were unthought of. City streets were littered with human and animal filth, water came from contaminated wells, rats, fleas and lice were universal.

Crowded together in such filthy environments, every city dweller was inevitably exposed to infection every day of his life. It is no wonder that the population of cities through all history has had to be recruited periodically from the country. Few cities have ever been able to maintain their population by their reproduction, but the attraction of gregarious life has always been sufficient to bring a constant stream of the ambitious from the healthier, because less densely populated, countryside. And on a larger scale we see almost the whole of ancient and medieval history dominated by the periodic out-pouring of nomadic tribes from the steppes and mountains of eastern Europe and central Asia down to the areas of civiliza-tion and cities in China, India, Mesopotamia, the Mediter-ranean basin and western Europe. The nomadic life is the healthy life, and the children of nomads survived until their numbers were too great for their steppes to support them. After each outpouring, the conquerors adopted the city life of the peoples they dispossessed, and disease saw to it that no longer did their children survive in the numbers that had been theirs in the nomad existence.

It will be our task in subsequent chapters to discuss the reasons why *all* dwellers in the unsanitary cities did not die of infectious disease. Here we are looking only at the general ecological problem of human existence in crowded communities. We might reasonably expect that if a densely populated area remained isolated from all other populous regions, an equilibrium condition would eventually be developed, irrespective of what parasites were initially present. It is equally reasonable to expect that the introduction of some important new parasite into the area would seriously disturb this equilibrium. Human history gives many examples of such conditions. Prior to the European discoveries, many of the Pacific Islands were quite densely populated. There were a few endemic diseases, but, on the whole, the people were very healthy. When the trader, the missionary and the blackbirder had finished their work, epidemics of a dozen or more infectious diseases of European origin, plus general demoralization, had reduced the population of such groups as the New Hebrides to approximately one-tenth of the original number.

In the European cities, with which epidemiological history mostly deals, there was always some degree of contact with other cities. New parasites might creep like the Black Death from city to city with the rats and their fleas, enter them with conquering armies as syphilis did in its sweep through Europe at the end of the fifteenth century, or spread invisibly from carriers like the cholera a hundred years ago. Sieges, floods or drought brought famines to make other violent disturbances of the balance between man and his parasites. There was never an opportunity to develop a *modus vivendi* with all the microbes and larger parasites which assailed him.

Suppose we leave the insanitary past and survey the conditions of present-day civilization from the same point of view. Two things have happened. First, we have found methods of preventing certain types of infection which were of the greatest importance in the old days, those spread by filth, or, to be more direct, by human faeces, and those transmitted by animal parasites or semi-parasites such as fleas, lice and mosquitoes. Efficient sewerage and water supply, plus ordinarily decent cleanliness, have thus rid us in temperate climates of typhoid, dysentery, cholera, plague, typhus and malaria. We have not been able, and perhaps never will be able, to block the spread of those diseases which are spread by what is technically called 'droplet infection'. Colds, sore throats, influenza, measles and the like are all passed from person to person via tiny drops of saliva which are sprayed into the air during coughing, shouting and so forth. As long as human beings in large communities have to go about their business, such dissemination of infection will continue. If anything, the greater size and mobility of modern city populations has probably increased the opportunities for the spread of these infections. This brings us to the second significant change of modern times. This is that the extent and speed of travel between all civilized countries has more or less converted them into a single closed environment in the biological sense. The infectious diseases of Europe, North America, Australia and New Zealand are almost precisely identical. There is now a real opportunity for those parasitic microbes, whose attack we cannot prevent, to reach the state of relative equilibrium with the host species which we have been postulating as the normal climax of interaction between organisms. For many diseases that seems to have been accomplished. The common diseases of childhood, measles, chickenpox, diphtheria, whooping cough and mumps, have their epidemic prevalences and occasionally kill, but the proportion of deaths falls from decade to decade. Where medical science is well advanced and the new drugs available to deal with the complications that used to be the main cause of death and serious illness, there is now almost no mortality from these diseases. The germs responsible continue to survive, yet their activity rarely has any perceptible influence on the general life of the community.

All these childhood diseases are followed by relative or complete immunity against a second attack. As we shall discuss in much more detail later, they affect childhood precisely because they are followed by immunity. Taking measles as an example, what ordinarily happens is something like this: after a year's almost complete absence of the disease from the region, a child becomes infected, perhaps from someone from another city. From this child a number of 5-, 6- and 7-year-olds are infected, perhaps at school, and a fairly rapid spread occurs to all exposed children not yet insusceptible in virtue of a previous attack. This will mean, as a rule, children who have just commenced school and younger pre-school children in the same homes. Almost every susceptible child exposed to contact with another child in the early stages of infection will contract the disease. There may be some children who come into contact with infection, but receive so small a dose of the virus that no real infection follows. Those children who are infected and have a typical attack of measles will practically all recover completely if they were well nourished and healthy at the time of onset. Some of the weaklings and an occasional unlucky healthy child will develop pneumonia and die. The epidemic will spread progressively through a city or a country, twelve or fourteen days between successive crops of infections, and under ordinary city conditions will not diminish greatly until a high proportion of susceptible children is infected. As each passes through his infection, he becomes immune and the germ finds progressively greater difficulty in spreading. Eventually measles disappears from the community, but in the meantime the virus is spreading similarly through other communities. In about two years' time another crop of susceptible children has appeared, and sooner or later the measles virus re-enters the community and the cycle is repeated.

It is a common simile to compare the spread of epidemics to forest fires. Where the fire has once been, it does not recur until fresh undergrowth has grown up. Perhaps we could make the analogy a little closer if we imagine a forest of a rather special type of tree—a tree which I fear has no real existence anywhere. In its youth this tree has a trunk from which sprout shoots of inflammable leaves, but the upper part of the tree, from which most of its ultimate development takes place, is much less inflammable. If a fire passes over the young trees, most of them lose their lower shoots only and remain alive. It is a characteristic of our tree that once these lower shoots have been removed they never grow again, but until this is done they keep on growing. Sometimes when the fire is especially intense, a whole young tree may be consumed, but most of them survive and are no more susceptible to fire. The forest is a windless forest, and the fire spreads slowly and irregularly. Sometimes it misses a patch for years, but sooner or later it covers the whole area, creeping back to regions it has once passed as soon as sufficient young trees have grown up to allow its passage. One little point in this analogy is worth stressing. When those patches of forest which have missed the fire for many years are at last reached, the overgrown inflammable material blazes fiercely, and many more trees are likely to be destroyed here than elsewhere. When measles was introduced into the Sandwich (Hawaiian) Islands, just such a conflagration occurred. Practically all the population went down with the disease, and many thousands died.

In some such way we can picture the natural history of measles. We can only consider the interaction between man and the measles virus as an equilibrium when we look at it over a large population and for a long period. For the individual community the interaction resembles much more a widely swinging see-saw. Nevertheless, it is a clear example of one method by which man and an agent of infectious disease have become adapted to one another without serious damage to the host species, and with steady survival of the virus concerned.

As an example of another method by which this same type

of mutual toleration is developed, we may consider the activities of the virus of psittacosis. Psittacosis, or parrot fever, became a matter of almost international importance in 1929 and 1930, owing to the large number of human infections which were derived both in Europe and North America from infected parrots imported from South America. Like many other infectious diseases, psittacosis was first recognized as a serious epidemic disease of human beings, but as its nature became gradually understood, it grew clear that the epidemic phase was only an accidental and relatively unusual happening. It is worth while going into the story of the elucidation of psittacosis, for it is an excellent example of the way interest in infections tended to shift from the medical to the biological aspects. The scientific study of psittacosis is relatively recent. It began early in 1930, when research workers in England, Germany and America almost simultaneously announced that the disease was due to a filterable virus, and not, as was previously thought, to a bacterium. Thirty years later it became clear that in fact the microorganism in question was neither a virus nor a bacterium but something to be classed along with the rickettsiae that are responsible for typhus fever and the like, as an intermediate. For our present purpose it is quite immaterial how we classify it. The real significance of the discovery was that the responsible germ had been isolated and methods developed of finding out whether or not it was present in a sick man or a sick parrot. This is the necessary preliminary stage before we can go any further toward understanding the natural history of the germ.

The next big step took place three years later in California. In the United States, after the epidemic of 1929–30, there was a rigid prohibition on the importation of South American parrots, and it was hoped that this would be sufficient to get rid of the disease. But now that the disease had become familiar to doctors, cases kept on being recognized, and most of these had no connexion whatever with imported parrots. The sources of their infections were nearly all American-bred budgerigars. There was one relatively large outbreak traced to a consignment of these birds from a Californian aviary, and a large-scale investigation of the conditions in the budgerigar breeding establishments of the States was set going by the Californian authorities.

Most people know the budgerigar, also called the shell parakeet or lovebird. It is a native of Australia, very common in the sparsely timbered grasslands of the interior. The wild bird is predominantly green in colour, but under domestication various colour varieties have appeared and been developed by selective breeding. Now there are varieties of every colour, from nearly white to deep blue, with dozens of blends of yellow, green and grey. In most parts of the world it comes a close second to the canary as the most popular cage bird, and there is quite a large minor industry devoted to their breeding and sale. In America, budgerigar breeding on a large scale was almost confined to California, from which large numbers of birds were exported to the other States.

In the Californian aviaries there was ample opportunity to observe the behaviour of the psittacosis virus. Over half of the 104 aviaries examined were infected. In many of these it was known that a considerable proportion of young birds became sick, and that some died, but others, also infected, had no undue mortality amongst their birds. Meyer, who was in charge of the investigation, came to the conclusion that in the infected aviaries most of the fledglings contracted the disease from droppings of older birds. The infection might or might not result in visible symptoms, but in any case most birds recovered. By the time they were eight months old, the budgerigars were free from all signs of the infection. If it was present at all, the virus now remained only in very small amounts hidden away and almost completely harmless in the cells of the spleen or kidney. Enough of these carriers persisted, however, to infect the young at the next breeding season. On the basis of these results, measures were set going to eliminate the disease, and a very considerable success was achieved.

In the course of this work, Meyer imported 200 wild budgerigars from Australia, assuming that these would be sure to be free from infection. A month or two after arrival in America, a few of them were noticed to be sick, and it was found that they were infected with psittacosis. They had had no known opportunity to become infected in California, and it seemed that they must have brought the virus from Australia. It obviously became necessary that Australian bacteriologists should look into the conditions in their own land, which had heretofore been assumed free from the disease. In Melbourne we undertook to make the necessary investigations. As a preliminary, a batch of young parrots was purchased from the nearest bird shop. About a third of them were infected with a mild, but perfectly definite psittacosis! I need not go into the details of our subsequent investigations, but they showed that most of the common Australian parrots and cockatoos were liable to be infected in the wild state. Sometimes almost every bird in the batches received direct from the catchers was infected. Other lots showed only a few with signs of past infection, and none actually carrying the virus. Each of the three main families—cockatoos, parakeets, and lories—provided its quota of infected birds.

At the time these investigations were made we were inclined to look on the virus of psittacosis as something that had evolved with the parrots in Australia and had been spread with the budgerigar to the rest of the world. Subsequent years, however, had seen a steady widening of the range of birds known to be infected with viruses of the same general character as psittacosis. In the Faeroes, in the North Atlantic, cases of severe pneumonia began to occur around 1933, almost always in women and at the time of the year when large numbers of young fulmar petrels were being killed and prepared for food. A few years later it was established that the women were being infected by psittacosis virus, that the infection was widespread amongst the fulmars and that the young petrels were as commonly infected on the bird cliffs of the Faeroes as the nestling budgerigars in the aviaries. In America, England, Australia, and South Africa the semi-domesticated pigeons of the cities have been found carrying a mild form of the virus. Hens and ducks and a variety of sea birds have also been added to the list, and it is hard to avoid the belief that we are dealing with a very ancient, almost universal infection of birds.

The conditions in Australian parrots may, however, still be taken as representative of the way these viruses survive in nature. It is not practicable to carry out the same detailed investigation of wild birds as is possible with aviary budgerigars, but our results were just what would have been expected if conditions in the wild were much the same as in the aviaries of California. The nestlings in all probability become infected from their parents, suffer a mild attack, and rapidly recover, but carry the virus in their bodies for at least a year. In this example, then, we have a well-balanced, mutually successful interaction between parasite and host. In the natural state it seems that very few parrots die or are even discommoded by the infection.

We may round off the story of psittacosis with an account of a small epidemic in Melbourne which we investigated some years ago. It is an instructive little tale. In Australia, white cockatoos are popular pets: they are good talkers, and can at least appear to be both intelligent and affectionate. The demand is supplied by bird-catchers, who take the young from the nests in hollow trees just before they are able to fly. In the city, the birds are sold in animal shops and by casual dealers. The epidemic with which we are concerned arose from a batch of cockatoos kept for some weeks by a hawker in very confined and dirty quarters. Two serious human cases of psittacosis, one in the wife of the hawker, were diagnosed, and an investigation of the circumstances was made by the health authorities. It was found, first, that all the remaining cockatoos in the backyard shed were sick and heavily infected with psittacosis; and secondly, that altogether a total of fourteen people had probably been infected from this batch of cockatoos. Only five of the cases, however, were severe, and there were no deaths.

Here we return to the medical sphere: something had tipped the balance in favour of the parasite. It is reasonably certain that those cockatoos, left to a natural life in the wild, would never have shown any symptoms of their infection. In captivity, crowded, filthy and without exercise or sunlight, a flare-up of any latent infection was only to be expected. The virus multiplied and spread throughout the body. Large amounts of it passed out with the excreta, soiling the feathers. When the birds fluttered they were always liable to fluff up a cloud of virus-laden dust and infect anyone in the neighbourhood.

Psittacosis is not intrinsically a very infectious disease. It is very rare for infection to pass from one human being to another. To produce dangerous illness the virus must be inhaled into the lungs, and ordinarily this is likely to occur only when infected parrots or cockatoos scatter the virus into the air by their movements. In one or two instances, sick parrots brought to a laboratory have infected people in all parts of the building by the spread of such dust on air currents along the corridors.

Our Melbourne epidemic was only a small one, but it created a good deal of public interest, pointed a moral against the iniquities of bird-catching, and for the first time made it clear that the mild natural psittacosis of our wild cockatoos could light up to an intensity capable of infecting man.

Perhaps these examples are sufficient to indicate the general point of view which we must adopt in regard to infectious disease. It is a conflict between man and his parasites which, in a constant environment, would tend to result in a virtual equilibrium, a climax state, in which both species would survive indefinitely. Man, however, lives in an environment constantly being changed by his own activities, and few of his diseases have attained such an equilibrium. The practical problems of prevention and treatment demand principally an understanding of the results of new types of infection on the individual and the community, and of the stages by which a condition of tolerance is reached. When such knowledge has been gained it is a simple matter to apply it to the interpretation of those diseases which have reached their climax state.

Two interdependent sciences have arisen to deal with the problems of infection. Immunology is concerned with the response of the *individual* to invasion by microorganisms. What determines whether he lives or dies, what are the physiological processes by which the disease is overcome, and what is the basis of the immunity to further infection which so often follows the attack? Epidemiology deals with the large-scale phenomena of infectious disease, not only with epidemics but with the less dramatic, more or less constant, prevalence of disease in human communities. Its concern is with the community or the human race as a whole, not with the individual, but it is self-evident that its methods and generalizations must be based largely on what is known about the individual's reaction to infection. It is the aim of this book to present a simple account of the microorganisms which cause disease, of the processes within the body which are called into action against them, and of the way infection persists and spreads within the community. It is written not from the point of view of a physician or a pathologist, whose interests must necessarily centre on the human aspect, but with the outlook of a biologist, to whom both man and microorganism are objects of equal interest.

CHAPTER II

THE EVOLUTION OF INFECTION AND DEFENCE

We can deal with no restricted field in studying the nature of disease. The whole range of living beings comes into our province, for there is probably no species of organism which has not at some time been either host to a parasite or a parasite itself. Many have filled both roles. Infectious disease is universal, and any attempt to imagine how it arose in the course of evolution will inevitably take us back to the very earliest phases of life.

The astronomers and geologists have now given us a fairly detailed picture of the origin of the solar system and of the gradual development of the surface characteristics of the earth. Most authorities now believe the earth originated by aggregation of cosmic dust and reached approximately its present size some two to three thousand million years ago. Eventually it developed a solid crust covering only a portion of the surface and floating on the future ocean beds. Above this was a dense atmosphere in which nitrogen, water vapour, carbon dioxide and volatile hydrocarbons were predominant; probably little free oxygen was present. As cooling progressed, the water vapour liquefied and formed the earliest oceans. Up to this stage there was no possibility of life. We can be quite certain that no living organism existed on the earth at the time of its formation, and almost as certain that by no conceivable process could life reach the earth preformed from any part of the universe. Living organisms must at some time have arisen from non-living material on the earth. The orthodox conjecture is that the early seas accumulated large amounts of various soluble compounds of carbon and the other lighter elements which had, as it were, formed the scum of the surface of the mass of molten iron and lava which made up the bulk of the planet at the time of its formation. It is likely that the primitive atmosphere contained no free oxygen and that much more of the chemically active ultraviolet light reached the surface of the earth than is the case today. Bernal has suggested that in the mud banks intermittently exposed at the edge of shallow seas the conditions were appropriate for the appearance of an enormous variety of organic compounds. Here there would be opportunity for adsorption of substances to the reactive surface of clay particles, for exposure to ultraviolet light and also for protection of unstable compounds from undue exposure. In some such situations the first precursors of living matter may have appeared.

Steadily increasing knowledge about the chemical structure of the smallest organisms has stimulated some detailed speculations about the nature of these intermediates between not-living and living matter. The last year or two has also seen a sudden emergence of the possibility of actually studying matter from other planets than our own. This has made more than one biologist dream of bringing the problem of the origins of life right into the laboratory. It would need only a handful of mud from Mars with its contained microorganisms to keep every first class biochemical laboratory in the world busy for years sorting out the common features of two separate emergences of living matter. However, any discussion of the possibilities would be quite outside our present scope. All that need be said is that in one way or another giant molecules or the crude beginnings of organisms commenced the process of incorporating dissolved compounds of carbon and other elements into growing self-persisting units. The essence of life is this quality of incessant incorporation of any chemically suitable material into living substance which, in its turn, continues the process.

Of all the possible voyages in an imaginary 'Time Machine', a biochemist would probably find a journey to the age when these first developments of living matter were occurring the most enthralling. One can imagine strange changes taking place relatively rapidly in the margins of those primeval seas, thick with possible foodstuffs, almost like the broths we now use to culture bacteria. Once the process of living began, it was probably an accelerating process. New forms would feed on the debris of older ones. There would be widespread and frequent changes in the chemical constituents of the seas, often, probably, destructive to the living forms whose activity produced them. Once life had begun, there were tremendous possibilities for the development of more effective variations. Any successful form would develop in myriads, and amongst these some fresh and more successful variation would soon emerge and spread in its turn.

As soon as living matter emerged, it became subject to death: it was of necessity a complex labile system which could be irreparably damaged by changes in the environment, e.g. excessive heat, so that no further growth could occur. These two alternatives, growth and death, set the stage for the working out of the evolutionary process. What grows most rapidly and avoids death most successfully will survive. From the beginning, that has been the criterion by which all living organisms have been tested. Perhaps it is in regard to infectious disease that the working of this principle can be most clearly seen running through the whole history of life. Almost it might be said that life itself is no more than a disease of matter.

As evolution progressed, the primitive unorganized living material gave place to the first microorganisms. These must have been loosely organized units of living matter which could function adequately only when their size lay within certain limits. To allow continued growth and yet retain a more or less definite size, the process of reproduction was evolved. Each unit, by division or some other method, now gave rise to other descendant units with the same potentialities as itself. For a long time, we can be certain, the primitive organisms fed as most bacteria do now, by the absorption of substances dissolved in the surrounding water.

At some point in the evolution of these early forms a certain standard chemical structure appeared which was so supremely successful that it displaced all the alternatives that may have developed along with it. To a biochemist interested simply in the chemical mechanisms of living matter, the resemblances between a man and a primitive bacterium are more striking than the differences. There are, for instance, practically no limits to the number of amino-acids that could be prepared by a competent team of organic chemists. Yet all proteins, whether derived from plant or animal, bacterium or virus, contain the same twenty varieties of amino-acids. The processes by which these amino-acids are synthesized seem to be common to all organisms which possess the capacity for such synthesis. Probably even more fundamental than the proteins are the nucleic acids, the complex molecules which carry the genetic 'information' that makes an organism develop to its characteristic form. From bacterium to mammal every living cell contains two sorts of nucleic acid known by the familiar initials DNA and RNA. Each is composed of four organic bases, three common to both types with thymine in DNA and uracil in RNA, phosphate and a sugar. All the differences between organisms seem to be based on the way these simple components are arranged in the giant coiled molecules of the nucleic acids. There is one group of viruses which has its DNA built on a different pattern, perhaps an indication of a dichotomy in the very early phases of evolution.

The energy requirements of living tissue have been studied principally in regard to mammalian muscle tissue and yeast. It is an extraordinary indication of the common origin of life that in such superficially dissimilar materials the very complex cycle by which glucose is oxidized and used to provide energy for cellular activities is almost precisely the same in each. In one form or another living substance must obtain from its environment all the elements needed for the synthesis of its own structure and a source of energy. In the green plant energy is obtainable directly from sunlight but for practically all other types of organism sugars or similarly oxidizable substances are used as energy sources and must be taken in as food.

We are concerned primarily with the evolution of the defence processes in animals, and we can pass over completely the development of the green plant and the whole vegetable kingdom. Our concern is with the great evolutionary discovery that the bodies of other organisms represented a concentrated and easily obtained source of foodstuff for growth. It was from that discovery that the animal kingdom developed.

Practically without exception, all animals live at the expense of some other organism. The simplest one-celled animals, the protozoa, of which the amoeba is the conventional example, live mainly by taking in and digesting bacteria or microscopic green plants (algae). Amongst the higher animals, some live directly on the substance of plants, others find their nourishment in the bodies of animals. All sorts of methods have been developed by animals to obtain various forms of living substance for their food, but this primary requirement is common to them all.

When we think about how this habit of living on other organisms was developed by the earliest animal forms, we cannot help being impressed with some important difficulties which must have been overcome. Let us take some primitive organism, rather like an amoeba, as our first animal. It is a blob of living jelly which, when it collides with a bacterium or some other microorganism, flows over and around it, engulfing it into its body substance. To obtain material which it can utilize for its own growth, our amoeba must disintegrate the complex substance of its prey into quite simple chemical units. It is the same problem for which our own complicated digestive system has been developed. In this we have the sequence of the starch-splitting enzyme in the saliva, the prolonged treatment with acid and pepsin in the stomach, then a change over to alkaline conditions in the intestine and a whole battery of enzymes to split the proteins and fats into simple molecules. The amoeba has to do the equivalent of all this with its captured bacterium, all within its own living substance, and with no specialized mechanisms at all. Under the microscope all that can be seen is the appearance of a clear space, a vacuole so called, around the food particle. Within an hour or two the bacterium or alga begins to disintegrate, and when only debris is left, the amoeba flows on and leaves it behind. A little thought will show that this seemingly simple process must involve some delicate chemical problems. A small living organism is taken into the substance of another, both are composed of fundamentally similar material, but the larger organism must contrive to disintegrate the chemical structure of the smaller one without damage to its own structure.

It would be orthodox to say that the amoeba, as it were, creates a stomach where it is needed around the particle, and into this space pours enzymes or ferments much like those used in our own digestive processes, and that these enzymes break down the proteins (and other complex components) of the engulfed bacterium to the small molecules that the amoeba needs for its nutrition. But that shirks the major problem—why do these enzymes not digest the amoeba's own substance, chemically so similar to that of its prey? No satisfactory answer to this problem has yet been offered. This is not to say that the phenomena are not governed by physico-chemical laws. Undoubtedly they are—all we are saying is that no adequate experimental technique has been developed which will allow us to describe the detailed happenings within the cell in physico-chemical terms.

If we are to describe and discuss such phenomena scientifically, we must for the present at least be satisfied with a simpler, more biological approach. Is there any simpler way of looking at this relationship between the eater and the eaten? It may be that something useful can be gained by concentrating on the most obvious aspect of all—that the engulfed micro-organism is not the amoeba itself. The fact that the one is digested, the other not, demands that in some way or other the living substance of the amoeba can distinguish between the chemical structure characteristic of 'self' and any sufficiently different chemical structure which is recognized as 'not self'. Here we seem to have an important general character of animal protoplasm which may provide a connecting thread to help link up some of the very diverse manifestations of the defence processes which we shall have to consider.

This power of recognizing the difference between 'self' and 'not self' is most clearly seen in the various processes by which animal cells engulf and digest other cells. There are, however, other phenomena in which a similar recognition of like and unlike appears. When we advance from the single-celled animals to multicellular types, the most primitive forms are represented by the sponges. Their cells are very loosely co-ordinated and retain a good deal of independent vitality. Some of the simpler sponges can be very readily disintegrated. Simply by squeezing them through butter muslin, one can obtain a collection of separate sponge cells in sea water. Most of them are still alive, and if they are watched, small groups of cells are seen to come together and build up a simple structure which, under suitable conditions, can grow to a normal organism again. From our point of view, the most interesting experiment along these lines is that in which two species of sponge were used. Owing to a difference in colour, the disintegrated cells of each species could be readily recognized, even when mixed indiscriminately. Such a mixture of cells in sea water was observed, and it was found that in forming the little groups of cells from which new organisms could develop, like fused with like. Again there was this dim recognition of 'self' structure as opposed to 'not self'.

In the development of methods of feeding by the intracellular digestion of other organisms, we have the first appearance of direct struggle for existence between species. Indirect struggle for the available amounts of nourishment must have gone on before, but this direct utilization of the living substance of other organisms was a new departure. It opened up a new and successful line of evolution from which all animals have developed, but at the same time it laid the way open to infectious disease. Let us look at the process from the point of view of the victim, the eaten rather than the eater. Suppose that by some modification perhaps of its surface, the bacterium on which the amoeba (or any other organism using the process of intracellular digestion) feeds becomes resistant to the digesting effect. If it is taken in by the protozoon it will be retained for an hour or two, and then discarded as useless, passing out like Jonah, none the worse for its sojourn in a primitive digestive organ. From this stage it is only one step further for the smaller organism to develop the power on its side of utilizing for food the substance of the organism which engulfs it. If the microorganism can multiply within and cause the death of the protozoon, we can quite reasonably say that the protozoon has died of infectious disease. Actually such happenings are only rarely seen in nature, probably largely because of the efficiency with which indigestible particles are evacuated from protozoa. It is very liable to occur, however, when protozoal cultures are not kept under the correct physiological conditions.

At the lowest level, then, we have an interaction between two organisms which, if it swings in favour of one, is an act of digestion, if in favour of the other, it is an attack of infectious disease. As we ascend the scale of animal life, we find the same essential theme repeated in infinite variation, and if we are to follow the development of the defence against microorganismal invasion, it is necessary to know a little also about the concomitant evolution of digestive processes.

In the simplest multicellular animals, the sponges, the mode of nutrition is essentially the same as that seen in the protozoa. Small organisms in the water still constitute the food supply, and these are taken up by cells, themselves very like certain types of protozoa. Within the cells they are digested and the debris discarded much as in the unicellular forms. The chief advance is in the co-ordination of cells to form an apparatus for the more efficient collection of food. The whole sponge forms a primitive pump, drawing in water with its contained microorganisms through a multitude of pores and discharging it through a small number of larger channels. In the process, the living food particles are taken up by the cells, and waste products, such as carbon dioxide and residues from digestion, are washed out from the tissues. The bulk of the living cells in the sponge are feeding cells, but there are some cells which have other functions to perform, and which receive their nourishment indirectly from the feeding cells. In some sponges there are primitive muscle cells, and in one group there are differentiated sexual cells involved in the reproduction of the species. From our point of view, the most interesting cells, however, are wandering cells resembling amoebae, which move about in the jelly-like structureless material at the base of the feeding cells. Their function seems to be partly to transfer nourishment from one part to another, but in addition they have the capacity to engulf and digest any food particles which may enter the deeper substance of the sponge. Such accidental entrants may serve as an additional food supply, but it seems clear that a major function of these wandering cells is to act as protective scavengers and remove any microorganisms which might otherwise utilize the tissue of the sponge as a source of food. This is the first indication in the animal kingdom of a mechanism to deal with invasion of the tissues by microorganisms.

Metchnikoff, who was the first to recognize that the study of comparative physiology might throw light on the nature of infection and immunity, called these wandering cells phagocytes, and this name can be generally applied to all such cells in whatever animal they are found.

As we go up the scale, we find a progressive increase in complexity of organization, and in specialization of cell function. In very rough outline, we have first a differentiation into an outer protective layer of cells and an inner tubular structure which is responsible for nutrition. This ground plan remains recognizable in all animals from the coelenterates (sea anemones, corals, etc.) upwards. In any actual organism, of course, the basic plan is complicated by all the accessories necessary for the animal to feed, move and multiply. A sea anemone is a highly specialized animal, and in the stinging organs on its tentacles it boasts one of the most extraordinarily elaborate offensive weapons in the whole realm of biology, but essentially it has not advanced beyond the two-layered stage. The internal cavity of the anemone is lined by cells specialized for feeding. Some of them seem to liberate enzymes into the cavity to initiate digestion of the shrimps or other small animals that are captured, but the great bulk of digestion is done within the cells which gorge themselves with fragments of food. If the food particle is too large to be taken in completely, the feeding cells crowd around it and digest it in a way which is half-way between true intra-cellular digestion and extra-cellular digestion, as seen in higher animals. The feeding cells of the primitive digestive cavity break down the proteins and other components of the food into suitable 'building stones' which can be passed on as required to those other cells of the organism not capable of taking up food directly. Part of this transfer of food material is carried out by wandering cells like those in the sponges which, for the most part, are found between the two main layers. Again, we find the more or less independent mobile phagocytic cells in between the two primary layers.

With the progress of evolution animals became more complex still, and new sorts of cells began to take a more and more dominant role. If we use the conventional names of ectoderm and entoderm for the two primary layers of cells, these new cells which develop in between them are called mesoderm. It is a convenience for the understanding of embryology to derive the various tissues of the adult animal from one or other of these three layers, although recent research indicates that the three are not so distinct as the older biologists thought. The so-called mesodermal cells are of special interest to us, for all the defence reactions are those of cells ultimately derived from these. Since most of the higher invertebrates and all the vertebrates have a basically similar structure, it may be advisable to give a brief summary of the various parts which arise from the three layers.

The *ectoderm,* as its name implies, is the outer skin of the embryo and gives rise to those parts of the animal which are directly concerned with its environment. It is the layer which as it were separates the organism from the environment, and at the same time is influenced by any changes from outside that impinge upon it. The skin epidermis is the most obvious derivative of the ectoderm, but the capacity of some primitive ectodermal cells to detect changes in the environment has been developed so that not only the sense organs but also the whole nervous system take origin from this layer.

The second layer is the *entoderm*—'inner skin'. This gives rise to the lining of the digestive tract and the various glands and appendages thereof, including the liver, pancreas and lungs of vertebrates.

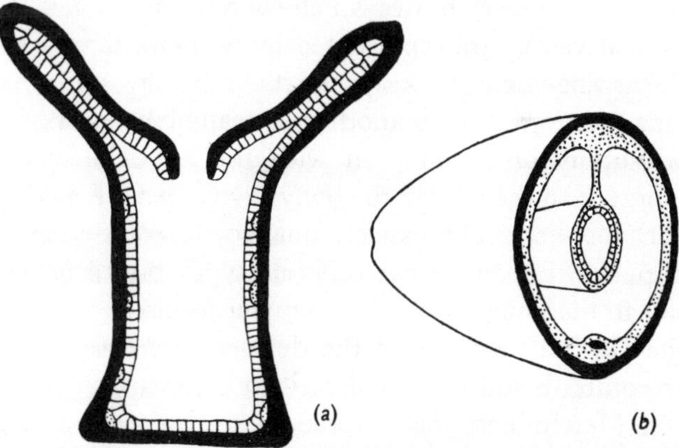

Fig. 2. The primary cell layers in two simple types of animal organism. (*a*) A two-layered organism of the sea-anemone type. (*b*) An unspecialized invertebrate such as the earthworm. The external layer (ectoderm) is shown in solid black, the digestive cell linings (entoderm) in rectangular blocks, and the mesodermal tissues by stippling. Both diagrams are highly conventionalized, and show only the general disposition of the cell layers.

The third, *mesodermal* layer, which was at first represented only by a few wandering phagocytes, eventually gives rise to most of the specialized tissues that are needed to convert the primitive two-layered organism into more efficient forms. From it arise particularly the muscles, the cells involved in holding together the various parts of the body, including in vertebrates the bones and ligaments, the heart, blood vessels and blood, the excretory and the reproductive systems—a very considerable list.

Before we reach the vertebrates, however, we must go a little further into the general way these mesodermal cells are arranged in some of the simpler invertebrates, an earthworm, a larval insect or a small crustacean. In these, as in vertebrates also, the mesodermal cells split into two main groups, one set surrounds the entodermal cells of the digestive tract and supplies the muscular wall and supporting tissues for various parts of the digestive tube, the other supplies all the supporting and accessory tissues for the body proper. Between the two there is a space containing fluid in variable amount—the body cavity. In the invertebrates which we have mentioned, heart and blood vessels are represented by no more than a rather crude arrangement to keep the fluid in the body cavity moving from one part to another. A really efficient system of blood supply only comes in with the appearance of the vertebrates. In the fluid of the body cavity we find once more, as perhaps we might expect, phagocytic wandering cells, perhaps showing one or two different types, but recognizably similar to the phagocytes of the simpler forms.

The classical instance of the defence processes in simple invertebrates is still the one described by Metchnikoff in the 1880's. Metchnikoff was a zoologist by training, and even when his interests were concentrated on the problems of infection and immunity he was liable to embark on researches with outlandish animals that no conventionally trained medical research worker would dream of using. Flat worms, cockchafer grubs, sea anemones and goldfish, all had eventually to contribute their mite to the development of the phagocytic theory. But the theory took its origin apparently from observations on an even more out-of-the-way creature, the water-flea (*Daphnia*). This is a small transparent crustacean living in fresh water and about the size its name would indicate. It is transparent enough and small enough to be observed directly in the living state under the microscope.

Metchnikoff observed the interaction between the water-flea and the spores of a primitive type of fungus which were numerous in the water of his aquarium. These spores were small, narrow and sharply pointed bodies which, when they were swallowed by the crustacean, were liable to penetrate the wall of the digestive canal and pass into the body cavity. When this occurred, the wandering cells of the body fluid were called into activity. They swarmed around the invading particle, covering it with their living substance and partly engulfing it. Soon it was evident that digestion of the living spicule was taking place. Its smooth shiny surface became pitted, its ends rounded, and in time it disintegrated into a walled-in mass of brownish debris.

Sometimes, when several of the sharp spores had entered the body simultaneously, or for some other reason, the activity of the phagocytic cells was ineffectual. The spores germinated, the fungus flourished at the expense of its host, and the water-flea died. Here, it seemed to Metchnikoff, was the prototype of all infectious disease, and of defence against it. The conception of the phagocytes as the defenders of the body was a dramatic and immensely fertile one. Metchnikoff spent most of the rest of his life elaborating it. For him the whole protective mechanism in all animal forms could be regarded as designed only to facilitate and make more efficient the phagocytic attack on the invading microorganisms of disease. Such enthusiasm provoked antagonistic theories, particularly from those who discovered and worked with the antibodies to be found in the serum of immune animals. Two schools of thought flourished, the followers of Metchnikoff, who saw immunity in terms of cells, particularly phagocytic cells, and the German school of immunologists who supported the 'humoral theory' that immunity was a function of the blood and body fluids, not of the cells.

Much water has flowed under the bridges since the days of those naive controversies. We are less inclined now to generalize or to think that the defence of the body against microorganisms makes use only of a limited number of processes. Yet it is probably still helpful to use Metchnikoff's ideas as a basis for our understanding of resistance to infection. On this view all the cooperative processes involving blood vessels, tissue cells and the various elements of the blood itself are directed essentially toward bringing phagocytic cells effectively to bear on the invaders. Any statement like this is necessarily superficial. In every word an infinitely elaborate series of processes and problems is implied. It cannot be true but it may be useful in bringing the sort of understanding needed for practical affairs.

This sketch of the evolution of the defence reactions of the animal body against invasion by microorganisms can supply only the roughest outline. In essence, it is little more than a reiteration adapted to a particular range of circumstances of the theme 'eat or be eaten'. Infectious disease is no more and no less than part of that eternal struggle in which every living organism strives to convert all the available foodstuff in its universe into living organisms of its own species.

Life is everywhere, and every nook and corner that can be exploited for a livelihood is filled. Every living organism is potential food for some other organism, and even if we confine ourselves to the animal kingdom we find an infinite variety of parasitic and semi-parasitic organisms which live at the expense of larger organisms. Every such parasite, be it virus, bacterium, worm or insect, is as much the product of adaptive evolution as its host. The mere fact of its present existence is positive evidence of success in the struggle to survive, and surely indicates a long and detailed adaptation to the particular conditions of its parasitism. The host species of every one of these parasites has also succeeded in surviving. In general terms, where two organisms have developed a host-parasite relationship, the survival of the parasite species is best served, not by destruction of the host, but by the development of a balanced condition in which sufficient of the substance of the host is consumed to allow the parasite's growth and multiplication, but not sufficient to kill the host. For such a balance to develop, long periods of interaction and selection between the two species must have elapsed, and any protective adaptations on the part of the host must have been stimulated by, and in turn would be likely to provoke aggressive adaptations on the side of the parasite. A stable balance is only rarely developed; more usually there are rather violent fluctuations, some of which appear as epidemics, but despite these, both species persist.

It would be impossible to attempt any more detailed account of the slow evolution of this balance between host and parasite. If we went beyond the general principles we have been discussing, it would be necessary to deal with every different type of parasite and almost every host species. In most instances we should have to draw much more on imagination and analogy than on fact in describing possible ways in which the relationship had evolved. In the next three chapters we shall discuss some of the more important parasites, those responsible for infectious disease in the ordinary sense of the term. We shall naturally be concerned only with the present state of affairs, but from this we can learn something of probable trends in evolution, particularly amongst the disease-producing bacteria.

On the side of the host we have an even more complex set of phenomena that will need to be looked at from both functional and evolutionary points of view. Immunology as we have said grew out of the practical needs of medicine. When experiment was needed the ordinary small mammals of the laboratory were used and the experiments were usually directed to human applications. It is only in very recent years that we have recognized that immunity had implications for fundamental biology as well as medicine. Even in 1961 our discussion of immunity must follow an uneven illogical course, moving continually between the practical and the speculative and only occasionally illuminated by flashes of biochemical or evolutionary insight.

Part II

THE AGGRESSORS

CHAPTER III

BACTERIA

While there are parasitic and semi-parasitic forms amongst all classes of living organisms, those responsible for infectious disease are practically limited to three great groups, the bacteria, protozoa and viruses. There are other parasites which may cause disease in man of much the same general quality as these, but they are very much rarer. We may mention worm infections, such as those produced by *Filaria*—the common cause of tropical elephantiasis—hydatid disease, due to the 'bladder' stage of a small tapeworm, and the hookworm infestation of many tropical and subtropical countries. Then there are a few infections with fungi and yeasts—ringworm of the hair is the best known—which on the whole resemble those of the less actively invasive bacteria. All told, however, these various left-overs probably do not produce more than a tenth of 1 per cent of the illness and death produced by the three main groups of microorganisms.

The general conception of a bacterium is familiar to anyone with a smattering of biological knowledge. They are very simple organisms in appearance (but not quite so simple when we study them in detail), small rods or spheres whose size is to be measured in small numbers of μ (μ = 1/1000 mm., 1/25000 in.). Some of them are surrounded by a fringe of mobile hairs (flagella) by which they can move actively. Others have flagella only at one end. A majority have no such appendages, and can move only passively. Inside the body of the bacterium, granules of different sorts can sometimes be seen, but there are no definite organs and no nucleus in any ordinary sense. Nevertheless with appropriate staining methods accumulations of nucleic acid can be observed which seem to be basically equivalent to the chromosomes of higher forms. Since 1947 it has been known that a simple form of sexual union between certain bacteria could occur and that genetic material could be transferred from the 'male' to the 'female' form. This has allowed some brilliant studies of the genetic control of biochemical processes in selected bacteria, but it seems very unlikely that sexual reproduction plays any major part in the life of bacteria in nature. For practical purposes we can regard bacterial reproduction as a simple matter of growth and division, the bacterium elongates, a central constriction forms, and what was one is now two. This is the only method of reproduction followed by most of the bacteria which produce disease. A few have an alternative method adapted to allow survival over a period in environments unfavourable for growth. A round hard-shelled spore appears in the middle of the organism, and inside this the germ can survive in dry conditions for years.

Bacteria are everywhere, in soil, air, water, and particularly in any type of dead organic material. They fill many important roles in the processes by which the various chemical elements pass into and out of living matter, but their pre-eminent function in Nature is to decompose dead organic substance to a form in which it can once again be utilized by plants and indirectly by animals. As living organisms, bacteria require food, both for growth and for the production of energy. This energy may be required in some species for actual movement, but the more important requirement is to maintain its own living structure. All actively living matter requires a constant expenditure of energy to maintain its own physico-chemical structure. In the very simplest of organisms we will encounter some apparent exceptions to this rule, but it undoubtedly holds for all bacteria. The substance of bacteria is built up of the same elements as any other organism, and the proteins, fats and carbohydrates they contain, although they have their own individual characteristics, are basically similar to those in our own bodies.

But whereas all higher plants and animals obtain their needs in the matter of food and energy in what are chemically very stereotyped fashions, an immense variety of processes is found amongst bacteria. There are some which obtain their energy by the oxidation of sulphur or of free hydrogen, some can derive their supply of nitrogen from the atmosphere. Our interest is confined, however, to those which regularly or occasionally produce disease, and to the forms from which these have or may have been derived, and we shall say nothing of the ways in which the unusual forms procure their nourishment.

In the last twenty years there have been quite revolutionary advances in the understanding of bacterial nutrition that are not easy to compress into any simple statement. The outstanding impression one receives from this recent work is the extraordinary synthetic ability of bacteria. Suppose we grow a large quantity of any common bacterium, wash the mass in a centrifuge and then dry the organism down to a white powder. Nowadays bacteriological chemists think nothing of obtaining several pounds of dried bacteria and analysing that amount for its content of whatever substance they may be interested in. It is only a slight distortion of the facts to say that the dried bacteria contain almost the same components as would be found in a similar weight of dried human tissue, liver or kidney, for example. There is an extraordinary basic similarity in the composition of living matter over the whole range of organisms. The proteins are built up of the same twenty amino-acids; the nucleic acids which are combined with protein to play essential parts both in nutrition and reproduction belong to the same two patterns; true fats, phospholipids and sterols are all found in the fatty fraction, and, built into the internal enzyme mechanisms, there are most of the vitamins that are needed by human beings.

Somehow or other all these, and many more complex

chemical structures, must be built up out of material taken up from the environment. The less specialized bacteria can do all this when supplied with little more than all the necessary elements in some water-soluble form, plus a source of energy. These bacteria will grow in a solution of glucose containing nitrate, phosphate, sulphate and chloride, sodium, potassium and magnesium with traces of iron and copper.

The bacteria that cause disease nearly always have more complex requirements: they may for example require several amino-acids ready made and some of the vitamins. It is believed that most pathogenic (disease-producing) bacteria are derived from more robust free-living forms which in the course of taking on a parasitic mode of life have lost their ability to synthesize some essential components. These must be supplied ready-made. When we talk about these food requirements for different bacteria we are referring to results obtained in biochemical laboratories where highly purified salts and organic compounds are available. In nature bacteria live in highly complex environments like soil or any collection of dead organic material. Chemically there will almost always be available in such environments all the elements needed for bacterial growth. Often, however, some components may be locked away in the proteins or other large molecules of organic material. If it is to be made accessible, appropriate enzymes capable of breaking down the material will need to be produced by bacteria in the environment. In practice all sorts of bacteria accumulate in decaying matter, and in one way or another the original substance is converted into the bacterial bodies which in their turn die and are used as food by other bacteria. In the process there is a steady loss of carbon dioxide and nitrogen to the air and of soluble salts to the soil. The end result when, say, a piece of meat is buried is the presence of a little more phosphate and other salts in the neighbouring soil, a small amount of indigestible bacterial polysaccharide and some increase in the complex brown substances that make up a characteristic part of humus.

Bacteria contain no chlorophyll, so that they cannot, like the green plants, utilize the energy of sunlight. They must derive their energy from the chemicals they absorb, often, but by no means invariably, by oxidation of sugars and the like. A great deal has been learnt of the various chemical processes which are involved in this liberation of energy, but the subject is far too technical to be discussed here. There is one aspect, however, which may be of importance in determining the influence of bacteria on the living tissues which they invade, and which must be briefly mentioned. The surface of a bacterium is much more than a simple protective layer or boundary between the organism and its environment. Through it passes everything that the bacterium takes in or excretes. The cell surface is of complex structure not yet fully understood. Complex polysaccharides are nearly always present, and in some bacteria these substances form a relatively thick sticky layer through which substances must diffuse to enter the body of the bacterium. Enzymes are probably present within the surface layers just as they are in the bacterial substance, but the older picture of the bacterial surface as a virtual mosaic of enzymes is now regarded as incorrect.

One of the triumphs of biochemistry in the last decade has been to decipher the processes by which glucose, the common source of energy for living matter, is broken down by bacteria to acetic acid, CO_2 and water. It is vastly more complex than the overall equation,

$$C_6H_{12}O_6 + 2O_2 = 2CH_3 . COOH + 2CO_2 + 2H_2O,$$

would suggest. There are twelve steps each directed by a special enzyme in which the sugar is combined with phosphate split into two parts, its energy concentrated into the form most available for use, the 'energy-rich phosphate bond' of the biochemists, and the residual acetic acid and CO_2 discarded into the surroundings.

There are other almost equally complex chains of reaction in regard to the turnover of any other of the cell components, but we have only a very partial understanding of where the enzymes concerned are located in the cell and how the 'production lines' are organized. There is much to indicate that particular groups of enzymes are held together in granular structures which can be extracted from bacteria by suitable methods.

It is quite impossible to understand anything of what goes on within any living cell without some knowledge of enzyme action, but in the present connexion all that need be stressed is that the living bacterium is a nest of enzymes with a turnover of energy that may be more than a hundred times as great as for the same weight of living human tissue.

The bacterial surface is particularly important. All the nutrients that the organism requires from the environment must pass through the cell wall and everything no longer needed must pass through in the opposite direction. It is obvious that there are subtle arrangements of enzymes on the surface to control the movement of these substances, as well as the structural components of the bacterial wall that have been much more actively studied in recent years. These are intimately concerned in the attack of antibodies and drugs on bacteria as we shall discuss in later chapters. Here we are only interested in noting the intensely foreign quality of a bacterial surface to any human or animal cell that it may enter. Even some of the actual chemical building blocks are completely alien and the various 'patterns' that give the specificity of immunity or of the different types of enzyme have nothing in common with those of the invaded cells. Any contact will be irritant or dangerous, and actively resented by the infected cell.

Since bacteria swarm in all dead organic material, it is only to be expected that some species will exploit the organic debris in or on the bodies of living animals. The residues of digested food in the lower parts of the digestive tract provide a particularly suitable source of food for many species, and it is calculated that about half the bulk of faeces consists of the bodies of bacteria. An immensely active struggle for existence amongst probably hundreds of species of bacteria goes on daily in our bowels, usually without interfering in the slightest with our existence. There are other less obvious localities also available in the body, the linings of the mouth, nose and throat, for example. Bacteria from outside are naturally always lodging here, and there are various mechanisms designed to clear them away. Mucus and saliva are secreted, and in part wash the surfaces clear of bacteria. The surface cells of these linings, and particularly those of the mouth, are constantly being renewed, the outermost which may be damaged by bacteria are being cast off continuously, and their places taken by others formed beneath them. Thus there is always a certain amount of non-living material available for nutrition in the mouth, nose and throat, and certain bacteria have become adapted to a life here. They live mainly on the dead or nearly dead cells lining these mucous membranes, and normally cause no disturbance.

Then we have to consider the scavengers of the skin. Here too the outermost cells are dead, and a continuous renewal from beneath is going on. A food supply is available, and automatically groups of bacteria have developed to utilize it. This applies particularly to the more sheltered parts of the skin, where the surface cells are not so readily rubbed off, and where they are liable to remain moist with sweat for considerable times, for example, in folds of skin or between the toes.

In these three groups of situations we have bacteria constantly present, not actually growing in living tissues, but in immediate contact with them. It would be curious if at some time or other these normally harmless organisms did not overstep their bounds and try to gain their living at the expense of the adjacent living cells. That seems to be the way in which many of the common disease-producing bacteria have in fact evolved. Amongst the common human diseases caused by bacteria, a great many are due to organisms identical with, or at least obviously related to, those found normally in one or other of these situations. And it is particularly impressive that when such bacteria produce disease, the region primarily involved is almost always that which normally harbours those harmless bacteria which the pathogenic type resembles.

In discussing human diseases, it will be necessary to be a little more explicit about the bacteria responsible than we have been up to the present, and a few names will have to be given. The technical names which have been applied to bacteria have usually been based on the shape of the organism, or on the way it grows in artificial cultures. Actually, from the point of view of the medical bacteriologists, these qualities are not of much importance. What bacteria do is of very much more moment than what they look like.

We may introduce most of the necessary names by considering the various groups of harmless bacteria that lurk about the body, and the related more dangerous forms, in a little more detail. Taking the skin first, we find one predominant type of bacterium, the *Staphylococcus*. Coccus is a general term for any bacteria of spherical or nearly spherical form, while the prefix refers to the habit this particular type has of growing in grape-like clusters. Cultures from any portion of the skin will always grow staphylococci, and it is natural that the common local infections of the skin, pimples and boils, should nearly always be due to the same type of germ. We must not be too precise about this relationship. The staphylococci we isolate from a boil are not quite the same as those we get from healthy skin, nor are the more dangerous staphylococci limited to producing skin infections. Blood-poisoning by these germs is rare, but when it occurred in the days before penicillin it was one of the most uniformly fatal of all blood infections. The acute infections of bones which often occur in childhood (osteomyelitis) are also usually due to infections with the *Staphylococcus*. Still, we can be reasonably certain that the staphylococci which produce infections both mild and severe have evolved from the natural inhabitants of the skin, and still show a predilection for living in and infecting the skin. The lining of the nose is essentially an enfolded area of skin and this is another site where staphylococci are nearly always present. Very often the disease-producing type will be found there without causing any inconvenience. In the not uncommon episodes when serious skin infection spreads through a nursery of newborn babies, it is often found that the infection stems from staphylococci carried in the nose of one of the nurses.

In the mucous membranes of the mouth, throat, tonsils, etc., we find a large number of bacterial species. Most of them are of the round coccus type. A group in which the cocci are strung together like beads on a necklace is particularly common in the mouth. These are the streptococci, of which there are many varieties, some harmless, some responsible for serious infections. Another type of coccus which is found in most human throats is the *Pneumococcus,* so called because it is the usual germ responsible for pneumonia. Yet another common group of natural inhabitants of the throat has no simple name, unless we call it the meningococcal group, after the one member of the group which is of medical importance. The *Meningococcus* itself is not infrequently found in normal throats, but only causes trouble when it spreads into the coverings of the brain and produces meningitis. There are many rather similar, but as far as we know harmless, cocci of this group in the nose and throat.

Again we find the same principle emerging, that normal inhabitants of the throat are closely similar to pathogenic (disease-producing) bacteria which produce infections of the throat or adjacent tissues. The commonest of all bacterial infections is probably tonsillitis, which is very commonly streptococcal in origin. Scarlet fever, another disease due to the *Streptococcus,* is also mainly located in the throat. The *Pneumococcus* and the *Meningococcus* have already been mentioned. Their names give the clue to the particular types of infection with which they are associated. The names remind us too that our present point of view neatly reverses that by which the knowledge of these bacteria was gained. Medical bacteriologists have naturally never been particularly interested in bacteria as such. Their interest has been human disease—what caused it, and what could be done about it when the responsible bacterium was isolated. When a particular germ could be isolated from the sputum of 90 per cent of cases of pneumonia, it was natural to call it the *Pneumococcus*. It was only later that bacteriologists began to recognize that the same germ was present in the throats of thousands of people without pneumonia.

The spherical or oval form characteristic of the various types of cocci is by no means the only shape to be found amongst bacteria. Probably the commonest of all the forms is the rod-shaped *bacillus*. In fact, there are so many of these that they have to be divided into at least a dozen different genera. The old term *Bacillus*, which was once the generic name of them all, is now strictly speaking only applicable to one small group, but we shall use it as a general name for all the rod-shaped forms. Amongst the normal bacilli of the mouth and throat we find again two groups, members of which resemble, and are named after, two pathogenic types. These are the diphtheroid bacilli, meaning those which are like, but not identical with, the diphtheria bacillus, and the influenza bacilli. Even at their worst, the so-called influenza bacilli probably play only a very minor role in influenza, but they do on occasion produce infections of the lungs. The diphtheria bacillus has a predilection for the throat which is known to everyone.

Finally, we can apply the same ideas to the bacterial inhabitants of the intestine. Very little is known about some of the bacteria which multiply in the bowel contents, and we need refer only to two groups, both of bacilli. The first contains the anaerobic bacilli, organisms which can grow only when oxygen is excluded from their environment. They are relatively numerous in the intestine, where oxygen is naturally lacking, but only become dangerous when introduced directly into a wound. Gunshot wounds are particularly liable to infection with anaerobic bacteria, especially when they are contaminated with soil which has been manured with animal faeces. Tetanus and gas gangrene were two very common sequelae to serious wounds received in France during the First World War. Both result from infection with anaerobic bacilli, but both must be regarded as being merely accidental results of the growth of the bacilli in tissues they could never naturally infect. Such infections are not really comparable, either to those we have already mentioned, or to those produced by members of the other great group of intestinal bacilli, which we must now discuss.

When the early bacteriologists made their cultures from the intestinal contents or faeces, there was one type of bacillus which almost always predominated on their culture plates. This was called *Bacillus coli communis*—the common bacillus of the colon or large intestine. Nowadays we know that this supposed species contains dozens of varieties of bacteria, and that even so, members of this group represent only a very small proportion of the bacterial species in the intestine. Their apparent preponderance was due mainly to the methods used for culturing the material. Nevertheless, these colon bacilli are very important, for they must be regarded as the parent group from which most of the bacteria which cause intestinal infections are derived. Sometimes we find infections occurring in various parts of the abdomen caused by bacilli which, as far as we can tell, are exactly the same as some found in the normal intestine. Recent work is making it possible to sort out different types amongst the colon bacilli, and it seems certain that two or three specialized types have been responsible for many cases of infant diarrhoea in England during the post-war years. More often the bacteria responsible for the various intestinal infections are distinct species, and although they have doubtless evolved from the *B. coli* stock, they have specialized as disease producers for centuries. The bacilli which cause typhoid fever and dysentery are the most important examples in human disease. Similar types have evolved to attack other animals, and not infrequently we hear of human infections which are caused by bacteria which normally infest rats and mice. Several outbreaks of food poisoning have been found due to food contaminated with bacteria present in the faeces of these rodents.

These examples should be sufficient to show how bacteria which are normally mere scavengers may develop a capacity to attack the living tissues adjacent to their normal habitat. Once they have developed such powers, they may, of course, extend their harmful activities to other parts of the body, but in every one of the examples we have mentioned, the predilection for one particular site of attack is clear.

Anyone with an ordinary layman's knowledge of medicine will recognize that the various bacterial infections we have been discussing are not equally infectious, in the ordinary sense of the term. Diphtheria, scarlet fever and typhoid fever are obviously infectious; boils, wound infections and infections of the urinary passages with the colon bacillus are, practically speaking, quite non-infectious. Actually we shall see when we discuss the question of the spread of disease in a later chapter that the distinction is not quite so clear-cut as it seems. Sore throats due to streptococci can show every degree of infectiousness from a tonsillitis that interests no one but the patient to a particularly virulent brand of scarlet fever. Still there is a real distinction between the two groups which it is important to understand. In general terms, the more a bacterium becomes specialized for a parasitic existence, the more infectious is the disease which results from its activity. The staphylococci which produce boils can survive and multiply harmlessly on the skin, only causing damage when the skin from some cause or other becomes unduly susceptible. The typhoid bacillus, on the other hand, if it cannot penetrate into the living tissues, is quite unable to persist long in the intense competition for the avilable food-stuffs in the intestine. When we come to study bacteria in the laboratory, we find that, as a rule, the bacteria which are responsible for the *infectious* diseases are more difficult to grow on artificial media than the less specialized ones like the staphylococci and the colon bacilli. There are many people who think that we might go a step further and say that bacteria, when they become completely specialized for a parasitic existence, may lose all power of multiplication outside of living cells, become smaller, and take on the form of a filterable virus, but we can leave such speculation till we come to deal with that group.

Without going as far away from the bacteria as this, we might yet expect that certain specialized bacteria might have so concentrated on a parasitic existence that they can be found only in diseased tissues. Their ancestors must have had a free living existence somewhere, but all indications of this have been lost. Amongst the organisms causing human disease, there are four which can be considered as highly specialized parasites, the tubercle bacillus and related bacillus of leprosy and the organisms responsible for the two chief venereal diseases, the *Gonococcus* and the spirochaete of syphilis. This last organism is not strictly a bacterium at all. It is one of a group of spirally twisted organisms, the non-pathogenic examples of which are found in decaying material and polluted waters. These four diseases have been known since classical times, and it is probable that the responsible micro-organisms developed from non-pathogenic ones many thousands of years earlier. The tubercle bacillus and the *Gonococcus* can be made to grow on specially prepared nutritive mixtures, but although countless attempts have been made to do so, no one has succeeded in growing either the leprosy bacillus or the spirochate of syphilis. Perhaps it might be more correct to say that no bacteriologist has ever devised a method by which *other* bacteriologists could grow these organisms successfully. There have been many claims to have done so, but none have stood the test of general confirmation. At present there are hopes that growth of these parasites in tissue culture will soon be possible but there is as yet no certainty of this. It is one of the greatest principles of all scientific work that nothing is accepted into the general body of knowledge until it has been confirmed by other competent workers in the same field.

CHAPTER IV

PROTOZOA

In temperate climates the great majority of infectious diseases are produced by bacteria or viruses; infections by protozoa are relatively very rare. In tropical and subtropical regions, however, we find four human diseases of first-rate importance which are caused by these minute unicellular animal parasites. Malaria is the most widespread and important, and, as well, we have sleeping sickness, kala azar and amoebic dysentery. There are also many economically important diseases of domestic animals which are due to protozoal infections. Research on the protozoa has followed rather different lines from those of orthodox bacteriological research. Most students of the subject have been trained as zoologists, and a large proportion of their work has been concerned with the microscopic appearance of the parasites and with their life histories in infected animals or human beings. Much less work has been done on the nature and extent of immunity which follows infection than in the field of bacteriology proper.

Protozoa are the smallest animal organisms. They are unicellular, and although they are on the average considerably larger than bacteria, none of the forms which produce disease can be seen with the naked eye. There are vastly greater numbers of completely harmless types of protozoa, and if we include the whole group we find a considerable range of size. The smallest forms of such types as the parasite of malaria are no larger than an average bacterium, while amongst the non-parasitic types there are a number which can be easily seen with a small hand-lens, and are actually a good deal larger than some of the smallest insects. A typical protozoon is easily recognized as a true animal organism, not to be confused with unicellular plants and bacteria. It is a single cell with a well-developed nucleus, usually capable of active movement and feeding by taking into its substance and digesting smaller microorganisms of various sorts. In the simpler forms such as the amoeba, movement and the taking in of food are both functions of the general cell substance. Portion of the semi-fluid protoplasm flows out into a sort of temporary organ, a pseudopodium, which then serves either to drag the amoeba along or to help engulf the microorganisms on which it feeds. When the amoeba becomes inactive, the pseudopodia are withdrawn and the protozoon becomes a featureless spherical blob of jelly. More specialized forms have developed quite elaborate permanent mechanisms to facilitate rapid movement and the more effective capture of food. Some free-living protozoal species can, however, obtain their nourishment wholly from soluble materials in their environment.

Protozoa are found in practically every situation which can provide both water and a food supply of smaller microorganisms. Any collection of fresh water in contact with decaying organic matter will usually contain protozoa of various types. Every amateur microscopist is familiar with *Amoeba, Paramoecium* and *Vorticella* from such situations, but there are nearly always many other forms not so easily identified. It is natural that protozoa should be constantly swallowed by all types of animals, and since the contents of the intestinal canal contain both water and an abundance of bacteria, we should expect certain forms to exploit this situation. There is, however, the important difference that life in the intestine must go on in the absence of oxygen. Only those forms which are capable of anaerobic existence can become intestinal parasites. Actually there is probably no species of vertebrate which is free from infestation by protozoa in its intestinal tract. At least a dozen species are known to be capable of living in the human intestine. Insects too are very frequently found to harbour parasitic protozoa in their digestive tracts. Originally such protozoa probably lived on bacteria and particles of semi-digested food, but like bacteria in similar situations, some of them have developed the capacity to live directly on the cells and fluids of their hosts. Our knowledge of the evolution of parasitic protozoa must necessarily be obtained only indirectly by comparison of the habits of the pathogenic forms with structurally similar free-living and semi-parasitic forms. Such studies do, however, provide a substantial basis for deduction, and have given rise to theories which offer an attractive interpretation of what otherwise would be a series of unconnected and very complicated phenomena.

The four important protozoal diseases of man (or for that matter practically all protozoal infections of vertebrates) can be divided into two groups: those in which the infection is transmitted directly from man to man, with the one human example of amoebic dysentery, and those in which the parasite is transferred by an insect intermediary—malaria, sleeping sickness and kala azar. It is generally believed that the first group is derived from protozoa which were originally harmless scavengers in the vertebrate intestine, while the forms in the second group are more or less highly specialized descendants of protozoa playing a similar role in the intestine of insects.

Amoebic dysentery is due to a relatively unspecialized parasite, an amoeba very similar to forms which normally make a living amongst the bacteria and debris of the intestinal contents, and not greatly different from the free-living amoeba of pond water. Instead of being content with a diet of bacteria, the disease-producing amoeba has developed a capacity to invade the tissues of the intestinal wall and draw its nourishment from red blood cells and fragments of damaged tissue. In a serious infection with the virulent form of *Entamoeba histolytica,* the amoeba seems to excrete enzymes which break down neighbouring cells—hence the name *histolytica*—and to gain its nourishment primarily by absorbing soluble material from its environment. This destructive action results in the formation of ulcers in the wall of the intestine and the appearance of the symptoms of dysentery. From the ulcers some amoebae may enter the blood and be carried to the liver. Multiplication of the protozoa in the liver produces the commonest complication of amoebic dysentery—a liver abscess.

From the biological point of view, we are dealing here with a development very similar to the change from the harmless skin staphylococci to the virulent ones which cause boils and carbuncles. Like the staphylococci, the dysentery amoebae may show wide differences in virulence. Many people may harbour the parasite without suffering any symptoms at all. In these individuals the amoeba probably causes only trivial ulcerations of the bowel. The reasons for these differences are still not understood. The possibilities are, first, that there are inheritable differences in the infecting strains of *Entamoeba* and the severity of a man's attack depends simply on whether he is infected with a highly virulent strain or not. The second possibility is that resistance will vary according to the state of nutrition and general health in the person infected plus, as in all such situations, the effect of genetic or constitutional differences in resistance. A third factor that may well be important is the coexistence of bacterial or viral infection in the bowel. It may be that the amoebae find it much easier to initiate infection in an intestinal lining damaged by infection of some other type. Where amoebic dysentery is rife we naturally find many opportunities for all forms of intestinal infection. There is probably a continual entry of new strains of amoebae each, as it were, being subjected to the test of survival in this particular intestine. Sooner or later in one set of circumstances or another the strain with or without the assistance of some other type of infection will find it possible to invade and damage the body. This is one of the infections in which there is little evidence of immunity following an attack, a fact which in itself suggests that the 'standard' amoeba requires some additional factor to allow it to produce serious illness.

We do not know for how long amoebic dysentery has afflicted human beings. It is probable that it was derived from an infection of the common Asian monkeys. The ubiquitous rhesus monkey of India usually carries an amoeba indistinguishable from the human *Entamoeba histolytica* but suffers no ill effects. South American monkeys on the other hand are liable to contract dysentery similar to the human disease when they are artificially infected. It is another example of the rule that long association of host and parasite is evidenced by little or no power to produce serious symptoms or death.

It is not so simple a story when we try to understand the evolution of such specialized parasites as those which cause malaria and sleeping sickness. In the case of sleeping sickness we have an infection, first of the blood, then of the brain, by a protozoon parasite which is transmitted by the bite of the tsetse fly. The parasites are members of a group of actively moving protozoa which in their typical form are called trypanosomes. Many, however, can take on a variety of appearances including a non-motile form analogous to the Leishmania which is responsible for kala azar. Only two species are capable of producing sleeping sickness in man, but several others produce rather similar diseases of domestic animals. The tsetse fly cycle will commence when the insect sucks in infected blood from some vertebrate carrier. Multiplication can take place in several regions of the tsetse's digestive tract. Everything suggests that this particular group of African trypanosomes evolved from species which lived harmlessly in the far end of the intestine. There is still some which multiply only in this situation, but the important forms that are responsible for sleeping sickness in man and fatal disease of horses have developed a complex cycle which eventually lodges the trypanosomes in the insect's salivary glands ready for injection into a new host. It takes about two to four weeks for this development to take place in the fly, and during this period it cannot transmit the infection. Once the salivary glands are infected, however, trypanosomes will be injected at each feeding. The tsetse fly remains capable of spreading infection for at least three months after the trypanosomes first reach the salivary glands.

We can see some of the stages by which this complex life history of the sleeping sickness trypanosome probably came into being by looking at the simpler life histories of some related protozoa. There is, for instance, one which infects the blood of some species of lizards. The infection is derived from a small biting fly by the very simple process of the lizard swallowing the fly. The parasite is liberated in the intestine and passes through the wall into the lizard's blood, where it multiplies. The next stage is for a new fly to be infected while it sucks the lizard's blood. The protozoa now find themselves, as it were, in their ancestral home and multiply in the lower end of the fly's intestine, behaving just like any protozoal parasites of insects which have no part of their life cycle in vertebrates.

The next step can be seen in one of the African tsetse flies which carries a trypanosome that infects crocodiles. In the insect the protozoon is limited to the lower end of the bowel and the crocodile is infected by contamination of the bitten points with the fly's faeces.

A rather similar, but probably independent, line of evolution was concerned in the development of the South American form of trypanosome disease (Chagas' disease). This protozoon is found naturally in armadillos and other native mammals. It is taken in by a species of bug which has catholic tastes and feeds on men as well as armadillos. The trypanosomes develop in the bug's intestine and pass out with the faeces. They do not get into the insect's saliva, and are not injected when the bug bites. Human infections develop only if the bug is crushed while it is biting, or if scratching of the spot works fragments of faeces into the puncture wound. Chagas' disease in man is a chronic infection of lymph glands and other internal organs which may be very difficult to diagnose. In 1959 it was suggested by a very distinguished protozoologist that Chagas' disease was responsible for Charles Darwin's chronic illness which has puzzled all his biographers. In the course of his travels in South America during the voyage of the *Beagle*, Darwin records that on at least one occasion he was extensively bitten by the huge *Triatoma* which carry the infection. His illness dated from the time of his return to England and perhaps helped to provide that almost unique combination of circumstances that allowed the idea of evolution to come to its full expression in *The Origin of Species*.

Kala azar, which in the period 1890–1905 was one of the major plagues of south-east Asia, is due to a protozoon that closely resembles that of Chagas' disease. Some authorities in fact believe that kala azar and some types of skin infection are all due to modern variants of the same species brought from South or Central America to Asia and the Mediterranean region in the first century after Columbus's discovery. Both in America and elsewhere these diseases, generically called Leishmaniasis, are spread by sandflies (*Phlebotomus*). The protozoon multiplies in the stomach of the sandfly to produce large numbers of motile forms and, much as happens in the flea infected with plague bacilli, some have to be regurgitated before the sandfly can take a new blood meal. Both dogs and human beings can be infected and, depending on the age of the victim and individual differences between protozooan strains, the result may be a limited skin infection (Oriental sore) or a general infection of variable severity.

Malaria needs a chapter to itself and here we need say only a little to bring its evolution into line with that of the other protozoal diseases. The organisms responsible for the three forms of human malaria are all spread by mosquitoes of the genus *Anopheles*. In simplified outline the mosquito injects a tiny malarial form into the blood which carries it to the liver. There it infects liver cells and multiplies to produce a store of descendants from which the red cells of the blood are infected. Multiplication for a few generations in the blood is associated with destruction of cells, each wave of destruction being the signal for a paroxysm of fever. Subsequently sexual forms appear which, when they are taken into a mosquito, unite to give rise to cysts from which a new generation of parasites can reach the salivary gland. At all stages the essential part of the process is multiplication inside a cell to produce a brood of descendants which then break out from the cell and pass to whatever type of cell is appropriate for the next stage in the cycle.

It is highly probable that the malarial parasites are related to the protozoa responsible for the diseases of rabbits and fowls that we call coccidiosis. In these the disease is primarily in the wall of the intestine. The whole process is broadly similar, but instead of infecting a mosquito the sexual form develops into a resistant cyst which passes out with the faeces. It is only by this form of the parasite that a new individual of the right species can be infected.

In this, as in the other examples of disease due to protozoa, we can only make speculative suggestions about the evolution of the microorganisms and of the diseases they produce. We shall have more to say about the general problems of infectious disease in later chapters, but here already we can see some outlines of the pattern that will emerge. It is very evident that when a parasite and its host have lived together for very many generations the association is a balanced one with little evidence of damage to the host. The African trypanosomes do no visible harm to the game animals that are their natural hosts, nor the *Entamoeba histolytica* to the rhesus monkey.

Partly because of the absence of simple technical methods for their demonstration, there has been relatively little work on antibodies and immunity against protozoal disease. There is evidence of immunity, but in most instances it is an 'immunity of infection' that disappears soon after the parasites are finally eliminated from the body. Individuals born and growing up in a heavily malarious environment will, if they survive, show no symptoms of malaria in adult life. They are infected, but they have developed sufficient immunity to keep the multiplication of the parasite down to a harmless level. Compared to the importance of immunity in bacterial and virus diseases, immune reactions are of only minor importance in protozoal disease. In the future we may find that the most important biological problem of protozoal infections is *why* they provoke so little immunity. There is therefore nothing to be gained by looking for artificial ways of emulating a nonexistent post-infection immunity and control of all these diseases has had to be sought on other lines.

The first is to modify the ecological situation so as to block some point in the cycle by which the parasite survives. The second is to find and use drugs which can damage the parasite while doing minimal harm to the cells of the host. Both approaches will be more appropriately dealt with in later pages.

CHAPTER V

VIRUSES

The golden age of bacteriology was in the 1880's, when Pasteur had laid the foundation of the science and the solid genius of Koch was providing the technical methods and the scientific point of view. Young men from Koch's laboratory had all the world of infectious disease before them to conquer. They investigated every disease which might be due to infection by some microorganism, and almost invariably found bacteria. The more fortunate workers found the right bacteria, and so established the cause of anthrax, diphtheria, typhoid fever and so on, but others were less fortunate. The bacteria which they isolated from cases of measles, influenza or smallpox turned out to have nothing to do with the disease, and it gradually became evident that there were some infectious diseases which were caused by agents smaller than bacteria and protozoa.

Quite early in the history of bacteriology, a Dutchman, Beijerinck, found that the agent responsible for the mosaic disease of the tobacco plant could pass through the pores of a porcelain filter candle which could keep back all bacteria. This was the first discovery of a filterable virus. Then, just at the turn of the century, two German workers found that the germ of foot-and-mouth disease of cattle could also pass through such filters, and established the existence of filterable viruses causing disease in animals. It was gradually recognized that other diseases such as smallpox and measles were due to filterable viruses, but it took years before adequate methods of experimental investigations were developed.

Around 1930 new technical methods rather suddenly made it possible to isolate and characterize a considerable proportion of the viruses responsible for serious disease. Since then progress has been rapid and when it was realized that the very simplicity of viruses had enormous virtues for biochemical attack on some of the most fundamental aspects of life, virology became literally one of the major branches of biology. It is true to say in 1961 that the most deeply studied of all living organisms are the bacterial virus T_2, the plant virus TMV and two animal viruses, those of poliomyelitis and of influenza.

To summarize the essence of what we know of viruses in a single chapter will only be possible if we concentrate rather closely on our special theme of their significance in disease of man and the animals that interest him.

It is not practicable to define a virus in any simple terms and the most practical definition is to say that a virus is a microorganism (or self-replicating agent of disease) which will multiply only within living cells of suitable type. To this we must add the requirement that it is too small for ordinary microscopic methods to be used in its study. The electron microscope is, however, now a standard laboratory tool and beautifully detailed pictures of even the smallest viruses are now available. Some would add an additional point to this definition by saying that a virus is composed of protein and one or other of the two standard types of nucleic acid that we call DNA and RNA.

A few years ago it was necessary to spend many words in describing indirect ways by which the shape and chemical composition of the different viruses could be established. With the immense advances in physical and chemical methods, we can now be more direct and positive. Before attempting to describe the structure of viruses, however, a little must be said about nucleic acids. These are now accepted as the key molecules that carry the 'information' that allows a cell or a virus to reproduce itself like to like. In the chromosomes of all cells we find the primary form which we can call simply DNA. It is composed of extremely long thread-like molecules which can be thought of as a tape on which information is recorded in code. The chromosomes have, in fact, often been compared to the strong room of a factory in which all blue prints, punch cards, electronic programme tapes, and the like, are stored to be issued as required. The second type of nucleic acid, RNA, has a similar but more workaday structure and function. It is produced in the nucleus to the order of the DNA but functions mainly in the cytoplasm of the cell. If we hold on to the same simile, the RNA represents the working drawings and the jigs which control the producing machines. In the cell RNA guides the production of proteins needed for enzymes and the other functioning parts or products of the cell. Reproduction of living material is guided by this cooperation of DNA and RNA. Without them any sort of reproduction is impossible, but viruses are unique in having either DNA or RNA but not both.

There are several basic patterns to be found in the structure of viruses responsible for disease of man and other animals. Fortunately at least one example of each group has been studied in detail. Without attempting to tell how the information was obtained we can describe the size, structure and composition of most of the important viruses within these type forms. One thing should be emphasized at once. We are describing the 'infectious phase' of the virus, the particles which passing from one infected host to another susceptible individual convey the disease. When a virus is actually multiplying in a cell it is something very different.

In a recent survey of the animal viruses, Andrewes has pointed out that about 90 per cent of those that have been described can be placed in six major groups with rather well-defined characters. These groups are defined on the size and structure of the virus and the type of nucleic acid that it contains. Andrewes has given names to each group but only some of these names have as yet been generally adopted. It will be logical then to describe viruses by taking one typical example responsible for human disease from each group.

The first group contains the smallest of the known viruses and polio virus can serve as our example. The unit in which viruses are measured is the millimicron (mμ) or 10^{-7} cm., and the diameter of these very small viruses which Andrewes calls Naniviruses (nana: a dwarf) is about 25–30 mμ. In round figures nearly one million such particles could be lined up in one inch. The individual particles are roughly spherical and consist of a regular arrangement of sixty spherical protein molecules in a 'cage' that encloses the RNA of the virus. There is nothing but nucleic acid and protein in the virus particles of this group of viruses and they are so uniform in size and character that they will pack into regular arrays. They are *crystalline* viruses. The polio viruses are the best known examples of a very large assemblage of similar small viruses that are found in the intestine of man and most other animals that have been studied. These have been called collectively the enteroviruses. In addition the viruses responsible for foot-and-mouth disease in cattle certainly belong to this group and it seems likely that some at least of the common cold viruses first isolated in 1959–60 will find a home here.

The next important group in order of size contains the viruses that are carried by mosquitoes and produce yellow fever, dengue and a variety of other diseases. Generically they are known as *Arborviruses,* not because they live in trees but because they are 'arthropod-borne'. These have not been so effectively studied as poliovirus, but everything suggests that they differ only in including a rather high proportion (30 to 50 per cent) of fatty material (lipid) in their structure. They may well have just the same amount of protein and nucleic acid (RNA) as poliovirus, but particles are a little larger, not so uniform in size, and a little more indistinct in electron microscope pictures.

The *Myxoviruses* include the various influenza viruses and a number of others including mumps virus. Although these viruses also contain only RNA, the particles are bigger and more complex. Expressed rather crudely, an influenza or mumps virus is a bag made up of protein and lipid within which is a coiled-up mass of protein-nucleic acid units, each of which is more or less equivalent to a small virus like polio.

The whole thing is from 80 to 100 mμ in diameter and roughly spherical. The outer coat (the bag) shows regularly packed protein molecules embedded in material which seems to be derived from the layer of fatty molecules on the surface of the cell in which the virus grew. The interior units are rather screw-like objects in which protein molecules are arranged in spiral fashion around a core that includes nucleic acid. The next group includes the *Adenoviruses* which are responsible for a variety of infections of throat, eye and respiratory passages. These have a geometrically regular shell of twenty triangular faces (an icosahedron) composed of protein molecules, with DNA this time inside the shell. The particles are about the same size as influenza virus and as they form in the cell nucleus they pack together into a crystalline array.

The next group (*Nitaviruses*) includes a number of important viruses of about the same size as the last two groups. Human diseases for which such viruses are responsible include herpes simplex (cold sores of the lips), herpes zoster (shingles), measles and chickenpox. This is not a very well-studied group and they are put together mainly because they all produce a characteristic change in the nucleus of infected cells. The only one that has been properly studied (herpes virus) has a geometrically regular structure with 152 protein units and contains DNA.

Finally, we have the *Poxviruses* which include the virus of smallpox and the closely related vaccinia virus used for vaccination against smallpox. This is considerably larger and oval in shape with its three diameters approximately 225 × 150 × 100 mμ. There is a complicated internal structure made up essentially of protein and DNA and resembling in many ways a bacterial spore.

Most of the viruses responsible for human disease have now been isolated and shown to fall into one or other of the groups we have just mentioned. This information, however, tells us very little about what happens when a virus produces disease or how we should expect to study viruses in the laboratory.

The next step then is to concentrate on the second half of our definition of viruses—that they can grow only in living susceptible cells.

This, of course, is the reason why the early bacteriolgists failed to discover the cause of diseases like measles and influenza. The viruses responsible were quite unable to grow on the nutrient mixtures which were so successful for the cultivation of bacteria. In recent years, much more refined methods have been used in attempts to persuade viruses to grow outside the living cell, but they have all been unsuccessful. It seems probable, in fact, that the viruses are too small to pack within themselves all the complicated mechanisms necessary for an independent existence. Virus multiplication within the host cell is completely unlike what happens when bacteria multiply in a nutrient fluid. Perhaps the best way to express the difference is to say that when a virus infects a susceptible cell we are dealing with the intrusion of one genetic system into the domain of another. In some ways infection is like fertilization of an egg cell. In each case genetic information has come in to interact with that originally present and to set the cell on a new course of behaviour. Once a virus particle has initiated infection in a cell it disappears just as a spermatozoon disappears at the act of fertilization. The infected cell is a new biological unit with its own natural history and only when a cycle of development has been completed does it again contain and eventually liberate a new brood of virus particles.

The limitation of virus growth to living cells makes it necessary to use methods for the experimental study of viruses which are quite different from the methods of orthodox bacteriology. Living cells are necessary for all such work and in recent years the trend has been toward the almost exclusive use of cells grown in tissue culture. Broadly speaking, experimental work with viruses has two requirements. In the first place we must have suitable conditions to allow virus growth which in practice means providing susceptible cells whether in an animal, in an embryo, or in tissue culture. Secondly we must have some sign by which we can recognize the fact that the virus we are dealing with *has* grown.

Thirty years ago all experimental work on virus was based on the use of small laboratory animals which when appropriately inoculated would show symptoms as a result of the multiplication of virus in susceptible tissues. Poliomyelitis in children was obviously a disease of the spinal cord and until nearly 1950 the only method for its laboratory study was to inject into the brain or spinal cord of monkeys. If the monkey showed paralysis with typical pathological changes in the spinal cord we could be certain that there had been polio virus in what was inoculated. Rather similarly, influenza virus was first studied in ferrets which are the only animals known to respond to infection with the virus with symptoms and tissue changes in the respiratory passages almost the same as those in the human disease.

Monkeys and ferrets are rather too large and too expensive for convenient use in the laboratory and for a very important phase of virus research the main aim was to adapt viruses so that they would multiply and produce lesions in the most convenient of all experimental animals, the mouse. There are no virus diseases of man that are 'infectious' in the ordinary sense for mice, but there are many which can multiply in one or other tissue if they are inoculated directly into that tissue. Most viruses which produce infections of the nervous system can be persuaded to multiply in the mouse brain if they are inoculated there. Influenza virus will multiply in the mouse lung and after a few transfers from one mouse to another will produce pneumonia in the form of red airless regions in the lung. Once we have a virus adapted to produce easily recognized effects such as death, paralysis or pneumonia, we are in a position to carry out quantitative work on such crucial matters as finding whether patients have developed antibody against the virus or in developing a vaccine against the disease.

The next development was the utilization of chick embryos for virus research. This has some important advantages over mouse inoculation. On the whole, embryonic cells are highly susceptible to attack by viruses and there are many different ways of inoculating eggs to allow virus to reach the most susceptible tissues. In addition there are no bacteria in a chick embryo inside its shell and we can see the effects of virus infection without being worried by doubts as to whether bacteria were partly responsible.

Most inoculations are made when the embryo is about halfway through its incubation. By this time a rather complex system of membranes and cavities has developed. There is the yolk which is the main source of nourishment for the chick, now almost surrounded by a living membrane (the yolk sac), then there are two water jackets, the amniotic and allantoic cavities containing clear fluid, and, close against the shell, the thin chorioallantoic membrane which spreads as the embryo develops till it completely lines the shell. This membrane has a rich blood supply, and is really a temporary lung, since its function is to take up oxygen from the air and liberate carbon dioxide. Probably the simplest way of using the chick embryo is to deposit virus on this chorioallantoic membrane. Suppose, for example, we place a drop of vaccine lymph, diluted to about one ten-thousandth of its original strength, on each of four egg membranes. The eggs are then returned to the incubator and opened after two days further incubation. When we examine the membranes we find that there are pock-like spots scattered over them. Each of these spots represents the point where a virus particle has lodged, infected a cell and set going the process which eventually produces a visible pock. By counting the number of pocks on each membrane, taking an average and doing the appropriate arithmetic, we can then calculate relatively accurately how many living virus particles were present in the original lymph. This was the first technique to be developed for using the chick embryo in virus work. Around 1940 it was found that influenza virus could be isolated by inoculating throat washings from patients into the inner amniotic cavity and that for many purposes the outer (allantoic) water jacket was an even more suitable site for influenza multiplication. A little later the yolk sac was also found to have special virtues for the growth of some viruses and particularly for those organisms which as it were lie half way between bacteria and viruses, the rickettsiae which cause typhus fever and similar diseases.

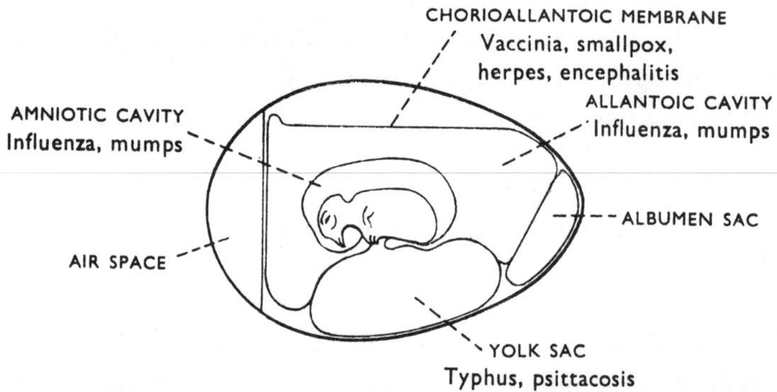

Fig. 3. A conventionalized diagram of the chick embryo about half-way through incubation to show the sites used for growth of different viruses and rickettsiae.

Tissue culture was applied to the growth of viruses as early as 1926, but it did not become the dominant technique until the 1950's. Embryonic cells, or adult cells which for any reason have taken on embryonic qualities, can easily be grown in tubes or bottles if they are provided with the appropriate mixture of salts and nutrient fluids and the necessary precautions taken to protect them from bacterial contamination. The commonest method is to let the cells grow on the surface of a glass container, but there are ways by which some cells can grow and multiply when freely suspended in the nutrient fluid. If we start from normal body cells, for example, cells from a monkey kidney, these will multiply readily for a few generations but not indefinitely. If these are to be used for the growth of polio virus, the usual procedure is to obtain a thin suspension of cells from the kidney by gentle treatment with the enzyme trypsin. These are then allowed to settle to the bottom of a thin layer of nutrient fluid where each cell forms a centre of multiplication. In a few days' time when there is an almost continuous sheet of cells, the virus is added and in another three to four days has multiplied to its maximal amount.

There are some cells, especially cells which have developed the heightened capacity for multiplication that is typical of cancer cells, which can go on multiplying indefinitely in tissue culture. Several such lines of cells are widely used in virus research, the best known being the strain HeLa from a human cancer. By using such strains we can free virus research completely from its dependence on experimental animals. A constant supply of growing cells is maintained and whenever an experiment is to be set up the required number of tubes or bottles are seeded with the cells and used after an appropriate period of preliminary incubation.

A method of growing viruses is of no particular use unless we can find visible evidence that growth has in fact occurred. Fortunately most viruses when they multiply in tissue culture damage or kill the cells. If we wish to find how much active poliovirus there is in a certain fluid there are two ways we can do this in tissue culture. Both depend on the fact that dead cells are easily differentiated from living ones. In the first we make a series of dilutions 1 in 10, 1 in 100, 1 in 1000, and so on. From each of these we place a standard volume into a small number of tubes that three or four days previously had been seeded with susceptible cells. The tubes are now incubated for four days and then examined with a lens or low-power microscope. If virus has multiplied the cells will appear rounded and granular and instead of a smooth sheet of cells on the glass there will be bare ragged patches. From the distribution of such positive tubes and of the negative ones with undamaged sheets of cells, we can easily calculate the amount of active virus in the original material.

The second method is a more elegant one. For this we have cells distributed over the bottom of shallow glass dishes and grown long enough to give a confluent sheet. The virus is added and left about an hour to allow the virus units to attach to cells. Fluid is now removed and the cell layer gently imbedded in a soft jelly. After further incubation we find the development of *plaques* of virus growth. These are round areas of damage that have been produced by the offspring of a single virus particle. From the cell initially infected the first generation of descendant particles has infected immediately adjacent cells and from them others further out have been involved until after four or five days we have a circular area a few millimetres across. The number of plaques is, of course, a measure of the amount of virus that was present.

With this background of knowledge about the sizes and general character of the viruses which cause disease in man and animals, we can go on to discuss the position of the viruses amongst living organisms.

First of all we want to know how widespread are viruses in nature, what sorts of organisms in addition to ourselves and our domestic animals are susceptible to virus diseases. The answer to that question is comprehensive. Every major type of organism which has been studied closely enough has been shown to be susceptible to attack by viruses of some sort. Even the bacteria suffer from virus diseases. Their viruses are called bacteriophages—eaters of bacteria. For the most part, bacteriophages are mere objects of academic interest, but occasionally they make some stir in the world. Their discoverer, d'Herelle, thought at one time that it was only a matter of collecting and 'training' suitable bacteriophages to eliminate bacterial disease from mankind. Unfortunately, when these ideas were applied in practice the results of treating bacterial diseases with appropriate bacteriophages were very disappointing. In regard to Asiatic cholera, however, there is some evidence that the activity of the cholera germ in causing disease, and more particularly in initiating epidemics, can be reduced by the administration of active bacteriophages to persons in the threatened area.

In a completely different field we may mention two instances in which the activity of bacteriophages against useful bacteria has been of economic importance. In New Zealand, as in other up-to-date dairying countries, the fermentation of milk in the production of cheese is initiated with cultures of streptococci specially selected for their power to produce acid and to give a satisfactory flavour to the cheese. A great deal of trouble has been encountered because these 'starter' cultures at various times seem to commit suicide and a whole batch of milk fails to curdle correctly. The difficulty was traced to bacteriophage action, but exactly why these specially selected strains should be susceptible to the virus has not yet been determined.

The other example is the diminution in productivity of a field of lucerne (or alfalfa) after it has been growing for a few years. Lucerne is a leguminous plant which obtains much of its nitrogen supply by the action of special bacteria living in nodules on the roots. According to certain workers, the diminished productivity of a stand of lucerne, which undoubtedly occurs in some regions, is due to the activity of bacteriophages in destroying or reducing the numbers of root nodule bacteria whose nitrogen-fixing activities are essential to the plant's well-being.

When three such different types of bacteria as the cholera germ, the milk streptococci and the root nodule bacteria are all susceptible to bacteriophages, it is only natural to expect that nearly all other bacteria will also be susceptible. This is the fact. For a long time the tubercle bacillus was the only important exception to the rule, but several phages were active against related bacteria and there is a recent claim which seems to be soundly based that the true tubercle bacillus can be attacked by one type of phage.

The relation of bacteriophages to the diphtheria bacillus is particularly interesting because for a diphtheria bacillus to produce toxin it appears to be necessary that it should be chronically infected with a low-grade bacteriophage. This type of chronic infection is termed lysogeny and examples can be found in virtually all the types of bacteria subject to phage attack. It is a condition which has opened up fascinating and subtle problems in regard to the relationship between the genetic materials of the bacterial host and the virus parasite.

During the 1950's bacterial viruses were very closely studied by biochemists and geneticists and we probably know more about their structure, composition and interaction with their bacterial hosts than we do about any other viruses. They are very small, but typical forms like T_2 have a surprisingly elaborate structure. There is a hexagonal head, a shell of protein within which is a tightly packed mass of DNA, an elongated hollow tail surrounded by a contractile sheath of protein and ending with a bunch of protein filaments that are responsible for anchoring the virus to the surface of the attached bacterium.

Two interesting findings amongst many can be mentioned. In the classical bacteriophage T_2 the structure of DNA differs from that of every other known DNA. From bacteria to man all DNA has a standard chemical pattern. Only T_2 and its relatives differ and one is tempted to think that we have here evidence of two independent origins of life on earth. The other feature of note concerns the readiness with which hybrid virus forms can be produced after double infection. For technical reasons the 'fine structure', of the chromosome of the virus T_2 and its relative T_4 is known in more detail than for any other organism.

There are viruses which attack plants, extraordinary numbers of them. Probably all plants are susceptible to some virus, but experimental work has naturally been concentrated on the diseases of economically important crops. The staple cereal crops are relatively immune to virus disease, while the solanaceous plants, potato, tobacco and tomato, are particularly susceptible. Plant viruses have nothing to do with disease in animals or man, and we need only touch on two points in regard to them which provide some useful information in regard to the biological position of viruses in general.

The virus of tobacco mosaic disease, as we have mentioned, was the first virus to be proved filterable, and, ever since, most of the fundamental work on the nature of plant viruses has been done with this example. In the tobacco plant the virus multiplies enormously, so much so that in the squeezed-out sap of an infected plant the actual bulk of virus is so great that it constitutes about 80 per cent of the total protein present. In the infected tissues of animals the actual weight of virus present is extremely small, and it is an expensive and tedious process to obtain any significant amount of purified virus for chemical examination. There is no such limitation with tobacco mosaic virus, and for nearly twenty years since Stanley first prepared it in near-crystalline form, it has been studied intensively. The excitement that greeted the discovery that something could at the same time be a virus and a crystalline protein has faded with the years. More than a dozen plant viruses have been isolated since then, some of them in crystalline form. Tobacco mosaic virus, TMV, still remains the favoured object of study and over the years all the techniques of modern biochemistry have been applied to it. We now can visualize its giant molecules as hollow rods made up of a thread of RNA spiralling down through the substance of the rod which itself is composed of hundreds of uniform protein molecules packed in a regular flat spiral. The individual molecules are rather small with a molecular weight of 18,000 and in 1960 two independent and essentially concordant results were announced giving the complete arrangement of amino-acids in TMV protein.

A spectacular discovery in 1956 by Gierer and Schramm showed that the RNA could be separated from the protein by a simple chemical method and was still infectious. This had great influence on the whole of biology because it showed by direct experiment what was gradually becoming clear for other reasons, viz. that all the 'information' needed to allow virus development including synthesis of its characteristic protein was carried in nucleic acid. It was not long before it was found that the same separation of infectious RNA was possible in the small animal viruses.

The other point of interest in regard to plant viruses that needs brief discussion is the existence of quite invisible latent infections. For instance, there are varieties of potato which grow perfectly normally without any of the usual signs of virus disease. If we rub a little of their sap on to the leaves of a tobacco plant, we find symptoms of a severe virus infection appearing in the tobacco. The potato variety consistently carries in its sap and tissues a latent virus. This phenomenon is very common amongst plants. Most of the 'new' virus diseases which arise in crop plants from time to time are probably derived from native plants which are infected in this latent fashion. The virus is transferred by plant-sucking insects, and, once it finds the new susceptible host, spreads widely. An interesting horticultural example concerns the 'breaking' of tulips. Until the middle of the sixteenth century, tulips were all self-coloured, i.e. the petals were of one uniform colour. At that period it was found that certain stocks developed variegations of petal colour which persisted as long as the stock was kept going from bulbs. When new plants were grown from seed, however, the flowers were again self-coloured and it was usually several years before 'breaking' occurred, giving the variegated more valuable form. Quite recently it has been shown that all that is required to induce 'breaking' at will is to inoculate the tulip with a drop of juice from certain lilies. 'Breaking' is really a symptom of a virus infection, usually derived from one of several species of lily which themselves show no symptoms whatever. When we come to consider questions of transfer of infection from one animal to another, we shall encounter very similar phenomena.

As to the viruses which infect animals, we find again that

every group of animals important enough economically to be the subject of detailed research has been shown to suffer from virus disease. Amongst invertebrates, the bee and the silkworm are the only domesticated forms. Both have their virus diseases, 'sac-brood' of bees and jaundice or 'grasserie' of silkworms. There is one known virus of fishes and one of frogs. The domestic fowl is subject to four well-known virus infections, and there are several others less adequately studied. Parrots suffer from psittacosis, and at least one other type of virus disease. Every domestic mammal is subject to poxes and plagues, nearly all of virus origin. Sheep-pox, cowpox, horsepox, swine fever, cattle plague, dog distemper, South African horse sickness, and so on, form an almost endless list that is constantly being lengthened. Man himself is subject to a wide variety of virus diseases. They range from the classical plagues of smallpox and yellow fever to trivial infections like herpes of the lips and the common cold. Most of the viruses responsible have been isolated in the sense of having been transferred to some laboratory animal in which symptoms can be produced or to some type of cell in tissue culture which shows visible evidence of damage by the virus. Tissue culture methods have been particularly successful in recent years. The viruses of measles and chickenpox as well as a wide variety of viruses responsible for ill-defined infections of the respiratory system or of the bowel have now been isolated and studied. The most notable recent achievement (1960) has been the isolation in England of a group of viruses responsible for some of the respiratory conditions lumped under the name of the common cold. There are only three important virus diseases which can still be studied only by the inoculation of human volunteers. They are German measles, hepatitis (infectious jaundice) and glandular fever, and there are hints that when we find how to isolate one the other two will be amenable to the same approach.

The list of viruses which have been isolated from human beings either suffering from disease or apparently healthy is now very large. In the first edition of this book 25 virus diseases of man were listed. Today it is impossible to give a definite number. As always happens in work with living beings, increasing knowledge tends to destroy sharp distinctions. We know now that there are large groups of more or less related viruses, all of which can infect human tissues but produce disease only irregularly or not at all. Under the circumstances we must give up any hope of stating simply that there are *x* virus diseases of man caused by *x* different viruses. We can, however, say something useful about the general types of human virus disease and perhaps list them as follows:

(1) General infectious diseases in which the virus is spread through the blood and is not localized predominantly in any particular organ, although skin rashes of one sort or another are common. These include smallpox, measles, German measles, chickenpox, and a group of mosquito-borne diseases of which only yellow fever and dengue are well known.

(2) Diseases in which a particular organ or system is specially involved. The most important single infection of the respiratory tract is still influenza A, but a positively bewildering variety of other viruses have come to light in recent years. Influenza viruses A2, B and C are well established and there is now a group of Parainfluenza viruses as well. There are nineteen Adenoviruses, three Reoviruses that can infect both respiratory and intestinal systems, and the newly found common cold viruses.

The digestive tract, especially the intestine, seems to be the primary site of action of another large group of viruses now collectively called the enteroviruses. Of these by far the most important are the three poliomyelitis viruses, but the Coxsackie viruses cause some important minor diseases and there are large numbers of other enterovirus types which are mainly important because of the difficulties of differentiating them from polio viruses. In addition the still unknown cause of infectious jaundice or hepatitis is probably a virus primarily located in the intestine.

Local infections of the skin and the conjunctiva (the inner lining of the eyelids) comprise herpes, *molluscum contagiosum,* warts, trachoma, inclusion blennorrhoea and Newcastle disease. Mumps affects the salivary glands and *lymphogranuloma inguinale* is a venereal disease that localizes particularly in the lymph glands.

Finally there are many infections which show themselves essentially by the damage done to the nervous system. Poliomyelitis and some others of the enteroviruses form one group, while rabies is the sole representative of another. In the tropics we find a wide range of mosquito-borne viruses capable of causing severe or fatal encephalitis and sometimes spilling over into temperate regions like Japan.

Probably there are about a hundred different viruses capable both of causing significant human illness and of being identified in a fully equipped virus laboratory. More than half of these are transmissible from man to man, but a considerable proportion are primarily infections of other animals reaching man in more or less accidental fashion.

It is usual to consider with the viruses another important group of organisms the rickettsiae which, like the viruses, can grow only in living cells although they are readily visible under the microscope and look like small bacteria. There are five main groups of diseases caused by these microorganisms: typhus and murine typhus fevers, the group of tick-borne infections of which Rocky Mountain spotted fever is the best known, the mite-borne scrub typhus of the Western Pacific region, Q fever, first of Australia but now known to be of nearly world-wide distribution, and rickettsial pox first reported from a New York suburb. They are all transmitted by insect or related parasites, lice, fleas, ticks or mites, but in some instances human infection results from inhalation of contaminated excreta rather than from the bite of the carrier.

It will have been gathered from this rapid survey of the activities of viruses that in many respects they must be regarded as a ubiquitous and rather highly successful type of organism. The problems of their evolution and of their relation to the better-known types of life, therefore, become of considerable intellectual interest. When we remember that apparently genuinely 'new' virus diseases have appeared during the present century, the interest becomes more than academic. Few things might have greater consequences to humanity than the evolution of a 'new' virus with the spreading power of influenza and the virulence of old-type smallpox.

Viruses as we know them today are capable of growth only within the living cells of some other organism. Present types then can have had no longer evolutionary history than that of the organisms at whose expense they live. There seem to be three possibilities. The first would assume that viruses are directly descended from primitive subcellular organisms which adopted a parasitic existence on the very earliest cellular organisms. As the evolution of animal forms progressed, viruses developed and adapted themselves to parasitize each new form as it emerged, always changing slightly, but never developing an independent mode of life. The second possibility is that viruses are descendants of pathogenic bacteria which had undergone parasitic degeneration to various degrees. Both these views implicitly accept viruses as autonomous microorganisms evolving as a result of reproduction, variation and selective survival like other organisms. The third possibility once sponsored is that viruses, particularly the smaller ones, are not autonomous organisms at all, but fragments of the cells they appear to parasitize.

Of these three possibilities, the first is intrinsically reasonable, and is perhaps the simplest possible hypothesis. It is perhaps only an intellectual prejudice to say that it is unsatisfactory because it merely solves the problem of the nature of viruses in terms of completely unknowable proto-organisms arising at the very dawn of evolution. No argument about

this hypothesis is possible. It may be true, but at least either of the others is 'metal more attractive' to a speculative mind.

Let us take first the possibility of parasitic degeneration. As we saw in dealing with bacteria, pathogenic forms which have specialized in a parasitic existence become progressively less capable of growth outside the tissues of its host. Highly pathogenic bacteria like the *Gonococcus* or the whooping-cough bacillus are difficult to grow on non-living mixtures. The *Gonococcus,* like some other bacteria, seems to grow readily inside certain body cells. So does the tubercle bacillus, and even more so the leprosy bacillus. The latter may represent an important step in the direction of parasitic degeneration. In size, appearance and chemical structure, the leprosy bacillus closely resembles the tubercle bacillus, but although it grows freely in the living cells of its host, it cannot be grown on any non-living material that has been so far tried. A further advance in this direction can be read into the characteristics of the rickettsiae. In man the rickettsiae are purely intracellular parasites. They look like small bacteria, but are considerably smaller than the great majority of true bacteria, and like the leprosy bacillus, cannot be grown on artificial media. The rickettsiae are nearly all transmitted by biting insects, mites or ticks, and seem to have evolved primarily in these invertebrates. In many insects there are structures in certain cells which appear to be undoubted bacteria. They have not been grown artificially, and they are passed on to succeeding generations through the egg. What part they play, if any, in the animal's economy is unknown. Some of the smaller types closely resemble rickettsiae, and it is possible that the pathogenic forms have developed from these harmless parasites (or symbionts) of insects and ticks. The rickettsia of Rocky Mountain spotted fever shows a specially close approach to these forms. It is harboured by a tick which is quite unaffected by its presence. So mutually adapted are parasite and host that the rickettsia may be transmitted through the egg from generation to generation. The typhus fever rickettsia

is transmitted by the louse, but in this case the adaptation of the insect host and parasite is much poorer. Infection of the louse with typhus is invariably fatal within a fortnight, evidence, according to Zinsser, that the louse has only recently taken on this role of vector. Then as a step between the rickettsiae and the smaller viruses we have the virus of psittacosis. This is the disease of parrots which we have already mentioned as an example of an almost perfectly balanced relationship between parasite and host. The virus particles, even in their smallest form, are easily seen with the microscope, and under certain circumstances the virus takes the form of organisms quite as large as many bacteria. Like the rickettsia they have both DNA and RNA and are susceptible to several of the antibacterial drugs. For these reasons they are not now regarded as viruses but placed as a subgroup of the rickettsiae. When we come to the true viruses, we find that the larger forms such as vaccinia or smallpox viruses are quite obviously of complex structure, have a chemical composition very like that of bacteria and in some of their immunity reactions behave in much the same fashion.

With smaller forms we can no longer see such resemblances to bacteria, but we can say that all viruses infecting animal cells show such a general resemblance in their behaviour that it is difficult to avoid the conclusion that in some way or other they are of the same biological status. According to the hypothesis we are examining, the viruses have been evolved from bacteria which specialized in a strictly parasitic way of life. Now it is characteristic of many though not of all parasites that, provided its species survives, the organism will tend to evolve in the direction of losing all unnecessary faculties, not infrequently being reduced until it is little more than a simple mechanism for providing sufficient nourishment to the reproductive cells. There are several well-known examples that adorn all the text-books. The most spectacular is perhaps the Malayan plant *Rafflesia*, which produces the largest flower in the world—five feet in diameter. As a flowering plant,

Rafflesia must have evolved from some fully functioning green plant, but it is now so intensely specialized as a parasite that it has no leaves, stem or roots. It is a mere network of feeding tubes which infiltrate the substances of living trees, abstracting sufficient nourishment to produce its extraordinary efflorescence. In the animal kingdom, we find the rather similar example of *Sacculina*, a parasitic crustacean which in its adult stage is reduced to a sac-like reproductive organ nourished by slender tentacles extending into the host's tissues. Less extreme examples are to be found in every group of parasites, and on a smaller scale it is what might be assumed to have happened in the evolution of viruses from pathogenic bacteria.

In discussing bacteria we have said something of the complex chemical activities mediated by enzymes on the surface or in the substance of the organism by which food molecules are incorporated and used to provide substance and energy for its requirements. Inside a living animal cell there are available similar mechanisms for the cell's own nutrition, and if a parasitic bacterium could divert these mechanisms to its own use it might be enabled to dispense with some of its own equipment of ferments and so forth. A corresponding reduction in size would become possible, and it is conceivable that such a process might continue until the organism is reduced to the absolute minimum, a fragment of matter still retaining the power of growth and multiplication, and capable of surviving in its own particular biological environment, but otherwise 'sans teeth, sans eyes, sans taste, sans *everything*'. The hypothesis seems to lead to a nightmare of futility, but how concordant it is with so many other hard biological and sociological facts. The evolution of living beings and of social organizations is determined only by their survival: neither pays the slightest heed to 'enlightened human opinion'.

The third hypothesis that viruses may have evolved from a cellular fragment that in one way or another had escaped from normal control has in recent years been discussed

chiefly in relation to the puzzling properties of cancer viruses in mice. With the development of refined methods of electron-microscopic examination, it appears however that these agents have the standard structure of viruses and are best regarded as low-grade viruses that have been derived from more typical viruses in the past. If we push the hypothetical origin of such and such a virus from a host cell fragment a long way back in the history of evolution, there is no way of refuting it. Once a self-multiplying cell fragment became free of normal control and capable of multiplying in another cell, it would become as subject to the process of evolution as a virus that had been 'born free'. If the requirements for survival were similar, we should expect their characters to converge until they were indistinguishable.

Even if we can never exclude this possibility of ultimate host cell origin, the hypothesis is an unattractive one from the practical point of view. So far all claims to have isolated viruses from normal cells have been better interpreted as either latent infection or laboratory contamination. Every worker concerned with virus research or the control of virus disease in the field must categorically exclude from his mind the possibility of spontaneous generation of viruses.

There is one group of viruses which on a superficial study of their behaviour in the field might well seem to qualify for an intrinsic origin from healthy cells. In England and on the Continent outbreaks of foot-and-mouth disease occur in a fashion most exasperating both to farmers and to those charged with control of the disease. No possible source of infection is obvious, and such far-fetched theories as spread of the virus by sea-gulls have to be invoked. It might be simpler to understand if, under certain unknown conditions, the virus could be produced spontaneously by the susceptible cells in cattle. But we can be absolutely certain that this does not occur, for the simple reason that by adequate quarantine foot-and-mouth disease has been kept out of Australia, and

no outbreak has ever occurred. The same holds for other important virus diseases such as rabies, sheep-pox, and cattle plague. From the practical administrative point of view, we must hold firmly to the biological axiom that, like every other living organism, every virus is genetically derived from pre-existing virus of similar but not necessarily identical type. On the available evidence, we must exclude our hypothesis of intrinsic origin, and accept one of the two we discussed before it. Most research workers on animal viruses prefer the theory that viruses are the diminished descendants of pathogenic bacteria or protozoa.

Part III

THE PROCESSES OF DEFENCE

CHAPTER VI

THE NORMAL DEFENCES AGAINST BACTERIAL INFECTIONS

Whenever the tissues of the body are invaded by microorganisms, one of three alternative results must ensue. The germs may multiply without effective restraint and cause death; they may establish themselves in the tissues and persist there indefinitely, or finally the invasion may provoke the tissues to react in such a way that the infection is completely overcome—all germs in the tissues are destroyed or eliminated and the patient recovers. The result of infection will depend to a large extent on the nature of the microorganism which invades the body, but by far the commonest sequel is complete recovery. It is our task in the next few chapters to discuss the processes by which bacteria and other microorganisms which may invade the tissues are dealt with and overcome. The most obvious example of such processes is seen in the course of recovery from a frank attack of some infectious disease, but for every such illness there are probably hundreds of occasions on which the same defence processes overcome incipient infections before more than trivial symptoms are produced.

It is common knowledge that after recovery from some infections at least the body acquires a resistance against any subsequent infection by the same type of microorganism. This phenomenon of immunity must take a central position in any discussion of infectious disease, but before we are in a position to describe the way an immune person or animal avoids or overcomes infection it is necessary to outline the normal defences of the body. By normal defences we mean those which are not dependent on any previous experience of the germ responsible for calling them into action. In practice it may be very difficult to be certain that any reaction against bacterial invasion is a normal defence in the strict sense of this definition. In the uterus the embryo exists in a sterile environment free from all bacteria, but immediately a child or an animal is born bacteria of many sorts begin to colonize its intestinal tract and every other available surface. A very interesting current phase of biological research is concerned with the rearing and study of 'germ-free' animals in which this primary bacterial colonization fails to occur. It is already clear that the early experience of bacteria in the bowel plays an important part in getting the organism ready to deal with more dangerous invaders. However, as it is only too certain that we and our descendants will never live in a germ-free environment, we must continue to regard a multitude of casual bacteria in and around us as normal.

Every infant enters the world temporarily equipped with most of the immunity of its mother against the germs she has encountered. This immunity transmitted from the mother's blood fades in a few months but probably provides important support to the infant in enduring the first phase of bacterial colonization. In all probability the infant has acquired some immunities of its own before it loses those supplied by the mother. Nevertheless, there is undoubtedly a sequence of responses to infection by bacteria which provides a standard form of defence against such invasion. The existence of an acquired immunity makes these responses more rapid and more efficient, but their general character is quite independent of previous experience of similar infection.

Let us take as a simple example a small cut in the skin which becomes infected with a fairly virulent *Staphylococcus*. The general sequence of events is familiar to most people. The gap between the cut edges is soon filled with a wedge of dried clotted blood, and there is a little redness along the edge and slight swelling. Next day there is a wider area of reddened skin, and the neighbourhood of the wound is painful to touch. Another day and the cut looks 'angry', a little yellow pus can be seen under the scab or exuding at one end of the cut. As a rule, the scab is soon lifted off, and a little discharging ulcer persists for a day or two. The redness, swelling and tenderness diminish, and in a week or two there is only a pink, slightly sunken scar remaining. In this simple series of events we have an epitome of the normal defence of the body against the less specialized invaders. If we are to understand the general nature of the processes responsible for this sequence of infection, inflammation and healing, it will be necessary to know something about those aspects of elementary physiology which are relevant to the defence reactions. These reactions are based very largely on the activities of the blood and the blood vessels, and most of our elementary physiology will be concerned with these.

All the organs of the body are supplied with blood which reaches them from the heart by way of the great arteries. In the organ these break up into progressively smaller branches till we come to the minute thin-walled tubules called the blood capillaries. It is in these capillaries that the various interchanges of nutritive material, gases and waste products between blood and tissues occur. From the capillaries the blood is collected by small veins which unite eventually to form the main trunk vein from the organ.

We shall be concerned very largely with the smallest blood vessels, the capillaries, and it is worth while discussing their nature and activity for a little. The larger vessels, both arteries and veins, are essentially just pipe lines, very intricately arranged pipe lines with capacities for regulating their bore in accordance with the requirements of the system, but concerned only with the physical function of supplying blood where and in what amounts it is required. The capillaries serve a more delicate function. Despite their very small average diameter, there are such enormous numbers present in every tissue that the blood passes through them relatively slowly, giving time for oxygen and nutritive substances to diffuse through to the tissue cells, and for carbon dioxide and other waste products like urea and uric acid to pass from tissues to blood. To allow such diffusion, the walls of the capillaries are made up of only a single layer of cells. Under the microscope, these cells show no indication of any special function other than to keep the blood from leaking out of the vessels into the tissues, but experiment shows that they are not mere passive units of a pipe lining. The capillaries can change their bore to a surprising extent. When a muscle is at rest, a large proportion of the capillaries in its substance close down completely. No blood passes through them at all. With exercise of the muscle, there is an immediate increase in the local demand for oxygen and food, and in response many more of the capillaries open up and allow an increased flow of blood through the part. This is one of the beautiful adaptations which ensure that there will be an adequate interchange of material between blood and tissues. An even finer control of this interchange is exercised by the cells themselves. Under normal conditions the blood at the arterial end of the capillary will be the 'freshest', i.e. it contains more oxygen and less carbon dioxide than at any other point of the capillary. If the cells of the capillary wall were all of similar character, this would mean that there would be much more active interchange at the arterial end than further along. To counteract this, there are differences in the degree to which the cells will allow the passage of material, those at the arterial end allowing less rapid diffusion than those at the venous end of the capillary. In this way things are evened out and all the tissue cells have an equal opportunity to obtain what they require from the blood.

It will be seen from this description of the capillary mechanism that the blood normally never comes into direct contact with the tissue cells. It is always separated from them by the cells of the capillary wall. There are some organs in which the blood passes into a network of spaces which are wider and more irregular than the capillaries in other parts of the body. These are the places where the blood is formed, or where its constituents as they wear out are removed, and in these regions the lining of the blood spaces is more complicated. The chief blood-forming organ is the bone marrow, which is the friable spongy tissue inside the shafts of many of the bones, particularly the ribs and the ends of the main limb bones. In adult life this is the site of formation of the red blood cells, and of a majority of the white cells or leucocytes. The mother cells from which these circulating blood cells are, as it were, budded off, line the irregular blood spaces that lie amidst the loose trellis of bone in these situations.

The final disposal of worn-out blood cells begins in certain cells which line the capillaries and blood spaces of the liver and spleen. These are larger cells than those which make up the normal lining of the capillaries, and from their activity in picking out from the blood stream dead cells and foreign particles, they may best be called the 'fixed phagocytes' of the body. Such cells are also found in other parts of the body, but these two organs contain a large proportion of the total, and we may neglect the others for the present.

As it circulates in the body, the blood is a dense suspension of cells, most of them the oxygen-carrying red cells, in a clear fluid, the plasma. About half its volume is occupied by the cells, half by the fluid portion. The red cells are, of course, of vital importance, but as far as we know they play no direct part in the defence processes; both the white cells of the blood and the plasma are of much more importance from our point of view. There are several different kinds of white cells to be found in the blood, but we need consider only the two most numerous types. The first of these is a cell with a very irregularly shaped nucleus, from which it derives its technical name of 'polymorphonuclear leucocyte'. Bernard Shaw wrote *The Doctor's Dilemma* around, if not precisely about, these particular cells, and since then everybody has heard about the phagocytes, the cells which eat bacteria. This is a more convenient name, provided we take care to differentiate them when necessary from the fixed phagocytes. Like the red cells, they are produced in the bone marrow. The second type of cell is a smaller one with a relatively large round nucleus, the lymphocyte.

The lymphocytes in the blood are only a very small fraction of those present in other parts of the body. Thymus, spleen and lymph nodes (or lymph glands) are very largely made up of these cells and there are numerous areas along the digestive tract where extensive accumulations occur. Tonsils and adenoids are masses of lymphocytes lying under the surface of the lining membrane of the throat and along the intestine there are smaller collections plus a specially large accumulation in the wall of the appendix. Obviously the lymphocyte has some important function in relation to defence and despite the fact that most physiologists are not satisfied that we know just what that function is, a good deal will be said about lymphocytes in the next chapter or two.

There are many lymphocytes in the bone marrow but they are produced elsewhere. Most authorities now believe that in the young animal the thymus, which is an organ lying just under the top of the breastbone, is the main producer of lymphocytes. In later life most lymphocytes are produced from 'germinal centres' of actively multiplying cells which are continually arising in spleen, lymph nodes and the other lymphoid organs with the important exception of the thymus. Since the appearance of these germinal centres is accelerated by infection or immunization, it is a reasonable speculation that they are making cells needed to deal with infection.

The plasma, or fluid part of the blood, is a liquid of extraordinary complexity and infinite interest. I suppose that in the last fifty years, literally millions of pages have been written about its properties in health and disease. In every hospital in the world dozens of analyses for one or other of its constituents are being made daily. For our purpose we can neglect many of these constituents, however important they may be in other respects. In rough outline, then, the plasma is a complex solution in water of various proteins and salts with smaller amounts of an almost infinite variety of substances which are either needed by the tissues or eliminated from them as waste products. It is the proteins with which we shall be chiefly concerned.

The blood protein with the most easily recognized activity is the one responsible for the clotting of blood. As soon as blood leaks out from the vessels as a result of some injury, a complex process results in this particular protein becoming insoluble. It crystallizes, as it were, into a network of threads which hold the rest of the blood together in the form of a spongy clot. If blood is taken into a test-tube and allowed to clot, after a time the clot shrinks and a clear fluid is squeezed out of its pores. This fluid is plasma freed from the unstable clotting protein, and in this state it is known as serum. It is obviously more convenient for most purposes to use a stable liquid like serum than one which is liable to go into a semi-solid state at the slightest provocation, and most of the experimental work on the changes in the blood which result from disease has been done on serum rather than on plasma. For some purposes it is more convenient to maintain the plasma in its original state by adding some anticoagulant such as heparin or sodium citrate.

The proteins which remain in the serum still form a very complex mixture which can be sorted out by several different methods which, however, do not give the same answers. The most useful present-day method is to separate the proteins by electrophoresis, that is, by taking advantage of the fact that when a solution of mixed proteins is exposed to an electric current each type of protein moves at its own characteristic speed toward the positive electrode. By a suitable instrument the serum or other solution can be made as it were to draw a graph of its own constituents, a tall peak corresponds to the fastest moving component, serum albumin, and this is followed by a complex of lower peaks. These correspond to a series of proteins of larger molecular weight than albumin, the serum globulins. Early graphs showed three peaks that were labelled α, β and γ. With more sensitive apparatus other peaks can be seen and in refined studies of this sort $\alpha 1$ $\alpha 2$, β, $\gamma 1$ and $\gamma 2$ components are recognized. These refinements need not worry us particularly as other ingenious methods will allow still further subdivision of globulin fractions. For our purpose we can neglect albumin and α- and β- globulins. They have important functions but are not directly involved in defence against infection. The gamma globulins, however, are of special importance because they include the antibodies, the classical defenders of the body. There are many types of antibody and it is only for a few that we can state what particular sort of gamma globulin they correspond to. It is sufficiently close to the truth to say simply that all antibodies are gamma globulins and leave it at that.

The gamma globulins are produced predominantly or perhaps wholly by cells closely related to lymphocytes which are called plasma cells. They are easily recognized in properly stained histological sections and in specially thin sections photographed under an electron microscope the intracellular machinery for the synthesis and liberation of the globulin shows up clearly as a complex collection of flattened tubles, the ergastoplasm. Many immunologists believe that all gamma globulin is antibody of one sort or another, largely because the newborn animal possesses no gamma globulin of its own and only begins to make it after it has experienced a few weeks' contact with the microorganisms of the environment.

This is a very brief and inadequate account of the infinitely complex composition and function of the blood but it covers at a superficial level most of the components which are known to be concerned in defence against infection.

We can now return to our analysis of what takes place when a small cut or abrasion is infected with staphylococci. The trouble starts when the bacteria, introduced at or after the time the wound was made, begin to multiply in the damaged cells and in the remains of blood clot and tissue juice in the depths of the wound. As they multiply they produce poisonous substances which damage or kill the adjacent cells. These damaged cells provide more food for the bacteria, but at the same time they set free a stimulus which calls the main defences of the tisues into action. One of the first steps, particularly in staphylococcal infections, is the clotting of the fluid in the local lymph channels which to a large extent prevents spread of the microbe to other parts of the body. Damage to living cells by almost any agent—heat, mechanical injury, chemical poisons—results in a liberation of a variety of soluble agents which can influence other cells. A good deal of progress has been made in sorting out the active constituents from the medley of substances that can diffuse from a damaged cell. The first to be recognized was histamine, a relatively simple organic substance closely related to the amino-acid histidine. From badly damaged cells or tissues more complex compounds, most of which seem to be of polypeptide character, can be obtained which attract phagocytes ('leukotaxine') and damage cells.

There are two simple ways of obtaining by personal experience an idea of the characteristic activities of histamine. The first is to apply a nettle leaf to the soft skin on the front of the forearm. The second is to allow a mosquito to bite some relatively unexposed part of the skin. Some people will find the mosquito bite ineffective, but in the average person both these types of mild irritation will give a histamine type reaction. In the first edition of this book the effect of the nettle was assumed to be due, in the first instance, to the damage by some unknown poison which stimulated the cells to produce histamine. Now we know that the example was better than was imagined at the time because one component of nettle poison is actually histamine itself. The nettle reaction because of its directness is more rapid than the mosquito bite. In both a little white weal commences to form and enlarge around the point of injury, while at the same time the region becomes itchy. As the weal enlarges, a red flush appears surrounding it. After an hour or thereabouts (if the place is not scratched meanwhile!) the weal gradually disappears, and is replaced by a pink swollen area which in its turn also gradually disappears. This simple little phenomenon, which is familiar to everybody, has been analysed in great detail by Sir Thomas Lewis, with results of great importance for the interpretation of all the phenomena of inflammation in the skin and elsewhere.

The sequence of events is almost wholly due to the action of histamine liberated from the slightly damaged cells, on the small blood vessels. In the first place, the cells of the capillaries relax and allow more blood to flow through; at the same time the wall becomes more porous and fluid seeps rapidly through into the tissues, causing the pale swollen area that forms the weal. The red flush around the weal is also due to the small blood vessels opening up and allowing more blood to pass through the skin, and so deepen its colour, but here the histamine acts in an indirect fashion by stimulating the nerves in the skin which are concerned with regulating the blood supply. As the effect of the histamine wears off, the excess fluid in the tissues returns to the blood, but the capillaries remain open and the resulting pink colour remains for some time.

Here then we have an arrangment whereby any damage to cells calls forth an increased local supply of blood and a passage of the blood fluids into the tissues which have been damaged. Now suppose we increase the injury and actually kill a few cells, say by pricking a few drops of silver nitrate into the skin. Everything follows the same course, except that a small red area persists around the point of injury, and after a day or two a little point of dry whitish matter appears at its centre, persists for a few more days, and then is thrown off as a tiny scab. This process involves the death of a certain number of cells, and the resulting reaction is naturally more complex than the simple histamine liberation of the previous examples, where only temporary damage to the cells was involved. With more severe damage there is a complete breakdown of the delicately balanced processes by which the internal structure of the cell is maintained. Everyone knows that when meat is hung for some days it becomes more tender. This is just one manifestation of the fact that nearly all dead and damaged cells undergo partial self-digestion. Some of their proteins are broken down to simpler nitrogenous substances whose molecules are small enough to diffuse easily out of the cells. In all probability the active inflammatory changes which occur in the neighbourhood of killed or severely damaged cells result mainly from the diffusion of such products of self-digestion. In any case it is evident that something diffusing from the damaged cells causes a slower but more prolonged opening up of the capillaries than histamine does and attracts the phagocytes of the blood to the part. Under the microscope the first thing to be seen is a tendency for the phagocytic cells to be drawn out of the blood by sticking to the walls of the distended capillaries. This is the first stage of a migration of phagocytes to the site of damage. The next step is for the phagocytes to penetrate through the capillary wall, and in very purposeful-seeming fashion to move through the tissue spaces to the cells killed by the silver nitrate. The dead cells are surrounded by phagocytes which form a transition zone between the dead and the living tissue, and by the action of their ferments commence the separation process which eventually results in the casting off of the dead cells as a small scab.

This example leads us on to the processes involved when, instead of a trivial damage by some chemical substance, the tissues are infected by a germ such as the *Staphylococcus*. The damaged cells produce both histamine and those other still unidentified substances which call forth the migration of the phagocytes. These wandering cells seep out from the swollen capillaries and penetrate the infected tissue. Any staphylococci they encounter are engulfed, but as a rule it will be some time before the invaders are overcome. This particular type of bacterium produces a poison which is just as destructive to phagocytes as it is to the cells of the skin, and many of them are killed by it in the early stages. The creamy coloured pus which appears in an infected wound is composed almost entirely of dead phagocytes. Soon we reach the state of affairs in which the originally infected and damaged area of tissue is almost replaced by dead phagocytes, while around it the still living tissues are packed with phagocytes which prevent the bacteria going any further into healthy tissue. In ordinary circumstances the phagocytic barrier is effective. The bacteria can invade no further, stray individuals are engulfed and destroyed, while behind the barrier the cells get to work on the processes of tidying up and repair.

So much for an example of defence against a simple local infection. If the bacteria in the tissues are not rapidly dealt with by the mobilization of the blood fluids and phagocytes, some of them will spread beyond the local region. The first direction of spread is through the lymph vessels to the lymph glands which receive the lymph from the infected region. The lymphatic system is an inconspicuous arrangement, the complexity of which can be demonstrated only by specialized methods of study. It consists of an intricate mesh of thin-walled capillary and larger tubes which ramifies through all the tissues. The lymphatic capillaries collect into main vessels which run to lymph glands and eventually by two large vessels into the large veins near the heart. The most obvious function of this system is to drain excess fluid from the tissues and return it to the blood. The lymph glands act both as filters to remove bacteria and possibly damaged cells, and as centres for production of lymphocytes and plasma cells.

Probably a few bacteria pass to the lymph glands from any bacterial infection, no matter how mild. They are caught by certain phagocytic cells in the lymph glands and are normally destroyed by digestion within them without any external evidence to draw attention to the process. As has been mentioned, blocking of the lymphatic vessels by clotted fibrin may play a part in stopping this passage to the glands. With more virulent organisms, and particularly those like some streptococci which liberate enzymes which can dissolve fibrin and break down any such barrier, there is more rapid spread to the lymph glands. A red line of inflammation may be seen running up under the skin and if the phagocytic cells in the gland cannot effectively deal with the invaders the result is an inflamed and tender swelling that may go on to an abscess if the organisms get really out of hand.

When we come to more severe infections, it is not so easy to be sure what is happening. The microorganisms get into the blood and are carried to all parts of the body, where they or their poisonous products may give rise to a variety of bodily reactions of which fever is the most constant and depending on the intensity of infection and the organs most severely affected, such symptoms as rash or haemorrhage, headache, delirium or coma. In addition, nearly all severe infections if they are not rapidly fatal, provoke in a few days changes associated with the development of immunity. Perhaps the simplest example to take at present is not a human disease, but that very artificial occurrence, an injection of bacteria into a rabbit's veins. Suppose we inject a rather big dose of bacteria, about 1,000,000,000, into a rabbit in this way, and by suitable experiments find out where they go to. The first fact which comes to light is that the bacteria very rapidly disappear from the blood. Though there may be millions to start with, the numbers are down to thousands or less in four or five hours' time. If the bacteria are not virulent for the rabbit, they are never found in the blood more than twenty-four hours after the injection. What becomes of the bacteria which disappear from the blood? They are not excreted by the kidney or by any other of the normal excretory methods, but find a temporary lodging in the various organs of the body. Two organs take up many more bacteria than any of the others—the liver and the spleen. Both these organs have a copious blood supply, and appear to be designed to act as filters which remove unwanted cells and particles from the blood. This filtering action is, of course, only one of the functions of liver and spleen. The former, particularly, has dozens of other important roles to play in the bodily economy. We have already mentioned the 'fixed phagocytes' which help to line the capillary spaces in these two organs, as well as in certain other situations, notably bone marrow and lymph glands. It is just as much part of the function of these phagocytic cells to pick out bacteria from the blood stream as it is to remove the worn out blood cells. So it happens that an hour or two after the injection we find that both spleen and liver are relatively crowded with living bacteria. In twenty-four hours' time, however, very few are left alive. They have been taken in and digested by the phagocytic cells. This happens to some extent irrespective of whether the bacteria are virulent for the rabbit or harmless. If the bacteria are virulent enough to kill the animal within a few days of such an injection, this means that the mechanism for removing them from the blood is not effective enough. In general, virulent bacteria are not so readily taken up by phagocytic cells, and a certain proportion will continue to multiply even when they are within the substance of these cells.

Many other changes in the body result from such injections, the rabbit's temperature rises, an increased number of blood phagocytes appear, and so on, but we may justifiably disregard these and look on the whole process as depending on the removal of bacteria from the blood by fixed phagocytes and their slow destruction by some form of digestion within these cells. The blood phagocytes seem to play only a secondary part in the process. They do take up some of the bacteria, and then, for some reason not well understood, become held up in the capillaries of the lungs. Their main function, as we have seen, is to deal with localized infections like those in the skin. For the serious emergency of bacteria loose in the blood, the more efficient activity of the fixed phagocytes is the main line of defence.

Many investigators have undertaken to find why a given type of bacterium is or is not virulent for some convenient laboratory animal. Virulent and avirulent strains are examined and a variety of differences observed. The only really significant finding is that a virulent organism is less readily taken up and digested by phagocytes than an avirulent one of the same species. The difference must depend essentially on the chemical nature of the bacterial surface. If infection is to be brought under control it would clearly be advantageous to change the surface to give the phagocyte an advantage. In the next chapter we shall be concerned with the part such a process plays in the development of acquired immunity.

CHAPTER VII

THE DEVELOPMENT OF IMMUNITY AFTER INFECTIOUS DISEASE

There are two characteristics of infectious diseases which are known to everybody. In the first place, every non-fatal attack follows a more or less definite course. There are initial symptoms usually rather vague, an onset which may be gradual or abrupt, then a period of fever or illness, and finally the fever disappears and convalescence begins. The second characteristic is that following recovery, the individual is not susceptible to the same type of infection for a period which may range from a few months to a lifetime. In the light of what we have said about the activities of parasitic microorganisms, we should expect these two characteristics to be intimately related. In the early stages of an infection like measles or influenza, the germ seems to have everything to suit it, and is multiplying rapidly. There is no reason to think that the viruses responsible change their character after they have been multiplying in the body for a few days. The change from fever to convalescence must be due to some modification in the bodily reactions, not to a change in the parasite. It is only to be expected that if the body has developed a power to overcome an established invasion by a particular germ it will for some time be even more capable of preventing any fresh invasion by the same type of microorganism.

Immunology is the science which has developed from the study of these phenomena. It now covers a much wider field and there are doubts arising even as to whether defence against microorganisms is, in fact, the primary function for which the immune process has been evolved. It is certain at least that in the laboratories new subsciences of immunochemistry and immunogenetics have developed which have no direct relationship to immunity against infection. Some aspects of these new approaches will need to be discussed, but from our particular interest in infectious disease we can still say that the central problems of immunology are the two we have mentioned. Why do people or animals recover from infectious disease, and why having done so are they subsequently insusceptible to disease due to the same type of infection? The first problem is both simpler and more directly connected with the matters we discussed in the last chapter. For our example of recovery we shall take a common human illness, pneumonia, which in the days before the successive advents of sulphapyridine, sulphadiazine and penicillin, was more minutely investigated than any other acute disease. Today no medical student ever sees a patient with typical lobar pneumonia. The infection is cut short with a few injections of penicillin and the patient recovers at home. To describe the course of acute pneumonia uninfluenced by the modern drugs, as we had to in 1937, is today little more than an exercise in the history of medicine, but it is only in this way that we can understand the natural process of recovery that not so long ago was all we had to depend on. This account of what happens in pneumonia is therefore left almost unchanged from when it was written a few years before the introduction of penicillin into medicine.

Pneumonia results when the *Pneumococcus,* which we have previously mentioned as one of the types of bacteria normally present in the throat, spreads down and multiplies widely in the substance of the lung. What allows it to do so is still rather a mystery. There are two particular types of *Pneumococcus* which are responsible for about 80 per cent of cases of pneumonia, while the remaining 20 per cent are due to one or other of about thirty other types. However, although these two types seem to be specially prone to produce pneumonia, they cannot do so in more than a small proportion of individuals. Everyone knows that the ordinary form of acute pneumonia is not infectious like measles or diphtheria. Some abnormal condition in the lungs must be necessary to allow the germ to develop its activity. Still, there is no mistaking its activity when it does develop. The patient becomes extremely ill and remains so for six or seven days. Then, if he is one of the fortunate ones, there is a sudden dramatic change for the better. His temperature falls rapidly to normal, delirium disappears, and the patient feels weak but infinitely better.

In the days before effective treatment was available, this crisis failed to occur in 20 or 30 per cent of patients. Some of these managed to recover in less dramatic fashion but most of them died.

In pneumonia, then, we have a clear indication that something very important should occur about the fifth or seventh day of the disease if the patient is to recover. A great deal of work has been done to find out what happens at this critical period, and we can now provide a fairly satisfactory account of it.

As the pneumococci multiply in the lung they damage the local cells, and processes, rather similar in essentials to those which we described as occurring near an infected wound in the skin, are set going. The capillaries distend and fluid leaks into the little air spaces of the lung, phagocytes too are attracted to the site of damage and follow the fluid. The result is that much of the lung becomes solid and airless, and is, of course, useless for breathing. The pneumococci keep on increasing their numbers and a few leak through into the blood; most of them remain in the lung, but their poisonous products diffuse into the blood and provoke such symptoms as fever and delirium. In these first few days the phagocytes are called out in great numbers, both into the blood and into the lung tissues, but they are ineffective. The pneumococci defend themselves as it were against the phagocytes by liberating a soluble gum-like substance which acts as a sort of smoke screen to confuse the attack.

The inefficiency of the phagocytes at this stage can be shown by direct experiment. If we take some of the patient's blood serum, a few thousands of his phagocytes and some of the pneumococci and mix them together, nothing happens. The pneumococci remain free amongst the cells and may even start multiplying. In the lung itself, however, the phagocytes can do better than in the test-tube. Where they have a solid surface to cling to they can overcome their disadvantages to some extent and even before the crisis many pneumococci are taken into the phagocytes and destroyed.

But once the crisis has occurred, the phagocytes appear to have learnt their job properly. Now they can engulf and digest the pneumococci, and very rapidly gain the upper hand. Parts of the lung may remain solid and functionless for some weeks longer, but the pneumococci are now being destroyed and prevented from producing their poisons. If we carry out the same test-tube experiment with blood serum, phagocytes and pneumococci, we find now that the phagocytes rapidly take up the germs, and in so doing destroy them. Other factors may also be involved, but there is no doubt that this sudden improvement in the activity of the phagocytes is the chief reason for the patient's rapid change for the better after the crisis.

In our experiments with the patient's blood we have so far used serum and phagocytes together, and we do not yet know whether the improved activity of the phagocytes was due to a change in them or to some change in the serum, or perhaps to both. There is no need to describe how such experiments are done, but we should mention that it is very difficult to induce a phagocyte to eat any sort of bacteria unless there is also serum present. That is why we always have the three components in the experimental mixtures. It is easy to see what sort of an experiment is necessary to decide whether serum or phagocytes are concerned in making it possible for the cells to engulf pneumococci. As soon as we start ringing the changes, we find at once that it is the serum and not the phagocytes which is important. In fact, the most convenient type of experiment is to use rabbit phagocytes instead of human ones, and test their power to eat pneumococci (*a*) when mixed with blood serum taken before the crisis, and (*b*) with serum taken afterwards. In the first mixture the pneumococci remain free, in the second they are nearly all taken up by the cells and killed. That makes it clear that some change in the serum makes the phagocytes more active or renders the pneumococci more susceptible to being attacked. Again it is not difficult to carry out the necessary experiments and show that the serum acts on the pneumococci, not on the phagocytes. There is something in the serum taken when the patient is recovering, which sticks to the surface of pneumococci and makes it easy for the phagocytes to deal with them. This something is quite a definite substance. It can be removed from the serum by stirring into it a lot of pneumococci. After the substance has had time to become attached to the bacteria, the mixture is put into a centrifuge. With this the bacteria can be driven to the bottom of the tube, leaving clear serum above. If we test this treated serum we find that it has lost its power to make pneumococci into an acceptable diet for phagocytes. But by suitable manipulation we can separate the substance from the packed lump of bacteria at the bottom of the centrifuge and show that it has the same sort of action as the original serum. This substance is called 'antibody'. This is a word we shall have to use frequently in this and subsequent chapters. It is by no means easy to define an antibody in any simple language, and it will probably be better to describe a few more examples of what antibodies do before attempting to say what they are.

Perhaps an even more conclusive way of showing the importance and effectiveness of such antibodies in the serum is by what are called protection tests in mice. The white mouse is very susceptible to infection with the *Pneumococcus*. If we inject with a hypodermic syringe even two or three pneumococci of sufficiently high virulence into the abdominal cavity of a mouse, the animal will die in about three days. If, however, we give the mouse, along with the pneumococci, a very small amount of serum from a patient recovering from pneumonia, it will survive indefinitely. By making suitably graded mixtures of the bacteria and serum and injecting them into mice, it is possible to measure quite accurately how much antibody there is in any given serum.

If we are correct in ascribing recovery from pneumonia to the appearance of antibodies in the blood, it should be possible to make certain that every patient recovers by simply giving him ready-made antibody. It is easy enough to make the right sort of antibody by injecting pneumococci into horses and using their serum after a proper course of injections has been completed.

Protective tests on mice show that such serum has much more antibody than ever appears in a human being with pneumonia, and great hopes were once entertained that the injection of serum would rapidly produce a 'crisis' and recovery in patients infected with pneumococci of the right type. The results of this serum treatment were rather disappointing. Serum undoubtedly helped some patients and saved a proportion of lives. As an example, in one large American investigation, about 250 patients with pneumonia were treated according to the best available methods, but were not given serum. Of these patients 33 per cent died. Another 250 similar patients in the same hospitals were given serum in addition to the usual treatment. The death-rate amongst these was still fairly high, 19 per cent, but was considerably lower than amongst those who received no serum.

There are several possible reasons why the results of serum treatment in pneumonia were so disappointing. In the first place, poisons produced by the pneumococci may have irretrievably damaged such organs as the heart before the serum could be given, or the portion of the lungs which was still air-containing and available for breathing may have been too small to supply the body's need of oxygen, even if the activity of the pneumococci had been overcome. Then the point must be considered that the antibody given in the horse serum is something foreign to the human body. It may stick to the surface of the pneumococci, but it may not render them so acceptable to *human* phagocytes as they would be if they were coated with human antibody. We can be reasonably certain also that there are a number of other reasons for the comparative failure of serum which have yet to be discovered. Infectious disease, particularly in man, is always a highly complex process, and although we may pick out certain factors such as antibodies, and rightly regard them as of the greatest importance, yet they can never play the whole part in bringing about recovery. Any critical reader will undoubtedly find many instances in this book where complicated biological processes are described in terms of one or two factors (always factors susceptible to experimental study), while a whole living background within which the chosen factors must be displayed is tacitly assumed to play no essential part in the processes. This is probably an inevitable feature of any scientific writing. Until the background factors not yet susceptible to experimental study are sorted out, it is only possible to deal with those aspects of the whole process which *can* be studied experimentally. All that can be done is to add a caution here and there that we are really more ignorant than sometimes we seem. Perhaps the best measure of our ignorance is given by our failures in practical medicine to achieve what incomplete theoretical ideas suggest should be possible. Still we should not forget that sometimes we can succeed brilliantly while we are still ignorant. The discovery of penicillin completely solved the problem of pneumonia years before we knew how the drug actually affected the *Pneumococcus*.

For technical reasons, the nature of the processes of recovery is more completely known for pneumonia than for any other human infection. Other diseases usually do not show the dramatic crisis which is so common in pneumonia, but there is little doubt that essentially similar processes lead to recovery. The body has to suffer a process of education before it develops the power to deal adequately with the invading germ. In all probability this education or modification of bodily processes involves cells and tissues as well as the blood fluids. The actual antibodies of the blood seem to play a predominant role in dealing with infection by pneumococci, but in other diseases their direct importance seems to be less. We can in nearly every case, however, regard the specific changes in the blood as an index that the body as a whole is developing an effective, if in some cases temporary, resistance against the invader.

Since pneumonia is not an easily transmissible infectious disease, we have no means of knowing whether one attack of this sort protects the patient against further infection by the same type of *Pneumococcus*. For clear-cut examples of immunity after an attack of disease, we can best take some of the infections due to the viruses. Measles, chickenpox and smallpox are all well-known diseases which hardly anyone ever has twice, but perhaps a better example is yellow fever. This is an exotic disease, and now rather a rare one, but it has the advantage over the commoner infections that the virus is more readily susceptible to experimental study. It is possible, therefore, to analyse the nature of the immunity which follows infection, along lines similar to those used for studying the process of recovery in pneumonia.

Yellow fever is a severe infection which is transmitted from man to man by mosquitoes. The virus is inoculated with the puncture of the mosquito's proboscis and spreads in the blood throughout the body. The favourite site for its multiplication is the liver, and the damage produced here is responsible for the jaundice which gives the name *yellow* fever to the disease. After recovery, the patient is completely insusceptible to reinfection, and as far as the evidence is available, he retains his immunity for life. The yellow fever virus can enter the body only in one way, by mosquito bite, and it can travel to the liver from the site of the bite by only one route, the blood. A completely effective protection could be obtained if, after recovery, substances capable of rendering the virus harmless appeared in the blood. This is in fact what happens.

By suitable methods, the yellow-fever virus, like the *Pneu-*

mococcus, can be made to produce a fatal infection in mice and just as the pneumococci can be rendered harmless by the addition of serum from a recovered patient, so can the virus of yellow fever. This power of the serum to kill the virus, or at least to render it harmless, persists through life. We can feel certain that when an infected mosquito injects the yellow-fever virus into a person who has recovered from a previous attack, the 'antibody' in the blood very rapidly attaches itself to the virus. As a result, the virus particles are taken up by the fixed phagocytes and killed. Had there been no antibody in the blood, they would have entered perhaps the same cells, but instead of being killed they would have multiplied and eventually have infected the whole of the liver, as well as other parts of the body.

Study of the power of serum to stop infection of mice with yellow-fever virus has in recent years made a great difference to our knowledge of the natural history of the disease. But that is a story which is best left for another chapter.

We have taken yellow fever as our first example of immunity following an attack of disease, primarily because of the effectiveness of the immunity and of the theoretical simplicity of the process by which it is achieved. There is another important reason for giving it pride of place. It is one of the few human diseases for which almost complete protection can be procured by a harmless imitation of the natural process of infection and recovery. The principle of the method is to inoculate a small dose of virus which has been so modified by living in the cells of mice or of chick embryos that it is incapable of producing serious disease in man. The attenuated virus multiplies in the body sufficiently to set the processes of antibody production in motion but produces no symptoms. Vaccination by this method has been proved highly effective provided care is taken that the virus used stays at the right level of attenuation. Many millions of servicemen were protected in this way during the Second World War. There were some unhappy complications because several large batches of American vaccine were inadvertently contaminated with the virus of one type of infectious jaundice, but everything suggests that the vaccine itself gave an immunity almost as solid as that following recovery from the natural disease.

Still, however exciting the scientific conquest of yellow fever may be, it does not personally concern most dwellers in temperate climates. Influenza undoubtedly does, and we must say a little about the way immunity against influenza is developed, for here the conditions under which the infection spreads are very different from those of yellow fever. Influenza is a virus infection of the linings of the nose, throat, air passages and lungs, but not of any other organs of the body. As everyone knows, it spreads very easily with any form of human contact. Droplets of saliva carrying the virus are liberated into the air almost with every breath, and are inhaled by some susceptible person. The virus enters and attacks almost the first cells it comes into contact with, and from there spreads over the various susceptible cells in the linings of the air passages. Almost all its victims recover from ordinary influenza, and when they do, antibody against the virus is found in their blood serum. But this antibody in the blood is not in the same favourable position as the yellow-fever antibody for nipping a new infection in the bud. The influenza virus can reach the cells susceptible to its action without having any contact with the blood. Nevertheless, a person who has recovered from influenza is quite immune against another attack of the *same sort of influenza* for a year or two at least.

The nature of this immunity is now reasonably clear. If spread of the virus over the lining of the air passages is to be prevented by antibody, this needs to be present not in the blood but in the film of moisture on the surface of the susceptible cells. In an attack of influenza, virus multiplies in the local cells and much virus and fragments of virus pass to the lymph glands and perhaps elsewhere. Antibody is produced and is easily detected in the blood a week after recovery. From the blood, some of it is always seeping through on to the mucous lining of the air passages. There is a fairly constant relation between what is in the blood and what is in the situation where it can best block the spread of influenza virus. It has been shown, however, that anything which produces a mild inflammation in the respiratory passages tends to swing the distribution of antibody in favour of the surface film. It is extraordinarily rare to have two attacks of genuine influenza in one season, and we can ascribe the immunity that follows the first attack to the presence of antibody on the respiratory surfaces perhaps increased in concentration by the persistence for some time of mild inflammatory changes. When immunity persists for two or more years it is probable that reinfection is not absolutely prevented but kept within very limited bounds by the increase in local antibody provoked by the beginnings of the new infection.

Not very long ago it was possible to claim that recovery from any infectious disease was primarily due to the development of antibody against the invader. Usually such a claim would be qualified by attention being drawn as well to the non-specific part played by normal defence mechanism but persisting specific immunity was regarded as self evidently due to the production of antibody. We know now that this is not correct. Antibody is undoubtedly important but it is not all important. The proof could hardly be more direct, for there are children who cannot make antibody but who can become immune to measles like a normal child. With the development of potent antibacterial drugs like penicillin, pediatricians began to notice that there were children who suffered repeated and severe attacks of pneumonia which needed skilful use of penicillin plus small blood transfusions to control. These children were found to suffer from an inherited defect, inability to produce gamma globulin and as a necessary corollary complete absence of antibody. This provided an obvious reason for their lack of resistance to bacterial infection, but it came as a surprise to find that when one of these children contracted measles he showed the normal symptoms, recovered in the same time as a normal companion and was just as firmly immune afterwards against a second attack. Clearly there are important aspects of acquired immunity that are not mediated by antibody. The modern approach is to look on the appearance of large numbers of what we now call 'immunologically competent cells' as the essential part of specific immunity. These cells play various roles in recovery, antibody production being only one of them.

The overall result of the complex of cellular reaction and antibody formation can perhaps best be visualized by saying that in the immune animal a virulent microorganism is dealt with as readily and in much the same fashion as a non-virulent organism in a normal animal. Antibody in particular seems to be the host's rejoinder to the development of specially invasive qualities by those microorganisms which have adopted a highly parasitic existence. If ordinary non-virulent bacteria enter the tissues or the blood, they are seized and digested by phagocytes of both types, but a fully virulent *Pneumococcus* is unaffected by phagocytes unless a corresponding antibody is present in sufficient amount. Then it is dealt with as swiftly as if it were the most casually insignificant of bacteria. The influence of antibody in virus infections is as we have seen not so all-important. Antibody is demonstrably more effective with some virus infections than others and it would be useless to make any general statement as to how it acts. Phagocytosis appears to be unimportant except as a means of mopping up virus that has already been dealt with in other ways. The important function of antibody is that it should meet and in some way block the activity of the virus so that it either cannot enter a fresh susceptible cell or cannot effectively multiply within it.

From the point of view of patient or doctor, these deep-seated physiological changes manifest themselves primarily in the two phenomena with which we opened this chapter—the process of *recovery* from acute infection, and the persistence of specific *immunity* after recovery is complete.

CHAPTER VIII

THE CHEMICAL BASIS OF IMMUNITY—ANTIBODIES

Since the beginnings of bacteriology as an experimental science in the hands of Pasteur, one of the main tasks of research workers has been to study the question of immunity from every aspect. At every stage the immediate requirement has been to find some *practical* way of imitating natural immunity so as to prevent some specific disease of man or animal. As so often happens in technical research on matters of immediate practical importance, valuable results were obtained long before there was any adequate general theory to account for such success. Vaccination with cowpox is an example of an empirical procedure that could have no theoretical basis until more than a hundred years had elapsed from the time of Jenner's discovery. Research on the more theoretical aspects of immunity has, of course, accompanied and arisen out of the more practical studies, and from it all there has grown up a new science of immunology. It is one of the borderland sciences, chemistry, physiology and bacteriology being the territories which adjoin it. In the previous chapter we have given a general account of recovery and immunity as shown in regard to one or two typical infectious diseases. Both recovery and immunity were ascribed in part at least to 'antibodies', substances which developed in response to infection and appeared in the blood. In virtue of these substances, the blood serum from recovered animals or men was capable of influencing the conflict between host and parasitic microorganism in favour of the host. The actual nature of antibodies was left unspecified. Our object in this chapter is to try to describe at the physico-chemical level what antibodies are and how they influence microorganisms. Here we will be concerned, not with medical or biological aspects of disease, but with such aspects of immunity as are susceptible to experimental study by the methods of the exact sciences. If antibodies are of the first importance in determining recovery and immunity, it is clearly essential to know as accurately as possible their chemical structure and the physical or chemical basis of their specificity. Such problems have provided an interesting field of study for biochemists, and in recent years ideas on these matters have become much clearer.

When a chemist wishes to study some substance or reaction, his first thought is to work with reagents which are as simple and as pure as possible. A living microorganism is a nightmare to the chemist, and the important chemical contributions to immunology have been due to the study of agents simpler than virus or bacterium. There are many relatively simple soluble substances which, on injection into animals or men, provoke the production of antibodies. One of the most extensively studied of these is the poison or toxin of the diphtheria bacillus and the corresponding antibody or antitoxin.

In this chapter we are not concerned with diphtheria as a disease, nor even with the importance of diphtheria toxin in producing the symptoms and complications of diphtheria. We shall merely accept the fact that the diphtheria bacillus under suitable conditions produces a highly poisonous substance, and try to provide a summary of what has been learnt from the vast amount of research on this toxin which has gone on since its discovery in 1887.

Diphtheria toxin has been prepared in pure form and shown to be a protein which apart from its extreme activity as a poison has very little to distinguish it from other proteins. There is a hint that it is a by-product, as it were, from one of the enzyme systems of the diphtheria bacillus, but no one so far has given any satisfactory interpretation of why the toxin is poisonous.

When diphtheria toxin is repeatedly injected in proper doses into a horse, the animal gradually becomes more and more resistant to its poisonous action. After six months it can be given a thousand times the dose which would originally have killed it. Concurrently with this development of resistance, it is found that the blood serum of the horse has developed a new property. If it is mixed with even relatively large amounts of toxin, the mixture may be injected into animals without producing any signs of poisoning. This effect of the serum may be compared with the action of soda in neutralizing an acid, and the process is referred to as neutralization of the toxin by what was at first a purely hypothetical component of the serum, diptheria *antitoxin*. In all probability the resistance or immunity of the horse is entirely due to this development of a specific antidote in the blood. We can measure the amount of antitoxin in the blood in various ways. The simplest one to understand is that originally worked out by Ehrlich, who was the first bacteriologist to apply exact quantitative methods to the problems of immunity. A certain quantity of the toxin, enough to kill say a hundred guinea-pigs, is put into each of a number of tubes. To each tube a graded amount of serum is added, and after a standard time each mixture is inoculated into two or three guinea-pigs. At the end of four days we find that some of the guinea-pigs, those which received small amounts of serum, are dead, but those which were given mixtures with larger amounts of serum are alive and as active as if they had never received enough toxin to kill a hundred unprotected animals. From such a series we can easily find the dose of serum which is just sufficient to protect guinea-pigs against the standard amount of toxin, and this gives us a value of the strength of the serum as an antitoxin. Tests made in this fashion are always used to determine the potency of antiserum prepared for use in the treatment of diphtheria. It is essential that the serum should be harmless to the patient, and that it should contain large and accurately measured amounts of antitoxin. To ensure that both these requirements are fulfilled there are national and international regulations as to how the various tests must be carried out. Thanks to these regulations, a doctor can be sure that a phial of serum labelled 10,000 units of antitoxin will have the same curative action on diphtheria, no matter where it was prepared.

But this is wandering from our subject, which is to define as far as we can the physical basis of immunity. Diphtheria antitoxin then is a substance produced by the body in response to a series of injections of toxin. There are many other poisonous substances which can act in the same way. Some, like diphtheria toxin, are produced by bacteria (tetanus toxin, for example) while the snake venoms and other animal poisons form another important group. All these can provoke the appearance of their own particular antitoxin. We must be clear that these antitoxins are specific: diphtheria antitoxin has no more action than normal serum on the tetanus toxin or on snake venom. Similarly, the antitoxin against rattlesnake venom is not of the slightest value in protecting a man against the bite of a cobra, however effective it may be against rattlesnake bite.

In diphtheria antitoxin we have a well-defined and potent substance, something which it ought to be easy to isolate and identify chemically. Actually, it took chemists a long time to decide what antitoxins were. It was clear that the real active principle was present in very small amount. Chemical studies showed some changes in the relative amounts of the different proteins, but there seemed to be no really new substance present. Gradually it became clear that antitoxin was not so much a new substance as a new quality pertaining to a substance present in every normal serum. Our present conception of antitoxin is still far from being expressible in accurate chemical terms. However disappointing this may be to a chemist, it leaves us free to discuss the problem in looser, more general terms, which will probably convey more to a reader interested primarily in the biological aspects of immunity than would the complicated symbols of the organic chemist.

The antitoxin is made up of molecules of globulin, which is one of the two chief proteins in the serum. These molecules are similar to those normally present, except for certain 'patches' on their surfaces. A protein molecule is relatively gigantic compared with the molecules that are dealt with in ordinary organic chemistry. It is quite large enough to have a surface modified in a special way. A useful mental picture may be obtained by thinking of a normal globulin molecule as a knobbly sphere of some plastic material and the diphtheria toxin molecule as a rather smaller body with two or three surface areas that are modified in some special pattern which we might picture as a knob and a spike. When these two come into contact nothing happens, but suppose that on part of the globulin molecule we have an area which fits exactly on the knob and spike pattern. Then we might imagine that when this modified globulin molecule (antitoxin) met a molecule of toxin the two complementary patterns would fit together and the two molecules unite firmly.

In rather crude fashion this gives a reasonably accurate idea of the current theory of the nature of antitoxins. They are globulin molecules, portions of which have their detailed atomic structure so modified that they fit on to and unite with atomic structures characteristic of the particular toxin concerned. For many years text-books have used the simile of a lock and key to describe this relationship. If the key fits the lock, firm union takes place, if it fails to fit, little or no union results.

Mainly because it is not known how the toxin produces its poisonous effect on living cells, we are unable to say in what way union with antitoxin renders the toxin non-poisonous. It is simplest and probably correct to picture the antitoxin as smothering all the activities of the toxin molecule beneath a blanket of bland unirritating protein.

It will probably seem a natural and appropriate reaction that the body should react to a dangerous poison by producing an antidote for it. We might expect that all poisons given in small repeated doses would provoke a similar response, and that non-poisonous substances would naturally have no such effect. But that, curiously enough, is not what happens. If we try to immunize an animal against poisons like strychnine, arsenic or prussic acid by the same sort of inoculations, we find that the most that can be done is to increase its resistance

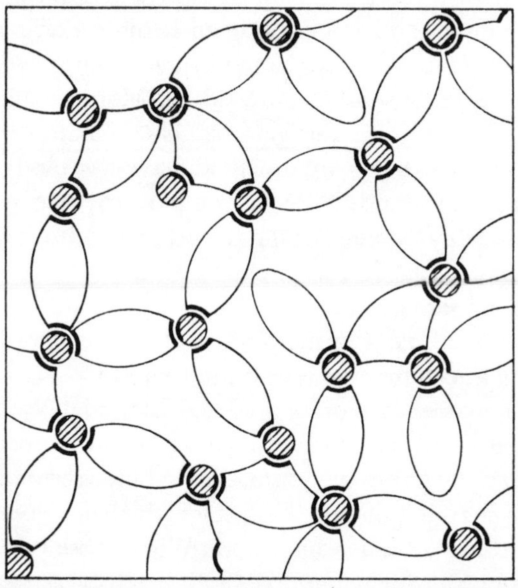

Fig. 4. A diagram to show the relation between toxin and antitoxin. The toxin molecules are shown as hatched circles, the antibody molecules as white ovoids with one, two or three specific combining areas. In the process of neutralization (or in any other type of antigen-antibody union) an interlocked 'lattice' structure of the type shown will be built up if the physical conditions are suitable.

slightly.[1] It may withstand twice the ordinary fatal dose, but there is never the enormous increase in resistance that can be induced against diphtheria toxin or the snake venoms. It seems that only one particular class of poisons can provoke these natural antidotes, and when the results are analysed it is found that the substances which can act in this way are all

[1] There are some poisons, of which morphia is the most important, against which a high degree of tolerance can be produced by the use of gradually increasing doses. This increased resistance seems to depend on a mechanism quite unrelated to the formation of antitoxin.

complex protein poisons with very large molecules. We might begin to wonder whether the important point was not that the toxin is a protein rather than that it is poisonous. What will happen if we inoculate an animal with some non-poisonous protein? If we inject a rabbit with some white of egg nothing obvious happens. The egg albumen is quite non-poisonous, but it does produce some change in the rabbit nevertheless. Suppose we collect serum from a rabbit before we start injecting, and store it in the refrigerator. Then we inject three or four weekly doses of egg albumen, and a few weeks later get a fresh sample of serum. Now we compare the two specimens of serum side by side by adding to each a few drops of a solution of white of egg. As we watch, a turbidity begins to appear in the second sample, and in an hour or two solid flakes begin to form and sediment to the bottom. The first sample, taken before the injections, remains quite limpid.

This phenomenon can be analysed in the laboratory, and it has been shown to be exactly analogous to the neutralization of toxin by antitoxic serum. The rabbit's serum after the injections contains globulin molecules which have been modified to 'fit' egg albumen molecules. When these two types of molecule meet, they combine and produce a compound which is insoluble and eventually forms a visible precipitate. This gives us a simple method of finding whether substances have or have not this power of producing a specific change in the animal's serum. Thousands of substances have been tested in this way, and in general the results have shown that only substances with very large molecules, and particularly proteins, have this power.

We are now in a position to define the word 'antibody' a little more definitely, and at the same time to introduce another convenient word, 'antigen'. Those substances, like toxins or egg albumen which, on injection into an animal, provoke the appearance of modified globulin molecules, are called *antigens* or antigenic substances, while the changed globulin molecules are said to compose the *antibody* in the serum. Nearly all proteins are good antigens, with one very important exception. Proteins from a given animal species are not antigenic when they are injected into another animal of the same species. Rabbit protein is antigenic when it is inoculated into a horse or man, but not when it is injected into a rabbit. This inability of an animal's own protein to function as an antigen within its body offers us some sort of link between the chemical and the biological ways of looking at antibodies. At present we are concerned not with living microorganisms but with non-living molecules of protein, and we may obtain a reasonably clear idea of the function of antibody in relation to such material if we think somewhat along these lines:

(1) The body resents the intrusion of any form of protein foreign to that of its own blood and tissues. This is of course a metaphor, but it represents something real and carries with it the far-reaching implication that in one way or another the body can recognize what is and what is not foreign to its structure.

(2) The most effective way of making a foreign protein molecule tolerable is to smother it with a layer of the body's own type of protein.

(3) The formation of antibody makes it possible to carry out this 'compulsory naturalization' of the foreign protein much more effectively and rapidly.

Sometimes, when the protein is actively poisonous, the antibody by this smothering function acts as a perfect antidote but we must look on this as happening more by accident than by design. The antibody is produced and reacts with the antigen irrespective of whether the latter is poisonous or not.

So far we have confined ourselves to simple antigens, molecules of toxins or of soluble proteins like egg albumen. The same principles hold for anything built up of proteins or other complex molecules foreign to the body, and of course for bacteria or other microorganisms which may invade the tissues of the body. In this book we are concerned only with infectious disease and this is no place to discuss the fascinating problems that arise when we deal with reactions to cells and tissues of different individuals of the same species that have been introduced into the body by transfusion or transplantation. Nevertheless the growing edge of thought about immunity in 1960 and 1961 has drifted away from its old obsession on the importance of antibody in defence against infection by microorganisms. In earlier editions we could suggest that the whole elaborate mechanism of immunity had been evolved to deal with microbial invasion. In a lecture given in December, 1960, I favoured the very different approach that immunity had evolved in the first instance as part of the process of controls which maintains the structural and functional integrity of the body. But even if the immune reactions to microorganisms are derived from something more fundamental, they are still of the greatest practical importance, and it is still legitimate to apply our earlier point of view of the action of antibody to them.

The surface of a virus or bacterium, as we have seen, is built up of a pavement of complex organic molecules, partly protein, partly gum-like substances of carbohydrate type. It is an active living surface designed to gather up food molecules from the environment, and as such it is intensely foreign and irritant to the body. At any cost that surface must be smothered with body protein and rendered non-irritant. Both the protein and carbohydrate fractions of the surface are antigenic, and after infection specific antibodies rapidly appear.

In the last chapter we described some of the changes which occur in the blood of a patient with pneumonia at about the time he begins to recover. There our interest was directed toward the significance of the serum antibodies for the patient's recovery. These antibodies can also be demonstrated by simpler tests based on the physical results of contact between antibody and the corresponding type of *Pneumococcus*.

If the serum is mixed with a thin suspension of pneumococci in a weak saline solution, we observe a phenomenon called agglutination. When very large numbers of bacteria are suspended in saline, the suspension appears as a dense white opaque liquid looking very like milk. If we dilute this down, it becomes progressively more milk-and-watery in appearance till we come to a stage when there are only a few hundred million organisms in each cubic centimetre. At this strength the suspension shows only a mild turbidity, a white haze that swirls slightly as the tube is shaken. The turbidity does not change visibly for many hours, but if the tube is left still for a week or two the bacterial sediment goes slowly to the bottom. When such a suspension of pneumococci is mixed with normal serum, nothing happens, but with the serum from the recovered pneumonia patient we see the same sort of change that occurred when egg albumin was mixed with its antibody. The smooth turbidity becomes granular, the granules enlarge to visible flakes, and finally these flakes sediment rapidly to the bottom of the tube, leaving the liquid above limpid and free from bacteria.

This agglutination of bacteria by appropriate antibody depends on the same principles as are involved in the precipitation of simple molecular antigens. In the serum are antibody molecules each with two or more modified patches on its surface. When one of these patches comes into contact with the particular type of antigen on the bacterial surface to which it corresponds, it sticks, and the antibody is anchored to the bacterium. Sooner or later another bacterium will bump against the same antibody molecule, and if circumstances are favourable, another union will occur. The antibody molecule will now be in the nature of a link, holding two bacteria together. Actually each bacterium will probably attach dozens of antibody molecules to its surface, so that the possibilities of cross-connexions being formed are enormous. In fact, a simple and quite legitimate way of looking at the phenomenon is to think that when antibody molecules become attached to the surface of a bacterium, they make it intensely sticky, particularly for others like itself. As the bacteria become coated with antibody and collide with each other, larger and larger clumps are formed, until they become easily visible and settle to the bottom. Agglutination then is just a simple physical consequence of the union of antibody to antigen molecules which, instead of being free in solution, are fixed in position as part of the surface of the bacterium.

Ways have been found of breaking up the pneumococci and bringing the surface antigens into a purified soluble form. It confirms our interpretation of the nature of agglutination to find that this soluble antigen, which is the gummy carbohydrate substance we mentioned previously, readily unites with the antibody which causes agglutination of the intact bacteria. This union results in the formation of floccules very like those in the agglutination tests, but built up by the linking up of molecules, not of visible particles like bacteria.

We might go into more detail about the agglutination of bacteria, how sometimes one sort of surface antigen plays the major part, sometimes another, how the appearances depend on the amount of salt and other substances present, as well as on the presence of antibody and so on. But the only thing that really matters is this power of antibody to stick to the particular antigen that provoked its appearance, and so to provide a coating, more or less complete, of body protein over the foreign surface.

Agglutination of bacteria as such probably plays little part in assisting the body to overcome their harmful activities. It is almost wholly a test-tube phenomenon, a more or less accidental by-product of more important immunity reactions. Nevertheless, the agglutination test has some important practical applications in both medical and veterinary work. These depend upon the fact that an agglutination test is very easy to carry out and occurs only when the right antiserum and the corresponding bacterium are brought together. An antiserum against the typhoid bacillus will agglutinate only typhoid bacilli, it has no action at all on dysentery bacilli or the ordinary bacteria which occur in the bowel. When a patient is suspected of suffering from typhoid fever, cultures are made from the blood and from the faeces. If a bacillus is obtained which has the general properties of a typhoid bacillus, the final proof that it is or is not that organism is obtained by the agglutination test. A serum which is known to contain antibodies against the typhoid bacillus is mixed with the suspected culture, and if agglutination occurs we know at once that the patient is suffering from typhoid fever. In this example the test has been used to decide the nature of a bacterial culture. It can also be used in the opposite sense to determine what type of antibodies are present in a serum. Let us suppose that an epidemic of fever breaks out which is not recognized as typhoid fever for some weeks. Some of the patients have nearly or completely recovered by this time, but we are anxious to be certain whether they have or have not had typhoid fever. The bacteria can no longer be isolated from these patients, but it is easy to obtain some of their blood serum and test it against a known culture of the typhoid bacillus. If agglutination occurs, we can be sure that at some time previously the patients supplying the sera have been infected with typhoid. With a little elaboration of the test we can be reasonably certain that it was their recent fever and not some long past infection that was responsible for the agglutination.

Tests of this sort can be applied to many human and animal infections. As an example of its application to an important economic problem of poultry farmers, we may instance the use of an agglutination test for the control of 'bacillary white diarrhoea'. This is a disease of newly hatched chickens which is transmitted through the eggs laid by fowls infected with a particular bacillus. The chickens from such infected eggs develop diarrhoea and infect all the other chicks of the brood. A high percentage of deaths is the usual result. To avoid these infections it is clear that chickens should not be hatched from the eggs of chronically infected fowls. Unfortunately adult fowls usually show no symptoms; it is only in the very young chickens that the bacillus is really dangerous. Nevertheless, even when there are no obvious symptoms, the fowl reacts to the presence of the bacillus in its tissues by producing antibodies, and by the agglutination test these antibodies can be detected in a few drops of blood. In practice, this has solved the problem of bacillary white diarrhoea. A small amount of blood is taken from each laying hen, and the serum from this is tested for its power to agglutinate the bacillus. Those hens whose serum agglutinates are or have been infected—their eggs are excluded from the incubators, and except for the inevitable occasional accident, the new batches of chicks remain free from infection.

There is another important method by which the presence of antibodies can be detected in the serum of an individual who is suspected of having been infected with some particular type of organism. This is the complement-fixation test, the best-known example of the method being the Wassermann test for syphilis. In essence, the test is to mix the serum with a known antigen in some convenient form and to determine whether or not union of antibody to the antigen occurs. In the case of the Wassermann test, if the evidence of antibody is obtained, it signifies that the patient has at some time previously been infected with the spirochaete of syphilis. The actual technique used in the test is complicated—most medical students find the Wassermann test the most difficult of all laboratory procedure to understand—and nothing would be gained by describing it here. Such complement-fixation methods are mainly applied to infections by organisms like spirochaetes and viruses which are not easily obtained in emulsions suitable for agglutination tests.

All these tests are in one sense very artificial ones; agglutination, precipitation and complement fixation are test-tube phenomena that give very useful information but are not directly relevant to the way the body protects itself against disease. There is, however, a group of tests for antibody against viruses which are closer to what we are primarily interested in. In Australia we have occasional outbreaks of a severe infection of the brain—Murray Valley encephalitis. This is due to a virus that is spread by mosquitoes and which can be isolated by injection into the brain of a mouse, where it produces a characteristic fatal disease. If a man or an animal has been infected with the virus and recovers with or without symptoms, his blood will contain antibody and the classical way to detect and measure such antibody is by a *neutralization* test. Measured amounts of serum and virus are mixed and inoculated into the brains of a number of mice. If antibody is present all those mice which received mixtures with a sufficient amount of the serum will survive; if there is none all the inoculated mice will die. Such tests are very important in detecting the existence of invisible infections by viruses and as we shall see later, it is impossible to understand the natural history of a virus disease unless we can do this. The other aspect of the test that concerns us is its direct evidence that something in the blood can actually render a dangerous virus quite harmless.

The discovery mentioned earlier that children with the rare congenital disease, agamma-globulinemia, were unable to make antibody yet responded normally and became immune to infection with measles, necessitated a change in attitude. Antibody is clearly not the only factor in defence, even against virus diseases.

Like many another facet of biology and medicine, what once seemed all important gradually falls into place as part of a wider scheme of things. We can prevent measles with antibody but antibody production is evidently only a minor part of the body's response to that infection. Like every other bodily function immunity depends on cells specifically adapted to that purpose and coordinated where necessary with the functions of other cells. In the theoretical studies of immunity in the 1960's, antibody will probably be used more as an indication that cells are actively tuned to respond to antigen, than as something to be studied in its own right. The real problems of immunity lie at the cellular level.

CHAPTER IX

THE WIDER SIGNIFICANCE OF IMMUNITY

It is almost inevitable for a biological scientist to feel that his own particular field of study is of the greatest importance in exemplifying general biological principles. The entomologist will find that the phenomena of protective coloration and mimicry amongst insects throw more light on the process of evolution than any other single group of facts. The economic zoologist, whose real job is to determine why the herring fishing is good one year and bad the next, finds himself concerned with all manner of problems. He must consider the set of ocean currents, the seasonal changes in temperature and composition of sea water, and all the resulting changes in the microscopic life of the sea before he can approach the all-important question of the herring's food supply. He may well be excused for thinking his own field a perfect epitome of ecological principles. Each biologist, in his turn, if he has any taste at all for generalization, will tend to see the major biological problems from that particular angle which is provided by his immediate specialized interest. As an immunologist, I feel likewise that we have to deal with material which has important bearings on general biological problems, and which the accepted biological philosophers have largely neglected.

From one point of view, the development of antibodies and of the associated immunity are of such obvious survival value to the species that no further explanation of their existence is necessary. It is not easy to be content with this point of view. All aspects of structure and function in a living organism have necessarily to be adapted to the present requirements of the organism, but they have also a continuous evolutionary history behind them. The capacity to become immune as a result of experience of previous infection is a most unusual type of biological reaction, and it is worth spending some time on the more general aspects of its origin and significance.

It is perhaps of particular interest that as this third edition is being revised in 1961 we are in the midst of a very deep-seated controversy about the significance of immunity and about the chemical and cellular basis of its manifestation. Broadly speaking the disagreement follows a classical pattern of biological controversy. Lamarck believed that the giraffe developed a long neck because generations of giraffes all strained to reach leaves higher and higher up the trees. Darwin and his successors taught that the environment selected for survival those animals which by random mutation and combinations of mutations had longer necks than the rest of their contemporaries.

In terms of immunity we can believe that something from outside (the antigen) stimulates cells to produce an antibody tailor-made, as it were, to fit and cope with the antigen. This is basically a Lamarckian view. Alternatively we might believe that the cells of the body were produced in a thousand different patterns each corresponding to one sort of antigen. When the antigen enters the body its corresponding type of cell is *selected* to multiply and produce antibody—Darwinian selection for survival at a cellular level.

Until recently the 'Lamarckian' approach to immunity was universal. Only in 1956 did Jerne see that a Darwinian approach was also possible. There is probably something to be learnt from both and we can develop the older view first.

It is a matter both of common knowledge and of scientific fact that any type of activity by a living organism improves with practice. Even an amoeba fed with non-nutritious particles of dye 'learns' to discharge them from its protoplasm with increasing rapidity as it gains experience. This process of learning by experience is, of course, most clearly seen in the reactions of the higher animals, with elaborately developed nervous systems.

In the simpler types of animals we can only call such

changes modifications of reactions as a result of past experience, but as we come to animals of more highly developed nervous systems, we can recognize the improved efficiency as something comparable to what we know as developing skill by practice in ourselves. Amongst the invertebrates we find that most activities are not readily modified by experience. The rigidity of the instinctive behaviour of insects is well known, but even with these there is nearly always some capacity to modify details of behaviour as a result of experience. The higher animals, particularly mammals and birds, have large complex brains whose essential function is to allow accumulated experience to play a part in determining what is the most appropriate response to the various cirumstances which the animal may encounter. In ourselves all education, conscious or unconscious, is dependent on the same ability of the nervous system to profit by past experience.

This obvious importance of the changes in behaviour of man and animals which depend on past experience is liable to draw attention away from the other biological phenomena of comparable character. There are several examples of such phenomena which do not depend on changes in the nervous system, and amongst these the immunological reactions, which have been occupying us for the last three chapters, are by far the best studied and most important. The acquired immunity which follows many infections is just as much a matter of 'learning by experience' as is the acquired ability to swim or to ride a bicycle.

The standard theory of antibody production which is still current in the text-books is basically an attempt to explain how such learning by experience can take place at the immunological level. The theory is usually attached to the names of Haurowitz, Mudd and Pauling. According to this, antibody consists of globulin molecules, each of which has been fabricated in direct contact with an antigen molecule. It is believed that a standard globulin molecule is synthesized in the form of a long straight chain of mutually linked amino-acids. This chain must subsequently be coiled up into a compact, almost globular, mass. There are many alternative ways of packing a chain into small volume and, on the Haurowitz theory, this packing when done in the presence of an antigen produces the antibody. Where the forming antibody molecule is in contact with the antigen, a pattern develops which is a 'mirror-image' of the pattern of the antigen. A crude picture of the process may be obtained if we imagine something comparable to the preparation of a cast, or more correctly the matrix for a cast, with plaster of paris. The matrix derives a pattern which is not the same as that of the object but has a complementary relation to it, so that when object and matrix are again brought together there is a perfect 'fit'. In the antibody-producing cell we have to imagine a steady production of such matrices. As soon as one has been formed it is detached from the antigen and sent out into the blood, leaving room for another to be built up against the same antigenic pattern.

There are serious difficulties about accepting such a process in detail, but it has provided a convenient way of picturing the formation of antibody and of stressing its complementary relationship to the corresponding antigen. If for the present we accept the Haurowitz theory, it is reasonable to expect that when cells have repeatedly responded to the antigen they will make antibody more effectively and quickly than at their first experience. If we give an animal a single injection of some antigenic substance, for example, diphtheria or *Staphylococcus* toxoid (toxin rendered non-poisonous by formalin), the antibody response is small and takes about a fortnight to appear. Now if after a month or two we give another injection of the same toxoid, quite a different result is obtained. There is a rapid and large production of antitoxin which commences about forty-eight hours after this second inoculation. This sharp difference between the responses of the normal and the previously treated animal is not of course explained by the Haurowitz theory. It is not very difficult however to devise supplementary interpretations to cover the facts. Clearly the antibody-producing cells are so modified that they can rapidly produce fresh supplies of antibody on renewed contact with the antigen, and histological studies make it clear that there is an actual increase in the number of antibody-producing cells. Cellular changes associated with infection and recovery are manifold and important. Most immunologists believe that some of these changes in cell reactivity are due to the attachment of antibody to cells which have had no part in *producing* antibody. The best-known evidence for such transfer of antibody comes from the study of a curious phenomenon called anaphylaxis. In the course of experiments on diphtheria in the laboratory, it sometimes happened that a guinea-pig which had been given one injection of antitoxin was given a second dose some weeks later. It was noticed that some of these guinea-pigs died in a peculiar fashion a few minutes after what should have been an innocuous and protective inoculation. To make a long story short, these deaths from anaphylaxis had nothing to do with diphtheria toxin or with the antitoxin as such. It was the antigenic foreign protein in the horse serum which was really responsible, and normal horse serum would have served just as well as antitoxin. The first inoculation provoked the guinea-pig to produce antibody against the horse protein. Much of this antibody passed out of the blood into the tissues, and when a second inoculation of the corresponding antigen (horse-serum protein) was made, antigen and antibody united. But most of the antibody was in the cells, and the union of the two reagents in the cells damaged them in much the same way that a bacterial toxin would. Histamine was liberated from the damaged cells, and if a sufficiently large dose was produced the histamine killed the guinea-pig in its own characteristic fashion—by an acutely fatal attack of asthma. The guinea-pig has well-developed muscular bands around the smaller air tubes in its lungs. Their natural function is not thoroughly understood, but they are curiously susceptible to histamine. Under its action they contract and block the passage of air to the functional portion of the lung so that the guinea-pig dies in a few minutes from asphyxia.

If the same sort of experiment is carried out with a dog, the second injection of the antigen into its veins is also fatal, but for a different reason. The guinea-pig dies from something very much akin to asthma, the dog from sudden damage to its liver. Fundamentally, however, the same principles are at work. The action of the antigen on the antibody-containing cells liberates histamine, and it is mainly or entirely because in the dog histamine has a damaging effect on the liver and very little action on the lungs that the anaphylactic reaction takes this form.

The paradoxical nature of these phenomena naturally evoked the interest of many laboratory workers, and this interest was quickened by the realization that related phenomena were sometimes to be observed in human beings. Thousands of experiments were made, and gradually the conditions under which anaphylaxis could appear were worked out. Two of these experiments are important enough to mention here. They provide the main clues to the interpretation of anaphylaxis. In the first experiment, a guinea-pig is injected with egg albumen or some other protein. After a suitable time, some of its blood is taken and injected into another previously untreated guinea-pig. Two days later the second guinea-pig is inoculated with the antigen. It dies in typical asthmatic fashion. Something in the blood of a guinea-pig that has been injected with a foreign protein can convey this acquired susceptibility to another untreated guinea-pig. Suitable experiments show that the same antibody which causes precipitation with the foreign protein is responsible. The second experiment is to take a piece of visceral muscle, intestine or uterus from a treated guinea-pig. The muscle is washed free of blood and serum, and then set up in an apparatus which gives a record of its contractions and relaxations. If the guinea-pig supplying the muscle had been injected with egg albumen, then if a solution of this protein is washed over the muscle it contracts strongly. Other foreign proteins, horse serum for instance, produce no contraction of the muscle, nor will egg albumen solutions do so with muscle from a normal guinea-pig, or from an animal treated with horse serum. By this second experiment we have shown that some of the antibody really is fixed in the tissues and not merely circulating in the blood. Research of this sort was all very interesting to the laboratory worker, but it has clearly very little direct bearing on natural processes. As someone said, anaphylaxis is decidedly a creation of the hypodermic syringe. This holds also in human medicine, anaphylactic shock of essentially similar character occasionally results when a person who has once been given horse serum is given a new injection containing the same antigen. Usually of course the injections are of anti-tetanus serum or some similar product.

In recent years there has been a relative waning of interest in anaphylaxis but a sharp increase in research on another cellular aspect of immunity known as delayed hypersensitivity. This differs from anaphylaxis in the important respect that it cannot be transferred by antibody. The capacity to react seems to be intrinsic to the cells themselves.

Most people have had some personal acquaintance with vaccination against smallpox. If a person is being vaccinated for the first time very little is visible at the site until the third or fourth day, when a little red swelling appears. This swelling gradually develops into a blister or vesicle which reaches its maximum size about the twelfth day, then dries up to a scab which falls off about the twenty-first day. This is the normal course, and we may compare it with what occurs on a re-vaccination in someone who is still immune as a result of previous vaccination. With such an individual, a small red swelling with a surrounding flush appears within twenty-four hours, much earlier, that is, than in non-immune persons. This swelling reaches its peak in three days and soon fades away, leaving only a brownish stain and no scar.

In the immune individual, the response of the tissues to

the invading vaccine virus is quickly called into action and carries out its defence reaction more efficiently. Part of this change is due to antibody in the blood, but the reaction seen in the skin is a typical example of delayed hypersensitivity. It is called *delayed* to contrast this type of reaction with the rapid acute reactions that are seen, for example, in testing a hay-fever subject for susceptibility to pollen extracts. Another well-known example of delayed hypersensitivity is the tuberculin skin test (Mantoux test) which in a person who has been infected with the tubercle bacillus gives a deep red patch appearing 24–48 hours after the injection.

There is still a good deal of doubt about whether these reactions are really relevant to defence against infection or not. Most conservatively-minded immunologists would probably prefer to say that such tests may give us much useful information but that it is unwise to look on the reaction as a purely defensive one. In fact there is much to suggest that much of the *damage* done in tuberculosis is due to reactions in the lung or other infected tissues of similar character. Nevertheless, if we keep such warnings in mind there is something to be said for the simple-minded view that a localized opening up of capillary blood vessels, which is what causes the red patch of a positive skin test, represents an adaptive character to allow leucocytes and other components of the blood to be brought to bear on a *local* invasion of some microorganism.

The process by which one of these delayed reactions develops in the skin of a man or a guinea-pig has been pictured as follows. The injected tuberculin or other antigen diffuses slowly into the surrounding skin. In the capillaries there are white cells (lymphocytes) which in some way are tuned to respond to contact with this particular antigen. Probably only a relatively small proportion of such cells have this 'tuning', but of these many will be attracted to the area. On contact with the antigen such lymphocytes react in a fashion which damages both themselves and the adjacent tissues. One result of the damage is to liberate soluble substances—drugs if you like—which are responsible for the opening up of the blood capillaries and the other changes in the inflamed patch of skin. In the tuberculin reaction histamine is probably not involved or plays only a minor part, but the substances responsible are liberated in essentially similar fashion.

To understand this important process by which a cell can react with an antigen and produce damaging substances, we can look at the more readily studied histamine reactions. Let us revert for a moment to our first example of the action of histamine—mosquito bite. It is almost certain that if we could find an adult who had never been bitten by a mosquito, and watch what happened when the first such experience occurred to him, we should see no reaction of the skin at all. The saliva of the mosquito and similar insects is not in itself irritating, but it contains protein foreign to the body and capable of stimulating antibody production. After repeated bites, enough antibody has developed to render the whole skin surface of the body sensitive to the protein of the mosquito's saliva. At each bite the local union of the antigen with antibody in the skin cells causes a liberation of histamine, and that is responsible for the 'mosquito bite'. Here is an example on a trivial scale of what was 'designed' to act as a protective mechanism turning out to be a positive nuisance. Mosquitoes would be much more tolerable creatures if they did not provoke all the swelling and itchiness which is the mark of histamine liberation.

It is no doubt important that man should possess effective mechanisms for dealing with infections by bacteria and viruses, but it is a pity that these arrangements are sometimes set moving by antigenic substances not in the least like microorganisms. In the spring and early summer the air is laden with pollen grains from every sort of flowering plant, but particularly with grass pollen. Inevitably much of the pollen is filtered out of the air as it passes through the nose. For many people the pollen grains absorbed by the nasal lining act as an antigen, producing antibody in the blood and 'sensitizing' the body cells in the usual way. The result of renewed contact with the same type of pollen is hay fever. As each pollen grain lodges on a cell of the nasal lining or of the moist surfaces of the eye and eyelids, the contact results in histamine liberation with swelling, redness and increased secretion. Hence the stuffy nose and sneezing and the puffy, sore and itchy eyes which can make a hot day in the country a minor torture for the too facile producer of antibody.

Hay fever is only one of the human ills which can be traced to this same unfortunate inability of some people to decide which antigens are worth reacting to and which are not. Asthma, which like anaphylaxis in the guinea-pig, is mainly due to a contraction of the muscular bands around the smaller air tubes in the lungs, is very frequently due to an acquired susceptibility—we can hardly call it an immunity—to some common substance which can reach the lungs in the form of fine dust. Quite a few cases of asthma have been traced to the orris root in face powder, others to the dust from the feathers used to stuff pillows or mattresses. Often it requires a well-developed detective faculty in the doctor if he is to find the substance responsible, and of course until he does find it the patient is not likely to lose his asthma.

Although the symptoms of hay fever and asthma are limited to their own special regions, this is only because the antigen can reach susceptible cells in these particular situations more readily than elsewhere. Probably every cell of the patient's body has this new abnormal susceptibility to the offending material. The skin cells are certainly susceptible, and it is by testing the skin with various likely substances that the specialist in these diseases discovers what material is likely to be responsible for the symptoms. If, for example, the patient complains of hay fever in early summer, the obvious things to test are the pollens which are liberated at that season. So a series of superficial scratches are made on his forearm and on each is placed a drop of extract made from one particular pollen. In a few minutes the pollen to which the patient is sensitive will be shown by the appearance of an itchy raised weal around the corresponding scratch.

Another minor ailment which can be traced to the same automatic activity of the antibody mechanism is the serum sickness which often follows about ten days after the administration of serum against diphtheria. The child develops an itchy rash, particularly around the place where the serum was injected, there is a rise in temperature, and often severe aching pains in joints and muscles. To understand this reaction we must remember that diphtheria antitoxin is a solution of horse-serum protein. The fact that it has the power to neutralize diphtheria antitoxin does not alter the fact that, to the human being, it is something totally foreign, against which an antibody begins to appear in the blood. In most cases relatively large amounts of antitoxin have been given, and some unchanged horse-serum protein persists for a week or two, especially near the place where it was inoculated. Wherever the antibody now circulating in the blood comes into contact with antigen in or on tissue cells, there is a liberation of histamine and the appearance of corresponding symptoms.

This long digression about the cellular aspects of the immunity reactions and their importance in medicine must not keep us from our main object, which is to elucidate the wider significance of immunity. The conception we have developed is that there are certain cells of the body, probably the fixed phagocytes, which take up from the blood or lymph any micro organisms or other material foreign to the tissues. Most theories of antibody production consider that this represents the first phase of the process. Within recent years however there have been increasing doubts on this point. In the 1920's the fixed phagocytes were regarded as wholly responsible for antibody production. Gradually it became evident that the actual production of antibody was a function of cells of the lymphocyte series which could be called either large lymphocytes or immature plasma cells. The current problem is whether they are stimulated to produce antibody by direct contact with antigen or whether the fixed phagocytes (now generally called macrophages) play an essential preliminary part.

All we can say at the present time is that both types of cell are present in the antibody-producing tissues and that such tissues respond to the foreign chemical structure of the micro-organisms by elaborating and, after some days, pouring out into the blood special protein molecules, antibodies whose function can perhaps be best understood if we call them 'reminders'. There are several distinct sorts of antibody which differ in the extent to which they remain free in the blood or are built into cells of various types. These antibody 'reminders' are like plain-clothes detectives with perfect memories for criminal faces; when they come into contact with their 'opposite number', this is recognized as a dangerous individual which has on some former occasion penetrated the defences either of the body or of society. It or he must be apprehended. So the blood antibody fastens on to the micro-organism and makes it ready for the phagocytes to take in and digest. The cell with its antibody 'reminder' responds vigorously to the invader, its liberated histamine and other products setting in action the local response of blood vessels and phagocytes, which is best fitted to eliminate the infection. Finally, just as in human communities we have a policeman at the gate of the police barracks, so in the body those cells of the type which produce antibody are themselves provided with 'reminders'. Contact with the 'remembered' antigen seems to stimulate some to liberate antibody, others to multiply and produce a new generation of antibody-producing cells. Both responses serve to increase the effectiveness of the defence—police reinforcements, shall we call them?

Now this elaborate mechanism will probably strike the reader as something ingenious, but eminently reasonable, and with easily developed analogies to defence processes in the social and political field. Yet, on the physiological and biological aspects, the process is an unusually difficult one to understand. Everything points to more than one type of cell being involved, and there are probably several steps in a process of which we can only see the beginning and the end. A bacterium or some other antigen is taken into one cell and, after a time, another cell begins to liberate the corresponding antibody. Two facts must be kept in mind in thinking about that process. First, the amount of antibody produced is much more than would be needed to unite with all the antigen molecules which are comprised in the bacterium, and secondly antibody may persist in the blood for many years after the infection which caused it has been completely eliminated, while the capacity for rapid antibody production to a 'remembered' antigen may last even longer. If these are facts we are compelled to think of the antibody-producing cells as cells which in one way or another are capable not only of producing antibody of some particular type but also of passing on to their descendants the same capacity to respond to one particular pattern of antigen with special ease and rapidly produce the needed antibody.

Until 1956 it was regarded as self-evident that antibody production was a rather straightforward sequel to the entry of foreign protein into the body. The antigen was taken into a cell, setting in train a process of stamping a complementary pattern on the globulin being produced by the cell so that it was released as antibody appropriate to react with that particular antigen. We have already mentioned some of the difficulties of this point of view. With increasing knowledge about the process by which protein is synthesized in the cell in conformity with what we can call the information stored in the chromosomes, many further difficulties arose. In addition the great activity during the 1950's on the phenomena of transplantation of skin and tumours drew special attention to the previously neglected problem of 'self and not-self'.

Today (1961) it is quite impossible to state simply what is the accepted way of interpreting the phenomena of immunity.

Most immunologists would probably say that there is so much still to be learnt about the details of protein synthesis in the cell that it would be wise to wait a while before trying to explain the production of antibody. In the meantime although we know the Haurowitz-Mudd theory will eventually have to be modified or discarded, it has been useful in the past and is still adequate for all practical purposes. Since I have been largely responsible for pressing quite a different theoretical approach, I can hardly be expected to adopt this non-committal attitude.

The essence of the alternative approach which has been called the clonal selection theory is that the function of the antigen is not to initiate the process of building a corresponding antibody in the cell it happens to enter, but as it were to seek out cells that are already capable of producing just such an antibody and stimulate them to do so. To elaborate that concept requires a book in itself[1] and it would be quite inappropriate to do so here. However, if we take for granted the possibility that a complete range of antibody patterns can be developed during the embryonic development of any bird or mammal, the outlines of a selection theory of immunity can easily be sketched.

We start with the assumption that many different cell lines develop, each of which will eventually be capable of carrying a small number, perhaps two, perhaps up to 20, of patterns which will allow it to react with the corresponding antigenic patterns and only these. The only really important reason for suggesting a selection theory at all is to find some way of accounting for the crucial fact of immunology, that only *foreign* substances provoke immune reactions. This is accounted for by the assumption that all the patterns on cell lines have to run the gauntlet of being tested against the multitude of patterns in the developing organism almost as soon as they arise. There are good reasons for believing that contact in the

[1] Burnet, F. M.: *Clonal Selection Theory of Acquired Immunity.* Cambridge and Vanderbilt University Presses (1959).

embryonic period will result in the destruction or inactivation of cells capable of reacting with body constituents. This might be by the actual elimination of the cells concerned or by a sort of permanent blocking of the unwanted patterns, with the cell still able to carry any patterns that did *not* correspond to body constituents. By the time of birth then we can picture the body as in possession of a vast population of wandering cells carrying amongst them patterns of potential action corresponding to all the antigenic configurations that are *not* found amongst the body's own components.

The actual process of recognition can be visualized by thinking of what happens if a child is by some mischance given the wrong sort of blood transfusion. The child's own red cells are of course completely at home in the body. There is nothing in them which can stimulate the lymphocytes and other cells that have, as it were, grown up in their presence to harmful activity. The foreign cells, however, carry new components. Perhaps in the circulation, but more likely when the alien cells are being broken down in the spleen, the non-self configuration they carry will meet some of those lymphocytes which have the corresponding capacity to react with it. The stimulated cells will, if they find a suitable niche in spleen or lymph node, multiply, producing either more lymphocytes with the same potential reactivity or plasma cells which, either at once or under a renewed stimulus by the antigen, produce antibody. Quite soon there will be greatly increased numbers of cells capable of reacting with the antigen. In fact it may be many years before the proportion of what we can now call *immunologically competent* cells will sink to what it was before the first experience of the new antigen.

This interpretation is thus capable of overcoming the two main difficulties of the orthodox theory. If we had injected some of the individual's own red cells, there would by definition be no lymphocytes capable of reacting and initiating the process of antibody production. The previously unmet antigen will be *recognized* in the sense that it can make effective contact with some of the small proportion of lymphocytes which had been 'marked' in the process of embryonic development with this particular reactivity.

Multiplication of cells under stimulus with inheritance of the inborn capacity to react with a particular antigen provides at once a basis for the enhanced secondary response and for the persistence of immunological memory.

This perhaps is the place to emphasize the expendable character of the lymphocytes and other cells concerned with immunity. Anyone who has had a chronic sore throat knows how 'glands' in the neck may swell up and disappear again in a week or so. Such changes in lymph glands mean the production and destruction of millions of cells. The average life of a lymphocyte is probably only a week or two. If antibody production and the capacity to revive immunity rapidly on restimulation is to persist over almost the whole of a person's lifetime, there is no escape from the conclusion that the capacity to produce antibody must be transferable from a cell to its descendants. Under the old theory this would have meant the acceptance in a rather special sense of the inheritance of acquired characters. This is for well-known and valid reasons a serious heresy against the whole of biological experience. One of the main reasons why geneticists in particular tend to favour a selection theory of immunity and antibody production is because of the absence of any known instance in which the environment can directly change the genetic character of an organism in a needed direction. It is an article of faith with geneticists that that change in genetic character depends on genetic processes of which the important ones are mutation and the various types of interchange and combination associated with sexual reproduction.

We must be clear that this discussion of inheritance of immune capacity applies only to limited populations of cells within the body. There is no inheritance of immunity in the full sense of the word. The child of a father strongly immune against a certain antigen is born with no more of that antibody than any other child. If a mother has antibody in her blood, this passes into her infant's blood during pregnancy, and at birth both mother's and infant's blood contain almost the same amounts of all antibodies. This antibody, however, is essentially just like antibody injected with a syringe; it has not been produced by the infant's own cells, and when after three to six months it gradually disappears, the child's body is, as it were, a clean slate upon which, as the child encounters its inevitable infections, each new antigen may make its mark. Neither from father nor mother is there any real inheritance of immunity.

CHAPTER X

WHAT MAKES BACTERIA DANGEROUS?

So far we have tended to take a rather optimistic view of infectious disease. It is a necessary manifestation of the struggle for existence between species, and viewed broadly, the interaction between host and parasite is a balanced one. The microorganism passes from host to host. Only an infinitesimal proportion of the individuals produced by its multiplication in each host survive, but they are sufficient to ensure the continuance of the species. The host species on its side has developed during its evolution the normal defences against infection, and, as well, each individual during and after first infection by any particular microorganism develops some degree of specific immunity against it. This double mechanism of protection does its work well so long as the general efficiency of the body is maintained, and so long as the attacking microorganism is not of abnormally high virulence, but sometimes it fails. In this chapter we want to discuss what happens when the defences fail. Since much more is known about the details of infection by bacteria than about viruses diseases or protozoal infections, we shall confine ourselves to the problem as it concerns bacteria. Why do the bacteria which normally can be held so easily in check sometimes find it possible to multiply almost without hindrance and kill the patient in a few days unless speedy and effective treatment is available? Such catastrophes are rather outside the order of nature. Sudden death of the host automatically destroys any possibility of the invading microorganism passing to another host. There are only one or two significant exceptions to this rule. Anthrax is one of them. In the carcass of a sheep dead of anthrax, the bacillus takes on the spore form in which it can resist heat and desiccation for years. The spores from the rotting carcass may infest the ground, and at any time give rise to infection of fresh sheep. Here death of the host forms part of the cycle necessary for spread of the infection. A rather different example is found in regard to plague. When a plague-infected rat dies, its fleas desert the cooling body and will spread infection to any new susceptible host, rodent or man, that they can reach. In the case of plague, death of the normal host (the rat) is not necessary for the maintenance of the infection in that species, but it does play a very important part in causing human infections.

These exceptions are important, but they do not invalidate the general rule that death from any type of parasitic infestation or infection is to be regarded as an accident rather than a normal occurrence. Still, all men die, and if we include childhood deaths, it is probable even today that more than half of all human deaths are due essentially to microorganismal invasion. It seems that our general picture of infection as a balanced conflict between parasite and host in which both species survive, is one of those theoretical conceptions which need continuous qualification if they are to describe what actually occurs in an extremely complicated world.

It will be obvious that the fatal result of any infection will depend both on the microorganism and the host, and we can also feel certain that, except for certain abnormally fatal epidemics, the state of the host is of far greater importance in determining the outcome than is the virulence of the microorganism. It is a truism to say that a tremendous amount of death directly due to infection is really determined by malnutrition or unhealthy environmental circumstances, in other words, by poverty. The excessive height of the infantile and childhood death-rates in slum areas makes this perfectly clear, and it is unnecessary to do more than mention the inevitable concurrence of pestilence with famine in all primitive or semi-civilized peoples throughout history. It is only common sense to believe that well-nourished, clean and properly exercised human beings will be better fitted to resist infection than less fortunate individuals. Medical experience and statistics, as far as they are applicable to the question, are in agreement with common sense. In comparing the well-nourished with the under-nourished, however, it is important that comparison should be made only between groups which have been exposed to much the same amount of potential infection. It is a commonplace that the healthy country recruit goes down to barracks' infections much more readily than the weedy city dweller. The important difference in this instance is not one of nutrition, but of the two individuals' previous experience of infections.

Experimental bacteriology has not been very successful in discovering why under-nourishment should favour a fatal outcome to infections. It is not possible to point to any particular aspect of the defence process and say that it is at this point that under-nourishment interferes. There is only some general lowering of bodily efficiency that tips the balance in favour of the microorganism. Curiously enough there are some infections in which the opposite effect may be observed. Experimentally, it is well known that in work with foot-and-mouth disease virus, the experimental guinea-pigs must be well fed and in perfect health if they are to show the typical signs and symptoms of the infection when they are inoculated. Underweight guinea-pigs show hardly any result of inoculation at all. Amongst human diseases, there is a general impression that infantile paralysis is more likely to attack a well-nourished 'healthy' child than one who is not thriving. As far as experimental work has gone it is in agreement with this impression. Mice can be partially protected against the effect of a modified poliomyelitis virus if they are kept on a diet deficient in vitamin B_1. It is possible that viruses, as it were, demand that they have healthy cells to parasitize, while most bacteria with their less rigid nutritional requirements can flourish as well in an under-nourished body as in a healthy one. For them it may be only the efficiency of the defence mechanism as influenced by nutrition that counts. Inherited weakness in resistance to infection was often suspected but only in recent years has its existence been verified and its nature become susceptible to study. The most important example, agammaglobulinaemia, has been mentioned more than once and there are several others. An occasional unfortunate infant dies after vaccination against smallpox because he is quite unable to develop either antibody or the more primitive cellular immunity. One can be sure that more such inborn deficiencies will be recognized in the future. This may help us greatly in the understanding of the processes of immunity for rather often the genetic abnormality is in regard to a single gene controlling a single phase of the chemical functioning of the body. Possibly rather similar to these inherited defects are some conditions which arise in the course of leukaemia (cancer of the white blood cells) and similar diseases, or following treatment with certain drugs, in which normally harmless moulds, bacteria or viruses may produce fatal infection.

To pass from these rare but often illuminating conditions to more familiar matters, we must consider one important reason why infections with normally harmless bacteria may be fatal. If by some accidental circumstance a germ reaches one of the 'sheltered' regions of the body where normally there is no contact with the environment, it is likely to produce a much more serious result than in its natural (or at least usual) habitat.

The best-known example of such susceptibility of sheltered regions of the body is puerperal fever, which results from streptococcal infection of the uterus immediately after childbirth. The infection is severe, and in the days before the sulpha drugs and penicillin about a quarter of the cases ended fatally. The uterus after childbirth is in rather a disorganized state, its stage of active function is over, and it has not yet commenced the process of shrinking and reorganization which will return it to the normal non-pregnant form. There is always at this stage a certain amount of blood clot and dead tissue cells to provide food for any bacteria which may enter the uterus, and the blood supply of the organ is in a makeshift, intermediate stage, poorly adapted to deal with the emergency of an infection. If a sufficiently virulent *Streptococcus* does reach the uterus, a very serious infection results.

There are effective bacteriological techniques for tracing the origin of such streptococcal infections as puerperal fever. Essentially these methods simply provide more delicate ways of telling whether two streptococcal cultures are or are not identical. It may be found, for example, that amongst the persons in contact with a woman with puerperal fever there is a nurse who has a mild sore throat due to streptococcal infection. Cultures are prepared from the infected puerperal uterus and from the nurse's throat. If it is found that the two cultures are identical at all points, and that no other persons in contact with the patient carry this type of *Streptococcus* in their throats, we can be reasonably certain that the patient was infected with streptococci from this nurse's throat. As far as is known, probably 80 or 90 per cent of puerperal infections are derived from mild or trival throat infections, sometimes in the patient herself, more often in those around her. In the usual place for streptococci, the throat, these germs do very little damage, but when the same type of germ enters the uterus, there is a 20 per cent chance that the infection will be fatal unless treated. It must not be supposed that only mild throat infections can cause puerperal fever. A virulent quinsy or scarlet fever, or indeed any severe streptococcal infection, would be even more dangerous, but naturally any such sufferers are kept as far away as possible from a maternity hospital. The mild throat infections are important mainly because they are unnoticed or not considered of sufficient importance to justify disturbance of the routine of midwifery practice.

Another interesting example of the way a relatively harmless bacterium can be responsible for fatal infections if it happens to reach the wrong place, is given by the Bundaberg tragedy of 1928. Bundaberg is a town in Queensland where, in the summer of 1928, an immunization campaign against diphtheria was in progress. Children were being given three inoculations under the skin of a mixture of diphtheria toxin and antitoxin, in order to provoke the production of antitoxin and concomitant immunity to diphtheria. This particular type of inoculation has long been superseded by more effective and safer methods, but at the time it was a thoroughly orthodox and usually effective procedure. By a chain of unfortunate circumstances, a bottle of the inoculation mixture became infected with a *Staphylococcus*, the common bacterium of the skin, which causes boils and such like. The bottle was left in a cupboard in warm subtropical climate for a week and then used for inoculating twenty-one young children. Unknown to the doctor, the material now contained millions of staphylococci which were injected under the skin of the children. The result was disastrous; twelve of the children, particularly the youngest ones, died within forty-eight hours, some of the others were severely ill but recovered, while four showed practically no symptoms beyond the formation of a small abscess at the point of inoculation.

The tragedy of course created intense public interest, and a Royal Commission was immediately appointed to investigate the circumstances. It was at once discovered that the bottle of toxin-antitoxin mixture was heavily infected with staphylococci, and that similar bacteria were present in the local abscesses which formed at the site of inoculation in those children who survived. The obvious inference was that the staphylococci had caused the deaths, but the extraordinary rapidity and severity of the symptoms was quite unlike the effect ordinarily produced by staphylococcal infections. The Commission was reluctant to accept this conclusion until every conceivable alternative had been investigated, but in the end decided that it provided the only explanation of the tragedy.

Almost everyone has at some time or other suffered from staphylococcal infections, but these are infections which take place by some natural route and in which the germs reach the unprotected inner tissues in very small numbers, if at all. A fully developed boil contains millions of staphylococci, and extends into the deeper layers of the skin, but the staphylococci are surrounded on every side by a thick defensive army of phagocytes. Elsewhere, too, any normal type of infection by these bacteria will be associated with an adequate or nearly adequate phagocytic response, sufficient at least to slow down the spread of the staphylococci into surrounding uninfected tissue. But at Bundaberg something totally unnatural occurred. It is biologically unprecedented for several hundred million staphylococci to appear suddenly in healthy normal tissue underneath the skin. In seventeen of the children this unnatural invasion overwhelmed the local defences, and the bacteria multiplied and spread throughout the body killing twelve and making the other five dangerously ill. Four children, however, were hardly affected at all; they had no symptoms until two or three days after the inoculations. Then they noticed a tender lump where the injection had been made and within the next few days saw a small abscess develop here. These children had a local defence adequate to deal even with this invasion. It is probably significant that most of them were older children who might be expected to have had more 'training' in dealing with staphylococci. Almost certainly they had in previous years developed enough antibody and immunity against staphylococci to render their phagocytic response to the invasion vastly more effective than it was in the unfortunate non-immune children.

Every surgeon knows that there are some parts of the body which must be shielded against any form of bacterial infection with the utmost care. In any operation to the knee joint, for example, bacteria must on no account be left in the joint cavity. If they are, an acute septic infection of the joint will probably result. In the mouth, on the other hand, a dentist thinks nothing of extracting a dozen teeth and leaving gaping holes connecting the inside of the jawbones to a cavity full of bacteria. Yet in ninety-nine cases out of a hundred the jaw heals quite uneventfully. As always, the body is fitted to deal with the commonly occurring emergencies, but has no special competence for dealing with emergencies so rare as to be of no significance to the survival of the species. Teeth are always liable to minor damage, and bacteria are always present to slip into any cracks between gum and tooth. An efficient local protective mechanism against bacterial infection in this region is a necessity for the survival of any toothed animal species. Infection of a large joint like the knee will occur in nature only as a result of severe injury, usually associated with compound fracture of bones. Such an injury to any wild animal is invariably fatal; the most effective antibacterial mechanism in the lining of the joint would make no difference to the result. So it is that because the dentist's manipulations are similar in character to minor natural accidents, he is almost free from worries about bacterial infections, while the surgeon, whose knife invades regions which in nature would be exposed to the environment only in the course of fatal injury, has to develop a rigid technique for the exclusion of bacteria.

While we are discussing the differences amongst body tissues in their reactions to infection, we should mention two special regions. The first is the central nervous system, the brain and the spinal cord. As the most delicate and important part of the body, this is very carefully shielded and insulated from the environment physically and physiologically. There is even a special physiological arrangement which prevents soluble substances in the blood from entering the actual substance of the nervous tissue. It is very rare for infection to lodge in the brain, even if the germs are passing through it in the blood. As a natural corollary of the existence of this elaborate shielding of the nervous system, if bacteria do enter it by any means, they are very liable to multiply and cause rapidly fatal illness. Meningitis, which is an infection of the surface coverings of the brain and spinal cord, is rarely caused by the common streptococci, staphylococci and pneumococci, but if such infection should occur, it demands strenuous treatment with penicillin, often accompanied by surgical measures, if the patient is to survive. Excluding for the present the tubercle bacillus, the germs which cause meningitis in childhood are chiefly two relatively harmless denizens of the human throat. The *Meningococcus* is the more important of the two. This bacterium is rather misnamed. A very minute proportion of the individuals infected with the germ develop any signs of meningitis. Normally it is a harmless inhabitant of the throat, but it has a distinctly greater aptitude for reaching and infecting the brain surface than any other of the germs living in the throat. The other fairly common cause of meningitis in infancy is a form of the so-called influenza bacillus, another inhabitant of the throat and air passages, and like the *Meningococcus* practically never producing any serious results there.

The other tissue which differs sharply from the rest of the body in its response to infection is the special type of bloodless fibrous tissue which forms the valves of the heart. These thin strong cusps of rather parchment-like appearance are continually surrounded by blood, and there is no need for blood vessels within them to supply nourishment. Sometimes, especially following an attack of rheumatic fever, some types of streptococci become implanted on a valve. They remain there, growing slowly but persistently, and gradually destroying the valve. The common cause of this disease, subacute bacterial endocarditis, is a type of *Streptococcus* very common in the mouth, and often associated with minor dental disease such as apical abscess. The commonest reason for its entry into the blood is the extraction of an infected tooth. In a normal person this little flush of streptococci into the blood does no harm, but in a person with a heart damaged by rheumatic fever it is potentially very dangerous. It is general practice to remove teeth from such a person only under the protection of a short course of penicillin injections. In any other tissue than the heart valve, the presence of the *Streptococcus* would provoke all the usual defence responses of blood vessels and phagocytes. But on the valve, although its blood supply in one sense is unlimited in amount, yet it is not suited to deal with unwanted bacteria. Red cells and white cells rush past at a speed comparable to that at which water flows from a bath tap. There are no capillaries through which the blood trickles gently, allowing phagocytes to stick to the walls and pass into the tissues where they are needed. So we have the curious anomaly of a relatively harmless bacterium producing steady and ultimately fatal damage in a situation where it is exposed to the full force of the blood stream, but remains unharmed by the agents in the blood which anywhere else would soon destroy it.

An infection results fatally for one or both of two reasons. Either there is an inadequate resistance on the part of the host, or the infecting microorganism is of excessive virulence. We have discussed some of the factors which may prejudice the host's chances in the stuggle—the part played by the changing virulence of the microorganism remains to be considered.

It is often easy to feel certain that the illness of some particular individual is due to infection with an unusually virulent type of bacterium. It is much more difficult to find an objective standard of virulence by which different strains of microorganism can be experimentally compared. Most experiments on the virulence of bacteria have to be rather artificial in character. Natural contact infection is always a chancy irregular process, and it can be used in laboratories only for some very special types of experiment. The only practicable way to measure the virulence of a bacterium is to find out how many of the germs have to be inoculated into an animal with a hypodermic syringe to be certain of killing it. For technical reasons, the usual experiment is to find the dose of bacteria which causes the death of half the animals injected.

If we obtain a culture of *Pneumococcus* from a patient with pneumonia and test its virulence for mice, we may find that the injection of 100,000 bacteria will kill four out of six mice, while 10,000 kill only one out of six. The number required to give a 50 per cent mortality would then be something a little under 100,000. Now if we inoculate a second mouse with a little of the blood from the heart of a mouse which has died from experimental infection with pneumococci, it will also die in a day or two. By successive inoculation of heart blood to fresh mice we can maintain a kind of artificial epidemic. If this passage of the germ from mouse to mouse is kept up for twenty or thirty generations, it will nearly always result in an increased virulence of the *Pneumococcus*. Some strains have been developed to such a degree of virulence by this method that a single living *Pneumococcus* will cause a fatal infection when it is introduced into a mouse. In such instances we know the ancestry of the germ, and can compare its characteristics in the relatively non-virulent form before passage through mice and in its later virulent form.

It is by no means certain that rapid passage of a germ from one patient to the next will produce a steady increase in virulence in any way comparable to the change in the *Pneumococcus* on mouse to mouse passage. Inoculation by needle prick is an unusual method for the transfer of infection in man. Probably the only clear evidence of increased virulence for man resulting from active multiplication of a bacterium in human tissues is provided by a type of accidental infection closely akin to inoculation. This is post-mortem room sepsis. Thirty years ago, if a pathologist performing a post-mortem on the body of a patient dead of some form of streptococcal infection were to prick his finger on the edge of a sharp piece of bone, he was in almost as great a danger as a man who had been bitten by a cobra. Unless the scratch was immediately dealt with by strong local antiseptics he was very liable to die as a result of infection with particularly virulent streptococci. During the fatal illness and for a short time after the death of the patient the streptococci had been multiplying rapidly in human tissues. They had learnt how to flourish in that environment, and when they were transferred almost immediately to other living human tissues they would usually continue to flourish, this time at the expense of the pathologist. The advent of penicillin has completely changed the situation, and we no longer hear of post-mortem room sepsis.

Sometimes, during an epidemic, there is a suggestion that the germ causing it increases in virulence as the epidemic progresses, but most of this apparent increase in virulence is really due to the increasing liability of infection as the disease becomes more widespread. In general, it is probably nearer the truth to say that any chance variation or mutation of the germ in the direction of greater virulence, however it may be produced, increases its disease-producing power, than to assume that frequent transfer from host to host itself causes changes in the germ, giving it greater virulence. Undoubtedly common germs seem to take on greater virulence when they have unusually free opportunities to spread from person to person. The *Meningococcus*, which we have already mentioned several times, very rarely produces meningitis in adults, except amongst soldiers in crowded camps. Infections spread by the respiratory route always seem to flourish in such camps, but it is difficult to say that rapid passage of the bacteria from person to person actually raises the virulence. What probably happens is that spontaneous variations occur in bacteria, just as they do in all living organisms. With such a rapid rate of multiplication there are increased opportunities of variation, and if the variation is in the right direction, it may rapidly replace the original form. If the microorganism causing an epidemic is susceptible to variations in the direction of higher virulence, then opportunities for rapid spread amongst susceptible persons will cause an apparent increase in virulence by the selection of the fittest, i.e. most virulent, bacteria.

There is another rather similar phenomenon which is likely to show itself in military camps. It may happen that two different microorganisms spread more readily in company than apart. In some American army camps during 1917 there were some serious outbreaks of measles. Measles is due to a virus, and is not in itself particularly serious, but in these camp outbreaks it had gone into partnership with a dangerous type of *Streptococcus*. The measles virus produced a mild inflammation of the respiratory passages, opening the way for the more dangerous activity of the *Streptococcus*. Many died of streptococcal pneumonia, and complications like infection of the middle ear were very numerous. The bacteriological history of the great pandemic of influenza in 1918–19 will never be known in its entirety, because at the time the influenza virus was unknown, and only the associated bacteria could be studied. Such reports as were made, however, show that sometimes bacteria were of great importance in causing or aggravating the fatal pneumonia which was so common. The types of bacteria found in the lungs varied from one country to another, and even in different stages of the epidemic in the same country. It seems as if a very active virus swept over the whole world, finding almost all individuals susceptible to it, and in its passage made all sorts of temporary alliances with pathogenic bacteria spread by the same respiratory route. The virus initiated the illness in every case, but when a fatal outcome resulted it was almost always the bacteria which were finally responsible.

The important question now arises as to whether we know anything about what makes one of two strains of the same bacterium more virulent than the other. It is obvious that we can never have a complete answer to this question until we know everything about both host and parasite, but it may be possible to provide an incomplete but nevertheless useful answer. There are certain aspects of bacterial structure and behaviour which are correlated with virulence to the susceptible host.

With such organisms as the *Pneumococcus*, the *Streptococcus* and the anthrax bacillus, we can isolate virulent strains from fatal cases of the corresponding disease, and we can also obtain harmless or avirulent strains. Avirulent strains may be developed by various methods, most of which involve growing the originally virulent strain under rather abnormal conditions. As it habituates itself to growth in the new environment, it will usually lose some or all of its power to multiply in living tissues. Some strains lose their virulence more readily than others, but with suitably chosen methods it is nearly always possible to reduce a virulent strain to complete harmlessness. When the virulent and non-virulent types are compared it will be found that, for each of the three species we have mentioned, there is a consistent difference between them. Under the microscope the virulent forms, but not the avirulent ones, are seen to be surrounded by a relatively thick mantle of transparent rather gummy material. This coating, which is generally referred to as the bacterial capsule, is transparent and not readily stained by dyes, so that special methods for demonstrating its existence under the microscope are necessary. The bacteria are mixed with indian ink, and a thin smooth film of the mixture is made on clean glass. The bacteria will then appear as translucent holes in the opaque background of the ink. If this smear is now stained with one of the ordinary dyes used for making bacteria easily visible under the microscope, we can see quite easily whether there is an 'invisible' capsule or not. With a non-capsulated, avirulent bacterium, we find that the holes in the ink film are almost completely filled with the stained body of the germ. With a virulent capsulated type, the hole in the ink is wider, and between its margin and the pink- or blue-stained bacterium there is a wide transparent zone—the capsule.

Tests made with phagocytes in the way described in chapter VII will show that the capsulated virulent strains are insusceptible to phagocytosis—i.e. they are not taken into the substance of phagocytes and digested—if serum from a normal non-immune animal is present in the mixture. The avirulent non-capsulated forms are readily taken up by phagocytes.

There is only circumstantial evidence so far that the presence of a capsule interferes with phagocytosis, and therefore makes the bacterium more virulent, but it is enough to call for a close study of the capsule. Chemical studies have shown that in most cases the capsule is composed of gummy material which is chemically a complex carbohydrate rather closely related to gum arabic, dextrin and suchlike substances. This gummy material is partly soluble; molecules are always being set free, and in the body or in the culture tube free soluble carbohydrate will always be present in the immediate neighbourhood of the germs. Now for phagocytosis to occur with any readiness, the foreign particle or bacterium must first be coated with a layer of body protein. It is one of the qualities of these bacterial polysaccharides that body protein does not readily combine with them. Only a very small proportion of normal protein molecules can combine, and before these can reach the bacterium they are almost certain to meet some of the free dissolved polysaccharide and combine with that instead. So the bacteria remain uncoated with protein and uneaten by phagocytes. This state of affairs can be altered only by the appearance of antibodies, as we described in an earlier chapter. Against bacteria of this type the only antibody of importance is that directed against the polysaccharide. As antibody accumulates in the blood, it provides more and more protein molecules which can combine with the polysaccharide and the protective screen of soluble molecules is soon mopped up. Then the antibody is free to attach itself to the bacterial capsule and surround the germs with a film of antibody protein which, in the test-tube, will cause agglutination of the bacteria, and in the body will allow them to be taken up by phagocytes. We are here repeating from a slightly different point of view the same story that a virulent bacterium in an immune animal behaves like an avirulent one in a normal animal.

As in every other chapter of this book, we can discuss only those examples which have been sufficiently studied in the laboratories. The explanation which has been given for the difference between virulent and avirulent bacteria is certainly valid for the well-studied bacteria which were mentioned earlier. For the pneumococci it seems to be almost the whole story. Undoubtedly other factors play an important part in determining the virulence of some bacteria. One of the best known is the production by bacteria of poisonous toxins. The power of the diphtheria bacillus to produce disease depends very largely, but not wholly, on its power to produce the characteristic toxin. All the important symptoms of diphtheria result from the action of toxin on the cells of the body.

Without its toxin the diphtheria bacillus would be a mere harmless inhabitant of the throat, which might at most produce a mild tonsillitis. If the body can become immune against the toxin by the development of antitoxin in the blood, this is all that is required to reduce the diphtheria bacillus to the status of a non-virulent form. Antibodies which promote phagocytosis of the bacilli may also be developed, but their part is relatively unimportant. Scarlet fever and tetanus (lockjaw) are two other diseases which are due almost entirely to the action not of bacteria as such, but of the toxins they produce. Research on these three diseases has centred very largely on the toxins and corresponding antitoxins, and methods which have been developed for the artificial production of antitoxins have now given us ways by which all three diseases could be almost entirely eliminated.

Though we have stressed this difference between bacteria like the *Pneumococcus* and the toxin producers, as exemplified by the diphtheria bacillus, we must recognize that the difference concerns only the dominant characteristics. In addition, each has a little of the quality of the other. There is one type of diphtheria bacillus which, although it produces toxin, seems to owe its greater virulence to qualities of its bodily surface, and, to counter this virulence, antibodies of the phagocytosis-promoting kind may be necessary as well as antitoxin. Similarly, the *Pneumococcus* has poisonous effects not so easily demonstrated as for the diphtheria bacillus, but probably of some significance in infections. Most bacteria which cause disease lie somewhere in between these two types, showing varying degrees of invasiveness (which depends on their surface structure) and toxin production.

Part IV

THE NATURAL HISTORY OF INFECTIOUS DISEASE

CHAPTER XI

HOW INFECTIONS SPREAD

If we are to make any attempt to prevent or check epidemics of infectious disease, it is obvious that the most helpful thing we can know is how the infection spreads from person to person. Just to know that an infection is spread by contaminated water or milk or, to take another example, by mosquito bite, will often be sufficient alone to allow adequate public health measures to be taken. Typhoid fever, for example, was being rapidly eliminated from England by attention to sewerage and water supply well before the typhoid bacillus was discovered. Even more striking is the story of yellow fever. In 1900 the American Yellow Fever Commission proved that the disease was mosquito borne, and on that basis yellow fever was almost wholly stamped out from Central America. But the virus responsible for the disease was not isolated until 1930.

In discussing the spread of infection, we ought logically to consider first the way in which the infective agent is liberated from the originally infected person or animal; secondly, how it passes from the infector to the new susceptible host; and thirdly, how it enters the tissues of the latter and provokes infection. In particular diseases, any of these aspects may be of great importance, but in practice we can divide infections into four main groups on the basis of the way infection is transferred. We shall eliminate for the present the various infections which may complicate wounds of any sort, whether external or internal. There are many important problems concerned with these so-called 'surgical' infections, and they show more deep-seated similarities to the typically infectious diseases than one might expect. In the old days there were veritable epidemics of septic complications in military hospitals, and in such conditions as puerperal fever and impetigo (skin sores in children) we have intermediate conditions which are, as it were, highly infectious diseases of trivial wounds.

Leaving aside wound infections then, our first group comprises those infectious diseases which infect primarily the digestive tract, usually concentrating on the lower part of the bowel. These are spread by the dissemination of faecal material containing the responsible microorganisms. Water, milk, food or eating utensils may be contaminated in various direct or indirect fashions. Fingers and flies are probably the two most potent agents for indirect transfer, but however devious the route from the source of infection, the microorganisms are eventually swallowed, and passing through the stomach infect the bowel. Apart from amoebic dysentery, due to protozoa, the best-known infections of this group are of bacterial origin. They include typhoid and paratyphoid fever, cholera, dysentery due to a wide variety of bacteria, summer diarrhoea of infants and bacterial food poisoning.

For many years it was thought that there were no virus diseases of the intestinal tract. In a sense that is still true, though in children it is common to find short episodes of diarrhoea which are associated with virus in the intestine and probably caused by it. On the other hand, the intestinal wall can be infected with any one of at least thirty viruses which include several that can produce disease elsewhere in the body, notably the three polioviruses and the virus of infectious hepatitis (jaundice). Apart from these, most of the virus infections of the bowel are almost silent, but occasionally a more virulent strain produces an unexpected epidemic with symptoms which may include fever, rash, headache and neck rigidity, or painful cramps of the respiratory muscles.

The method of preventing such diseases is obvious to everyone. Indeed, the one indubitable blessing of modern civilized life is the development of the technical methods and mental attitude required to eliminate them. That has been well done, and can be justly claimed as the best contribution the English-speaking peoples have made to humanity. Decent sewage disposal, pure water supply, pure food laws, control of milk supply and pasteurization, plus the cult of personal cleanliness have rendered most of these diseases rare in any civilized community. An outbreak of typhoid fever or a high infantile mortality from diarrhoeal disease is rightly regarded as a civic disgrace.

It is interesting to look back on the development of such a civic conscience and to realize that its all-important beginnings were based on a completely wrong idea of how infections like typhoid fever arose. In the early nineteenth century it was recognized that typhoid fever and filthy drains went together, but the stress was laid more on the smell than on possible infective principles (bacteria were, of course, unknown) in the objectionable drainage. By some transference of ideas, bad-smelling drains were also blamed for the incidence of diphtheria, and the incentive to remove these two diseases was largely responsible for the development of modern sanitary engineering. The process was well under way by the time the infectious nature of typhoid fever was clearly recognized, and it was a good deal later that the typhoid bacillus was found. Both these discoveries, of course, accentuated the necessity for keeping drinking water and sewage (to put it bluntly) out of each other's way.

For many years it has been the standard practice to protect against typhoid fever by inoculation with a vaccine, usually the T.A.B. vaccine which is designed to prevent paratyphoid fevers A and B as well. Antityphoid vaccination seemed to work very well during the two World Wars but, of course, the medical authorities of all armies also insisted on the best possible field hygiene. Perhaps it is a valuable commentary on how difficult it is to evaluate a single measure in preventive medicine when we have to confess that at the present time most critical bacteriologists are extremely dubious whether typhoid vaccination has any value whatsoever. It still remains a routine precaution, presumably on the basis that although we know that in a heavily infected area such as the Egyptian Canal Zone during the immediate post-war period, there was a high incidence of typhoid in well vaccinated British soldiers, the incidence might have been even greater without the vaccination. Vaccination will go on for a long time no doubt but 'environmental sanitation' is the only measure that can be relied on to eliminate typhoid fever.

There are still some riddles to be answered about intestinal infections. The results of sanitary progress are better than we should expect. The serious diseases typhoid, cholera and dysentery have been almost eliminated, but minor gastro-intestinal infections often seem to spread easily, and the evidence indicates that the poliomyelitis virus has infected most urban American children by the time they are eleven years old. Thread worms too seem to have an unholy capacity to spread by transfer of eggs from one child to another. Epidemiologists are finding, as so often happens, that because some practical procedure works this does not necessarily mean that the theory on which it is based is wholly sound.

The next method by which infection can spread is by far the commonest and most important in civilized countries, but has no really popular name. 'Droplet infection' it is usually called in technical accounts, or sometimes infection by the respiratory route. Suppose we have a cold, an early cold at the stage when there is a steady call on the handkerchief and a similar drip to the back of the throat. If the fluid leaking from the nose contains one of the rather numerous viruses which we now believe are responsible for the common cold, then there is not the slightest doubt that the virus is also present in the saliva and on the lips. When we sneeze, cough, shout or speak loudly, all these commotions in our mouths scatter droplets of saliva to be carried out with the breath.

Visible droplets settle to the ground and rarely convey infection. It is the very tiny droplets which are important. Unless the air is saturated with moisture, these droplets almost immediately evaporate. They are not much larger than the droplets which makes one's breath visible on a frosty morning and evaporate almost as rapidly. The frosty morning's breath is due to condensation of water vapour to tiny spheres of pure water which can again be dissipated completely into vapour, but the droplets of saliva contain other things than water. When they evaporate they leave as a residue a tiny light flake of dried protein in which are held any viruses or bacteria which were present in the droplet. Such flakes take a long time to settle in still air, and are easily carried about on air currents. Probably with every breath we take in a room where there are more than one or two people, some of these flakes from other people's saliva pass into our noses. There is an efficient method for filtering most of them out of the air before it reaches the lungs and when we get down to actual figures of infection as judged either by symptoms or antibody rises, we find that even with a virus of the high contagiousness of influenza, it is only a very small proportion of contacts that transfer infection. When Asian influenza reached Melbourne in 1957 it lasted six to eight weeks and died out when about 45 per cent of people had been infected as judged by a rise in antibody. On some reasonable mathematical assumptions each infected individual on the average transferred the virus effectively to an average of only 1.2 persons. Sooner or later with an increasing number of immune individuals this rate of spread becomes inadequate to maintain an epidemic and the outbreak then terminates.

There are several different situations which may be infected by germs taken into the nose and mouth in this way. Colds seem to start sometimes in the lining of the nose, sometimes in the larynx and then spread up or down, influenza probably results from virus particles lodging in the smaller tubes of the bronchial passages. Diphtheria and the various forms of streptococcal sore throat have a predilection for the tonsils, while the virus of psittacosis seems to be harmless unless it can be carried right down into the lungs. These differences may be reflected in regard to the alternative ways by which infections of this group can spread. They all require some degree of interchange of saliva, but anyone who has observed young children will know that saliva can be transferred from one to another by many other ways than droplet infection. I have heard of one small epidemic of diphtheria which ceased in a school as soon as pencils were treated as strictly private property and not in communistic fashion. Streptococcal sore throats, including scarlet fever, are rather frequently a result of milk infection, sometimes resulting from contamination of the milk by dairy employees with the infection, sometimes actually from a streptococcal infection of the cows. Since all food and drink passes the tonsils on its downward journey, it is only to be expected that those germs which tend to infect that region may be spread as readily in milk as by the droplet method. Psittacosis, on the other hand, has to reach the depths of the lungs, and to do so the virus must be in very finely distributed form and probably in rather large amount. Dust from infected parrots is the only common source of infection which fulfils these requirements. In one outbreak in Louisiana, probably derived in the first instance from egrets, there was a sequence of infections from patient to sick-bed attendants presumably associated with the intense virulence of the strain of virus concerned. In general, person to person infection does not occur and there is nowhere any suggestion that the infection can be transferred by food or drink.

When we add to those infections which have already been mentioned such common ones as tuberculosis, meningitis, measles, chickenpox, mumps and smallpox, it is clear that, in civilized countries, droplet infection is much the most important route by which infectious diseases spread. Whenever any exceptionally serious outbreak of one of these diseases occurs, efforts are always made to check its spread. Quarantine and isolation restrictions are enforced, and sometimes the wearing of gauze masks over the mouth and nose is required. It is doubtful whether such measures are of the slightest real value unless the occasion is serious enough to justify complete dislocation of community life. When a few cases of pneumonic plague appear, public opinion will allow and demand complete segration of the infected persons and their contacts, and enforce it with machine guns if necessary. Those who have to treat the patients will adopt rigid precautions which could only be applied in a well-equipped hospital. They will wear gowns and rubber gloves which can be sterilized after each visit to the patients, and protect eyes, nose and mouth with goggles and gauze masks. The spread of 'droplet' infections can be stopped in this fashion if stopping it is the full-time job of all concerned, but not if persons in the infected community have to go on with their daily business.

Any form of obstruction to breathing such as a gauze mask will never be popular with adults, and still less with children. Even if properly made and worn, the protection afforded is only partial, tiny infected flakes of dried saliva can pass through quite readily. When put to the test of practice, such masks have always failed to show any significant effect in stopping or slowing an epidemic. It is just possible that with a more effective protection such as could be afforded by a slight modification of the civilian anti-gas masks now available in most countries, a very considerable reduction in the incidence of some infections might be effected. Whether such an attempt would be worth making is a question not easily answered, which will have to wait till we discuss some of the general problems of epidemics.

In addition to these infectious diseases, there is also a general interchange of germs like streptococci and pneumococci which, on the whole, give very little indication of their presence in the throat. Repeated bacteriological tests, such as have been carried out on groups of nurses or medical students, often show that at certain times there are invisible epidemics. There may be a sudden appearance of one sort of *Streptococcus* not previously found in the great majority of the group with, perhaps, no more than an odd individual with a red and slightly sore throat. Such occurrences in themselves are trivial, but indirectly they may be of great importance. We described in the previous chapter how puerperal fever usually results from infection of the uterus with streptococci derived from the throats of those looking after the patient. In obstetric hospitals, a technique for dealing with this danger has been gradually developed. Any doctor or nurse with a definite sore throat must not be present at a confinement. Unfortunately, even a perfectly healthy-looking throat may carry dangerous streptococci, and the only safe policy is to assume that such streptococci are present and to take the necessary precautions. A gauze mask over the mouth and nose, although it is no great protection to the wearer, is relatively efficient in preventing the dissemination of droplets by the wearer, and is now worn as a routine by doctors and nurses at most confinements. The use of rubber gloves and of antiseptics which are particularly active against streptococci provide precautions against the second stage of transfer by hands which have been unknowingly contaminated by droplets of saliva.

The venereal diseases exemplify a third method of spread. There are five human diseases of this group: syphilis, due to a corkscrew-shaped organism called a spirochaete, which is something between a protozoon and a bacterium, two bacterial diseases, gonorrhoea and soft chancre, a virus infection (lymphogranuloma inguinale) and a tropical disease, due to an unusual type of bacterium. All these microorganisms are very readily killed outside of the body, and very direct contact is necessary for their transmission. Both of the common forms are readily cured by penicillin, and, more important from the point of view of prevention, the patient is rapidly rendered non-infectious for others. The virus disease lymphogranuloma venereum is not susceptible to penicillin but can be cured by some of the newer antibiotics. Since 1947 there has been a steady reduction of venereal disease in all Western countries. Syphilis has not yet vanished but primary syphilis is far rarer than it was twenty years ago and the late effects of the disease, such as general paralysis, are now seldom seen. This improvement is due mainly to the effectiveness with which penicillin treatment has been used, but in part also to the development of a more realistic social approach.

During the war venereal disease was an important military problem, and most of the measures which have been suggested were tried in various combinations. These included direct disciplinary measures, the provision of opportunities for sport and other leisure-time employment, moral and religious exhortation on the one hand, the issue of prophylactic packages to men on leave and the establishment of depots for disinfection after exposure on the other. These measures probably had a considerable effect, but they did not prevent the general rise in the incidence of venereal disease that has characterized every war in recent history. On the whole, there is a generally hopeful outlook that wider knowledge and freer approach to sex matters, plus the use of simpler and more effective methods of treatment, may gradually eliminate most venereal disease from the more advanced countries of the world.

In the three methods so far discussed by which infection is transferred, the germ enters the body by one of the natural routes. The last important method involves the 'unnatural' introduction of infection into the blood or tissue by the bites of animals, usually, but not always, insects or ticks. In this group we have the complication that the transmission of infection is frequently not from man to man, but from some infected animal to man. There are now no common human diseases spread by this method in temperate climates amongst civilized communities, but malaria, plague and typhus were once widespread in England and Europe generally, and would probably return with any breakdown of civilization. All these infections have their own peculiar characteristics, which are largely determined by the habits of the animal which transmits them. It is not easy to discuss them in general terms, and the best introduction is perhaps to give a table showing the more important diseases of the group, the animal responsible for transmitting the disease to man (technically the 'vector') and the species from which the vector derives the infection. This species is referred to as the 'reservoir' of infection.

The chief human diseases transmitted by animals

Disease	Type of micro-organism	Vector	Reservoir
Plague	Bacterium	Flea	Rat and other rodents
Malaria	Protozoon	Mosquito	Man, monkey
African sleeping sickness	Protozoon	Tsetse fly	(*a*) Man, (*b*) antelopes and other wild mammals
Kala azar	Protozoon	Sand fly	Man, dog
Relapsing fever I	Spirochaete	Louse	Man
Relapsing fever II	Spirochaete	Tick	Rodents, ticks
Yellow fever	Virus	Mosquito	Man, monkeys
Dengue fever	Virus	Mosquito	Man, jungle mammals (?)
Virus encephalitis	Virus	Mosquito	Wild birds
Rabies	Virus	Dog, jackal, etc.	Same species
Paralytic rabies	Virus	Vampire bat	Same species
Typhus (I)	Rickettsia	Louse	Man
Typhus (II)	Rickettsia	Flea	Rat
Scrub typhus	Rickettsia	Mite	Field mice and small rodents
Rocky Mountain spotted fever	Rickettsia	Tick	Wild rodents

Within the human diseases of this group we find an interesting range from diseases which, biologically speaking, have nothing to do with man to those for which he is the only susceptible species. At the former end of the scale we have such conditions as Rocky Mountain spotted fever or the scrub typhus of the eastern tropics. These diseases are due to rickettsial microorganisms which are in nature relatively harmless parasites of wild rodents transmitted from one to the other by ticks or mites. It is a pure accident that man happens to be highly susceptible to the infections. Then we have those parasites which are partially adapted to the human host, such as the germs of typhus fever and African sleeping sickness, and finally the diseases which are specifically human, such as malaria, dengue fever and yellow fever.

The necessity for the ecological outlook on disease is probably more clearly evident in relation to these insect-borne diseases than elsewhere. The most detailed study of the habits of mosquitoes has been necessary to provide an understanding of the epidemiology of malaria and to indicate methods of control. Dozens of species of *Anopheles* mosquitoes can transmit malaria, but in any one district there is usually one species of predominant importance. If malaria is to be controlled, this species of mosquito must be studied from every point of view. The larvae always develop in water, but different species may prefer very different environments. One may live only in swampy pools overgrown with vegetation, another requires water freely exposed to sunlight, some develop in brackish water, others prefer small casual collections of rain water. Any of these predilections for one particular kind of water may, according to local circumstances, make it easy or difficult to deal with malaria by attacking the larval mosquitoes. In the adult phase the feeding habits of the female mosquito become all important, its season and time of activity, its preference for human or animal blood, its tendency to remain in the neighbourhood of its last meal or to wander freely, and so on. Finally, these habits have to be correlated with the human situation in the region. If the mosquitoes are infected they must derive the parasites from a human source. In most malarial regions the reservoirs of infection are the children of the native populations in whom the transmissible stage of the malarial parasite is likely to be present in much larger numbers than in the adults who have developed a substantial resistance to the infection.

Yellow fever, another important human disease spread by mosquitoes, provides an interesting contrast to malaria. There are two phases in the natural history of yellow fever. In the African and South American jungles the virus is present as a parasite of monkeys, being transferred from one monkey to another by mosquitoes of the forest canopy. The classical yellow fever that once plagued the ports of West Africa and Central America probably derived from the jungle disease but an animal reservoir was no longer concerned. The virus passed from man to man and only one species of mosquito was involved in the spread of the disease. This mosquito (*Aedes egypti*) is predominantly found in houses, and only rarely flies any distance from a house in which it has once taken a meal of blood. The mosquito can only become infected with the yellow fever virus if it feeds on a patient in the first three or four days of his fever, and before it can transfer the infection to another human being a period of about ten days must elapse. This strict limitation of the period during which the patient's blood contains virus is in sharp contrast to the conditions with malaria, where chronically infected individuals may remain capable of infecting mosquitoes for years. Mainly for this reason malaria tends to be constantly present with only moderate seasonal variations, while yellow fever used to occur in epidemics with long periods of absence between them. Once these characteristics of the mosquito and of the disease which it transmits had been discovered by the American Army Commission in 1902, the elimination of yellow fever became a practicable proposition. The essentials were: first, to diminish the number of yellow-fever mosquitoes by destroying the larvae or reducing the number of their breeding places; secondly, to shield all recognized yellow-fever patients from being bitten by mosquitoes during the period over which their blood was infective; and thirdly, to destroy all mosquitoes in any dwelling where a case had occurred before they had time to develop infectiousness for other human beings. By such methods yellow fever has been eliminated from all the regions in which the classical disease once flourished. About 1925, it seemed likely that a few more years' work would see the end of yellow fever everywhere, but that was just before the recognition of jungle yellow fever, first in South America, later in Africa. As soon as it was clear that infected monkeys were probably distributed over nearly a million square miles of the Amazon basin the possibility of eliminating the disease became infinitely remote. We shall leave discussion of yellow fever in Africa to a later chapter, but a little more should be said here about the jungle situation in South America. In the forests of the Amazon occasional deaths from yellow fever occur amongst wood-cutters, porters and others working in the jungle. The cases do not occur in the form of epidemics, and there are no *Aedes* mosquitoes in these inland jungle areas. The disease has therefore totally different epidemiological characters from those of the classical yellow fever. Whenever a human disease is contracted only in uninhabited or sparsely populated regions, one can be reasonably certain that it is derived from some animal reservoir of infection. In the Amazon region the yellow-fever virus has infected the wild monkeys, and is transferred from one monkey to another and occasionally from monkey to man by the bite of jungle-haunting mosquitoes quite distinct from the true yellow-fever mosquito. The existence of such an animal reservoir will probably make the extinction of the disease impossible. It may be that South American monkeys have been infected with yellow fever since time immemorial, but there is much to suggest that the disease may have crossed the Atlantic from Africa three or four hundred years ago.

The development of a new animal reservoir of human disease in the historical period is probably not unique. It is still generally believed that plague was originally a purely Asiatic disease involving burrowing rodents in Turkestan and Siberia. At varying times after the ship-borne epidemic of plague that went round the world in 1900, it was discovered in California and South Africa that plague was present in wild rodents in the mountains of western United States and on the veldt in Africa. In both regions this was ascribed to spread of infected rats from the ports.

Another interesting example concerns the appearance in South America of rabies infections due to the bite of vampire bats. Since 1921, there had been recognized epidemics of paralysis amongst South American cattle. These became gradually more frequent, and in 1928 there was a very extensive outbreak which caused the loss of something like 30 per cent of the total cattle in Paraguay. The disease was found to be a form of rabies or hydrophobia, in which the violent 'mad dog' type of symptoms were replaced by paralytic ones. There is little rabies in dogs in South America, certainly not nearly sufficient to account for such widespread destruction amongst cattle. Gradually suspicion lighted on the vampire bat, though it was known that these bats had taken blood from cattle for centuries without causing any serious harm. In 1930 a further development was observed in the island of Trinidad, thousands of miles north of Paraguay. Here a similar disease broke out amongst cattle, but in addition about a dozen human beings contracted the same fatal paralytic disease. Again vampire bats were incriminated, and the crime was sheeted home by the discovery of several bats which actually harboured the virus.

Obviously it is a serious position if as seems likely the vampire bats all along the eastern half of South America are heavily infected with this virus. As far as one can gather, the disease spreads from bat to bat from bites given during quarrels in their roosting places, not by way of infected cattle or other victims. Some of the infected bats develop symptoms and die, some remain healthy carriers of the virus for months.

It is not difficult to protect human beings, who are bitten only during sleep, by suitable wire screening of houses, but protection of cattle will be a more difficult problem. In 1956 a new danger emerged with the recognition that rabies could be spread at times by ordinary insect-eating bats.

Clearly the vampire bat and even the less specialized types of bat will need to be studied in the same detail as the rat, the flea, the louse and the mosquito. In every one of the diseases spread by biting vectors or derived from animal reservoirs, very detailed ecological studies of the animals concerned are always necessary. Any sort of fact may be important. The seasonal incidence of plague in some parts depends on the fact that fleas die more quickly when the air is warm and dry. Two races of a mosquito species have developed different winter habits, one hibernates in cold places, the other frequents warmed houses—only the second race spreads malaria in Holland. Dozens of similar apparently trivial facts may turn out to be of value in controlling disease.

There is one additional point that sometimes has epidemiological significance. Sometimes a vector can transmit the pathogenic microorganism to its offspring by what is called *transovarial transmission* without the necessity for an intermediary infection of some vertebrate. The best known example is in tick-borne relapsing fever where transovarial transmission of the spirochaete through successive generations of ticks has been observed. The rickettsial disease, scrub typhus, is transmitted by a mite which in its normal cycle of development takes only one blood meal in the larval stage. Transovarial passage of the rickettsia in the mite is therefore a necessary phase in the process of human infection.

When the necessary facts about the habits and life history of vector and reservoir species have been obtained, the application of the knowledge to the prevention of the disease will depend mainly on economic factors. In heavily populated wealthy communities, control can nearly always be established, but in the tropics, where most of the problems lie, the relatively small and impoverished populations, plus the intense fecundity of animal and especially insect life, make most of the problems of prevention insoluble. The difficulties in regard to malaria will be discussed in a later chapter.

The four methods of spread which we have described, gastro-intestinal, droplet infection, venereal and by animal vectors, cover practically all the infectious diseases which have been adequately studied. There are a number of infections by worm parasites in which entry is by way of the skin, but except for one group of diseases, this type of infection is of no significance in the microorganismal infections with which we are dealing.

The exception is leptospirosis, the classical form of which is also called Weil's disease. Leptospirae are small corkscrew-type organisms which in man may produce fevers ranging from one with severe jaundice and often fatal, to a mild three-day fever that can only be diagnosed by appropriate laboratory tests. The organisms are natural parasites of rats, pigs, dogs and some wild rodents, and are excreted in the urine of infected animals. They can survive for relatively long periods in polluted water. These leptospiroses are characteristically occupational diseases. The sewer worker or the man cleaning up a fish market is liable to contract the severe form that comes from infected rats. Some years ago there were extensive outbreaks amongst Queensland sugar cutters working in wet fields that had been contaminated by a native species of rat with a special type of *Leptospira*. Another milder human disease common in Australia and central Europe where it is called *maladie des porchers* (swineherds' disease) is due to yet another *Leptospira*, named after a little orchard town, Pomona, in southern Queensland where it was first observed. Pigs and cattle provide the reservoir and again the organism is liberated in their urine. All these infections result from skin contact with contaminated water or mud, the organism penetrating not through intact skin but through cracks and minor wounds.

Probably we should include along with Weil's disease a number of local infections of the eyes and of the nose and throat, which may be all too easily transferred in such places as swimming pools. There is, in fact, a virus infection of the eyes which in America is usually referred to as swimming-pool conjunctivitis. The other important virus disease of the eyelids, trachoma, may be transmitted in various ways—flies, fingers, or towels used in common may be responsible for directly transferring infective material to the eyes.

There is one important disease which, so far as is known at present, is spread wholly by the doctor's syringe or its equivalent. This is the virus disease, serum hepatitis or homologous serum jaundice. It had been noted ever since blood transfusions became commonly used that occasional recipients developed jaundice two or three months later, but this was generally thought to be a result of some chemical damage to the liver. The first widespread recognition of the condition came in the early months of 1942 when about 80,000 American servicemen developed jaundice for no immediately apparent reason. Investigation showed that the factor common to all units in which cases of jaundice developed was that they had been inoculated with certain batches of yellow fever vaccine. Eventually it became clear that these batches contained a small amount of human serum which had been added to improve the keeping quality of the vaccine and that this was the dangerous component. Once this capacity of human blood, or preparations containing some component of human blood, to produce jaundice had been recognized, it became clear that similar jaundice could be transmitted in other ways.

The situation as we now understand it is that a small proportion, perhaps one per cent, of apparently healthy people have the virus in their blood. If a small amount of blood from such a carrier is injected into a number of people one-third to one-half of these can be expected to develop a mild illness usually accompanied by definite jaundice sixty to one hundred days after the injection. For a considerable period before and after the period of jaundice the virus is present in the blood and can be transferred to another individual by injection. Blood transfusion is probably not the commonest method of transfer. There have been many accounts published of long-lasting 'epidemics' of jaundice in venereal disease clinics where patients were being injected into a vein with arsenical drugs. Although it was routine practice to use a new needle for each patient, enough blood might enter the syringe for some to be transferred to the next patient and transmit the disease. Much work is being done at the present time to tighten up the precautions for sterility in treatment of this sort, and to find ways either of recognizing the existence of the virus or destroying it without damage to the life-saving properties of the blood or serum that may contain it.

It is almost fantastic that a disease of this sort should exist, and I think the greatest intellectual prize that a virologist can hope for is that some day he should be the first to explain what is the real natural history of serum hepatitis. It is the old question which is fundamental to the understanding of any infectious disease, how does the virus survive as a species in nature? If one had to guess the answer it might be that the virus is a variant, a mutant of infectious hepatitis virus which has developed the capacity to pass to the unborn child in the uterus without causing damage to its tissues or provoking antibody production that will destroy the virus. There is in the literature on viruses an account of a disease of mice, lymphocytic choriomeningitis, which in a stabilized mouse population shows no obvious evidence of its presence. The mice are, however, almost literally saturated with the virus, If an organ, say the liver, is ground up and a very small amount injected into a mouse from an uninfected stock, that mouse will die of the disease. In the infected group mice are infected long before they are born. Some of these embryos are stillborn, but most survive and carry large amounts of virus in their bodies till death. It has been suggested that if before birth the body tissues become used to the presence of a foreign material like a virus, they lose the capacity to treat it as foreign *after* birth and do not produce antibody. The analogy with serum hepatitis may be only a distant one, and some quite different explanation of the latter may eventually be found. Until we have some means of recognizing and growing the hepatitis viruses, we are not likely to make much progress. It is unfortunate that even with extensive use of the new tissue culture methods neither virus had been isolated by 1960.

CHAPTER XII

THE TRANSFER OF INFECTION FROM ONE SPECIES TO ANOTHER—ANIMAL RESERVOIRS

In the last chapter we discussed the various ways in which infectious disease may spread, and in dealing with the carriage of infections by insects, we had to say a good deal about animal reservoirs of infection. Several of the most important insect-borne diseases, such as malaria and typhus, are normally confined to the human species, but there are others, including such an important one as plague, which are almost entirely derived from animals. Transfer by insects and the like is not the only way in which a pathogenic microorganism can pass from some animal host to man. We have already mentioned how psittacosis virus is taken into the lungs in the form of fine dust raised by the fluttering of infected parrots. Then there are several bacterial diseases of wild or domestic animals which are liable to infect persons such as hunters, butchers or veterinary surgeons who have to handle animal carcasses or other infective material. In most cases the infection probably enters through cracks or scratches on the hands. Anthrax, glanders and tularaemia (a disease of hares and rabbits) can all produce severe and fatal infections in this way, but the actual numbers of cases are very small. Milk, as is well known, may be infected by bacteria derived from the cow's udder, and tuberculosis, undulant fever and some streptococcal throat infections may result.

In this chapter we are concerned, not with the mode of spread of such diseases, but with the general questions associated with the transference of infection from one animal species to another. Our chief concern will still be with those animal infections which give rise to human disease, but the same principles are evident when two dissimilar species of animal are concerned, or even when, on rare occasions, human infections are naturally contracted by another species.

It has often been pointed out that long-established endemic diseases are under normal circumstances mild diseases of low death rate. If any undue advantage is given to the parasite, such as under-nutrition or overcrowding by the host species, severe and fatal outbreaks may occur which, by diminishing the numbers of the host, will tend to rectify the circumstances which gave rise to them. It is self-evident that if both host and parasite are to survive, a mild, rather long-lasting infection, which does no serious damage to the host and provides adequate opportunity for the parasite to be transferred to other hosts, is the most advantageous relationship for both. Such a relationship is established by mutual adaptation of the two species concerned.

When changing circumstances allow the parasite to invade a new host species, the result will depend on so many delicately balanced factors that it is quite unpredictable beforehand. Perhaps the commonest result is for the parasite to find itself unfitted to survive in the tissues of the new host, not so much from the activity of defence processes as from inability to gain nourishment from the tissues. No real infection takes place. If, however, the parasite is capable of utilizing the substance of the new host for its nutrition, in the absence of any acquired racial or individual resistance it is liable to multiply excessively and produce a high mortality. In such circumstances the over-all result will depend on a complex of factors. High mortality following infection is not necessarily correlated with ease of spread from one individual host animal to another. No disease passing to a new host has ever exterminated that host species during the period for which records are available. In general, any period of excessive mortality is followed by a phase in which for one reason or another the mortality reaches a much lower level. The ways in which this more or less balanced situation is reached provide some of the most interesting phenomena in epidemiology.

There are two groups of infectious disease which show various stages in the process by which disease in one species can be transferred to another species, the second species in both cases being man. These are first, the rickettsial diseases, of which typhus fever is the best known; and secondly, the trypanosome infections spread by tsetse flies in central Africa.

The rickettsiae can be regarded as tiny bacteria which have become so specialized for living within the cells of their hosts that they cannot be made to grow apart from these susceptible cells. Almost certainly their evolution as parasites started in insects and ticks, many species of which still contain rather similar parasitic microorganisms, which are not, however, pathogenic to vertebrates. It was probably at first a sheer accident that one of these tick parasites should prove to be capable of living and multiplying in the rodent on which the tick fed. But once the transfer had been accomplished, a *modus vivendi* between the rickettsiae, the tick and the rodent had to become established. A typical example of such mutual adaptation has been revealed in the course of investigations on the spotted fever of the Rocky Mountain States in America.

In the state of Montana there is a valley of evil reputation, the Bitter Root Valley, where since the country was first opened up in 1880, prospectors, surveyors and settlers have been liable to a severe fever, with a mortality of about 80 per cent. Except for pneumonic plague, it is probably the most fatal infection known. It was soon discovered that the disease followed tick bite and was due to a rickettsial organism present in the tick. The natural history of the disease and of the ticks which spread it was elucidated in the Montana laboratory of the United States Public Health Service, and eventually a method of preventing the disease was worked out and shown to be practicable. The danger of this work was extreme. Before the method of protective immunization had been developed, seven workers in the laboratory had contracted the disease. In every instance it was fatal. Since the immunization of all workers has been a routine, fifteen more cases have occurred in the laboratory, with one death.

Ticks have rather a complicated life history with three main stages, larva, nymph and adult. The tiny larvae are hatched on the ground, and when opportunity offers, attach themselves to some small rodent. For a day or two they slowly engorge themselves with blood and then drop off on to the grass. Here they digest their meal, grow and prepare for the moult to the nymph stage. The nymph repeats the same process, also feeding on small rodents, but when its engorgement is complete it hibernates through the winter and emerges as an adult with the melting of the snows the following spring. The adult needs a larger animal to feed on, bears and wild goats being the chief native hosts, but cattle, horses and man are equally suitable.

The virus of the disease probably alternates between the tick and one or other of the small rodents of the region. The larval tick feeds on an infected rodent and takes in the rickettsia with its meal of blood. The rickettsiae multiply in the tick tissue and establish a harmless infection which persists through the life of the tick. With each subsequent feeding the host is liable to be infected by the bite. In the nymph stage the disease may be passed on to a new susceptible rodent; in the adult stage the normal hosts of the tick are insusceptible to the virus, and it is only by an unfortunate accident that man happens to be so susceptible to the rickettsia. The important business of passing on the infection from one natural host to the other is done in the larval and nymphal stages of the tick. The fact that the adult tick bite is also infective for man is a mere accident of no significance to the survival of the rickettsia.

The natural disease among wild rodents has never been observed. The only evidence that it exists is that a proportion of the wild rodents show immunity to the disease, of the type one would expect to follow natural infection. It is certain that, like the disease resulting from artificial inoculation of the virus in the same species, the natural infection is an extremely mild one. Long experience has made it certain that this virus is never responsible for the outbreaks of disease which occur when rodent populations increase abnormally. It is just possible that the rodents play no essential part in the disease, since a proportion of larval ticks hatched from the eggs of infected ticks are also infected. If this occurred regularly we might regard the whole condition as a tick disease only, the infections of rodents and man being both unnecessary accidents. However, most workers are convinced that the tick-rodent-tick cycle is much more important than the occasional transmission of the infection from infected female ticks to their offspring.

So far we have been speaking of the extremely virulent spotted fever of the Bitter Root Valley. A curious feature of the disease is that in most other parts of the United States the mortality is very much smaller and may be as low as 5 per cent. Amongst the sheepmen of southern Idaho, not very far from Bitter Root Valley, it is common enough, but is regarded as hardly worth worrying about. The rickettsia is the same in both parts, as far as can be judged by cross-immunity tests; the only difference between the strains is in their virulence. The reason for the difference is unknown, but one interesting suggestion has been made. In the Bitter Root Valley there is an abundance of species of small mammals, so that in the course of transfer by tick bite the virus is constantly having to adapt itself to slightly different tissue conditions in the different susceptible species. In the districts where the disease is less virulent, there are usually only one or two rodent species available as reservoirs. The suggestion is that constant passage from one species to another in the Bitter Root area has kept the adaptability of the strain higher than in districts where the same rodent species serves for each transfer. The idea is a reasonable one, but will require a good deal of experimental substantiation before it can be accepted. At the present time it is probably safer to consider that the differences in virulence for man are just accidental differences of local races and are of no significance for the survival of the virus. When an animal or plant community is isolated for a long period from the rest of its species, a local race usually develops showing some slight but constant differences from the type of the species. Sometimes these differences have functional significance, more often they seem to be merely fortuitous. There is no reason to suppose that the differences between the Bitter Root and the Idaho strains of virus are any more than similar fortuitous results of isolation.

To sum up, we have in Rocky Mountain spotted fever a highly fatal human disease due to a microorganism which in its normal hosts, the native rodents and the tick, produces hardly any signs of illness whatever. This virulence for man is a wholly accidental property of the virus, and is only shown in superlative degree by one local strain; other strains apparently similar in their natural cycle are much less virulent.

On the opposite side of the Pacific there is another rickettsial disease which is present from Japan southward through Formosa, the Philippines and New Guinea to North Queensland. In the west it is common in the Maldive Islands and Ceylon, patchy in India, and from Burma it is found continuously through Malaya and Indonesia to the Solomon Islands in the east. Its Japanese name was *tsutsugamushi* fever, but elsewhere it is usually called scrub typhus. It is a severe disease with a mortality that varies like that of Rocky Mountain spotted fever from one infected region to another and may be as high as 50 per cent or as low as 1 per cent. Like the American disease, scrub typhus is contracted away from human communities not in mountain valleys but on tropical islands, in grassy clearings at the jungle edge or in any other situation where the mite that carries the infection can flourish. During the war in the south-west Pacific, scrub typhus ranked next to malaria as the most important cause of disability and death from infectious disease. Nearly 7000 cases with 284 deaths were reported in the American forces. The carrier is one of two very similar mites which, in their larval stage, may obtain the single blood meal needed for their development from some small animal or from man. The rickettsia is never passed directly from man to man or from animal to animal. After its blood feed the larva becomes successively nymph and adult which live in the soil, and when eggs are laid by an infected female they contain rickettsiae which, in turn, develop in the new generation of larvae. The human infections play no part in allowing the survival of the virus, and its human virulence must again be regarded as a mere accident.

Typhus fever in the classical form, which has been the great attendant of war and famine in Europe for centuries, is a purely human disease. It is a severe fever with a characteristic rash, highly fatal in susceptible adults, particularly under famine conditions, but as a rule affecting children less severely. The body louse is the vector from patient to patient. It takes up rickettsiae from the blood and is itself fatally infected in the process. However, it has about a week in which to transfer the infection to another subject before it dies. In view of this method of transmission, typhus can flourish only in circumstances of poverty, overcrowding and filth. In the English history of disease, typhus figures mainly in connexion with the Civil War and as a disease of prisons, though it was not uncommon in the slum quarters of cities until the middle of the nineteenth century.

There is one feature of typhus which suggests that it is not an old-established human disease, its fatality for the louse. This is one of the few instances in which the insect vector of a human disease is seriously discommoded by the germ it transmits. The likely inference is that typhus of the louse is a relatively recent development, and that the disease has evolved in other hosts than man and the louse. The first indication that there were other methods of contracting typhus than by louse bite came from observations made in Australia soon after the first World War. Hone in Adelaide saw a number of patients with mild but quite definite typhus fever in 1919 and subsequent years. He was struck by the number of these patients who were employed in grain stores or in transporting wheat, occupations likely to bring them into contacts with rats and mice. Since none of the patients was louse-infested, he advanced the view that the disease was carried from rats or mice by some insect parasite. A few years later, in Queensland, there was an interesting relationship between a 'mouse plague', that is, a sudden enormous increase in the mouse population, and the appearance of numerous cases of typhus fever amongst farmers in the district. In both instances the connexion between rodents and typhus fever appeared to be unmistakable, but unfortunately no experimental proof that rats or mice were infected was obtained. The proof that typhus could be derived from natural infections amongst rats had to wait for American investigations in 1928. In the southern states cases similar to the Australian ones occurred, and it was shown conclusively that they were infected by rat fleas from rats chronically infected with the typhus *Rickettsia*. Since then similar conditions have been found to exist in many other parts of the world. In all probability typhus is an ancient disease of rats and mice, perhaps an even more ancient disease of the fleas that live on the rodents. The typical louse-spread typhus is a modern development.

In Mexico it is possible to see the change from rat typhus to human typhus in progress. Rat typhus is common, and when conditions for case-to-case transfer by lice are present, a patient infected with typhus of rat origin by flea bite may set up a small epidemic of the classical type. There are some slight differences between the rickettsiae which produce the 'rat type' typhus and those of 'louse type' infections, but they are no more than the differences between local races of the same species. Zinsser, in his fascinating 'biography' of typhus fever, *Rats, Lice and History*, suggests the probability that the European louse-borne disease originated during the long-drawn-out wars of the sixteenth century in Hungary when

Christians and Moslems alternately conquered and reconquered the country. No clear evidence of typhus fever is found prior to this period, but every war in Europe since has seen grave outbreaks of the disease. The greatest in all history was probably the epidemic which swept Russia during and after the Revolution of 1917, when cases were numbered in millions and deaths by hundreds of thousands.

The war epidemics of typhus have always been associated with famine, hardship and dislocation of social life. Under happier, if still crowded and filthy circumstances, typhus can take on a milder character. Following the general rule amongst infections, typhus is far milder in children than amongst adults, and in endemic regions such as the native quarters of North African cities a high degree of immunity may be developed by such mild childhood infections. Here we have reached the end of the process of transfer from rat to man. The mild disease of the rat passes accidently to man, it finds a new vector in the louse, and under circumstances of war and famine spreads widely and fatally, but where circumstances allow its easy spread in a stationary population, it eventually develops the character of a typical relatively mild endemic infection.

The second example of evolutionary changes in infectious disease associated with transfer to new host species is an African one, and concerns the infections produced by trypanosomes, protozoal parasites of the blood which are transferred by the tsetse fly. The most important diseases they produce are nagana, a highly fatal disease of domestic animals which has played a big part in limiting the area of European occupation in Africa, and sleeping sickness of human beings. The ancestral form of trypanosome responsible for these diseases is *Trypanosoma brucei*, which is a very common harmless parasite of many types of antelope and other wild game in the tsetse-fly country. A large proportion of the flies become infected, and any domestic animals or human beings entering the country are inevitably soon inoculated with the trypanosome. Horses, camels and pigs die rapidly, cattle more slowly, but equally certainly. Man is usually unaffected, even in heavily infected country where it is impossible to keep any domestic animals. In certain parts of Northern Rhodesia, however, there are rare but rapidly fatal infections of human beings by a trypanosome which, apart from this pathogenicity for human beings, cannot in any way be distinguished from the *T. brucei* of other regions where human beings are apparently not infected. This seems to be the first stage in the adaptation of the trypanosome to its new host, man. The next state is seen in the regions further north and to the west, where true sleeping sickness occurs. The trypanosome of sleeping sickness is closely related to *T. brucei*, but it is recognizably different in several respects. In man, it produces a mild infection of the blood which becomes serious only when the trypanosomes enter the brain and produce the symptoms that give the disease its name. It is a much less acute disease than the Rhodesian one. The trypanosome of sleeping sickness has only very rarely been found in the blood of wild animals, and it seems certain that most infections are carried by the tsetse fly from human to human, not, like the Rhodesian form, from animal reservoir to human. The parasite can be inoculated into antelopes and produces in them the same sort of long-lasting harmless infection as *T. brucei* does, but in nature it has become predominantly a human parasite.

In this series we see first a parasite which probably over thousands of years has developed a mutually tolerant relationship with its two hosts, the tsetse fly and the native mammals. When domestic animals and man entered the regions, the trypanosomes inoculated into them by the ubiquitous tsetse flies multiplied or failed to multiply according to purely accidental circumstances. Most of the hoofed domestic animals being relatively closely related to the native hosts of the trypanosome, but lacking their inherited tolerance, allowed free multiplication of the germ with fatal results. Human beings were much more resistant, but amongst the minor variations which are always occurring in living organisms one strain of *T. brucei* developed power to multiply in a proportion of the human beings into which it was inoculated. Most of these infections by unadapted strains are fatal to the new host, and as such are not likely to be widely disseminated from man to man. This is the present position of the Rhodesian trypanosome. The germ of true sleeping sickness has gone a stage further; it has developed a slower type of human infection which provides greater opportunity for transfer of infection to other human beings, and so for survival of the strain. Here we have an example of the general principle that, given sufficient time, and providing both species survive, host and parasite will eventually develop a mutual tolerance. Highly fatal diseases in nature nearly always represent the effect of first contact with a microorganism which has developed its parasitic habit in some different host.

The only instance yet recorded in which a microorganism has been successfully used to provoke widespread epidemics in a wild animal pest is the recent use of myxomatosis virus against the rabbit in Australia. This virus was isolated in Brazil from fatal cases of infection that appeared to arise spontaneously in European type laboratory rabbits. Its real origin was a mystery until a few years ago, when it was recognized that the wild rabbits around São Paulo were the reservoir of the disease and that it was transmitted to other rabbits, wild or European, by mosquitoes. The association of the Brazilian rabbit with myxomatosis has all the marks of an ancient and stabilized equilibrium. Instead of a fatal infection, the bite of an infected mosquito provokes only a small swelling of the skin and a transient invasion of the blood by the virus. The rabbit survives and is subsequently immune even to the minor results of primary infection. The European rabbit is only a distant relative of the Brazilian, and for it infection with myxomatosis virus is the same kind of biological accident as scrub typhus is for a human being. The disease is almost always fatal.

Australia's greatest pest is the rabbit, the European rabbit introduced around 1860 from England, and for many years the possibility of using myxomatosis virus to destroy it has been considered. It has two important and unusual characteristics that favour such use—its extremely high mortality rate and its strict limitation to rabbits. It is innocuous even when deliberately injected into human beings, domestic mammals or native Australian marsupials. Early attempts to initiate infection in wild rabbits were essentially unsuccessful. All the rabbits in a warren might die, but the disease spread no further. In these experiments the aim was to allow the disease to spread by contact from rabbit to rabbit, and it so happened that the tests were carried out in areas virtually free from mosquitoes. In 1950 experiments were begun in a different part of Australia near the upper Murray River and again the results looked unpromising. Then just before Christmas a wholly unexpected development occurred. Rabbits were dying, obviously from myxomatosis, on the river flats near Albury fifteen or twenty miles from the nearest rabbit warrens that had been experimentally infected. In the next three months myxomatosis spread rapidly over an area about as large as western Europe, concentrating its lethal action along waterways but sweeping north across New South Wales in leaps that seemed to be as much as a hundred miles at a time. The mortality amongst rabbits within the vast area involved was very patchy, but along the river flats there would often be virtual extermination and in areas of western New South Wales, where unusual rainfall had left much water lying, almost equally good results were obtained.

The virus could be spread by any mosquito or other biting insect which will feed on rabbits, the dominant carrier varying from one season to another. *Aedes* and *Culex* were important in the first summer, but in 1951–2 anopheline mosquitoes played the major part in another even more extensive outbreak over most of southern Australia.

In subsequent years myxomatosis persisted over the whole area, rising to a peak of activity whenever a summer prevalence of mosquitoes coincided with a recovering population of rabbits. From the first it was obvious that the disease provided a special opportunity for the epidemiologist. It was under study from its inception and has already provided a unique opportunity to follow the process by which a virus and its host can reach an equilibrium.

By 1957 both the virus and the rabbit population had changed. Within two or three years the myxomatosis virus being isolated in the field was of lower virulence. Instead of 99 per cent of deaths the figure was nearer 90 per cent and, more important, the time between infection and death was almost doubled. This new form of virus has been shown to survive much more effectively in the wild than the original extremely virulent form, or than the rare forms of much lower virulence which are sometimes isolated. Change in the resistance of the rabbit population was slower in developing, but by 1957 it was clearly evident. By this time there were areas in which rabbits had been exposed to five successive epidemics each at least 90 per cent lethal. This is a very stringent test for selective survival, and in the last set of tests for resistance amongst young rabbits from these areas the results were very striking. Using a virus killing 90 per cent of normal rabbits, the mortality in the group that had experienced all these epidemics was just less than 50 per cent. Many of the surviving rabbits suffered an illness that in the wild would probably have killed them, but even the Australian farmer is now beginning to see that 'myxo' is not as effective in clearing his land of rabbits as it was.

In 1960 there were still outbreaks of myxomatosis occurring but the effectiveness of the disease as a control of the rabbit had ended. Myxomatosis will probably persist as long as there are substantial rabbit populations in Australia, but in the settled areas the official policy is to foster professionally controlled poisoning campaigns with fluoracetate as the only practical means of extermination.

To return to natural examples of an ecological balance between pathogenic organisms and the hosts with which they have evolved, we may cite some other instances from Africa. The diseases in question have been recognized almost solely from their effect on domesticated animals introduced from abroad. There is no other part of the world in which large native mammals occur in such numbers both of individuals and of species. Amongst them are zebras, antelopes and wild pigs, all close relatives of common domestic animals. Diseases have developed amongst these, and through centuries the various parasites and their hosts have become adapted to each other. A large proportion of these infections are spread by biting flies or mosquitoes, so that when domestic animals enter the country they can be infected without necessarily coming into close contact with the natural hosts of the parasites. It is only to be expected that domestic stock will be particularly susceptible to infections whose normal host is a closely related wild animal. If, to take an example, a virus producing a mild infection of zebras is transferred by a mosquito bite to a horse, it finds a host whose tissues are of almost the same quality as the zebra's but lack the resistance which the latter species has developed to curb the virus. This may well be the origin of African horse-sickness, although actual proof has not yet been supplied. Amongst the diseases known to be derived from native animals are malignant catarrh, with the expressive Afrikaans name of *snotsiekte,* which is a natural disease of the gnu and affects sheep and cattle severely, and a highly fatal form of swine fever derived from a mild infection of the wart-hog. There are in Africa several other diseases of stock due to protozoa and viruses which must undoubtedly be derived from wild mammals. So far, however, the natural hosts have not been determined, an indication in itself that the natural diseases are inconspicuous.

Perhaps the most interesting of all such transfers of infection from one species to another is the infection of cattle with the virus of 'mad itch.' This is the name given to a rather rare disease of cattle in the mid-western states of America. The cattle develop an unbearable itching and almost tear their skin off against posts and the like for a day or two, then they develop signs of paralysis and invariably die. The virus was not difficult to isolate, and was found to produce fatal infections when inoculated in any of the common animals of the laboratory. Sheep and cattle were also highly susceptible to inoculation, but pigs were hardly affected, unless the virus was inoculated directly into the brain. Nevertheless, although pigs hardly ever died from inoculation, they became infectious for other pigs. A mild infection by the mad-itch virus passed from pig to pig in the experimental pens, spread apparently by the porcine equivalent of droplet infection amongst human beings. It could be shown that the virus was present in the nasal discharge of a pig sick with the disease, and that such discharge placed in a nostril of another pig resulted in infection. There was therefore a sharp distinction to be drawn between pigs and all the other animals tested. Monkeys, rabbits, guinea-pigs, sheep and cattle all died from inoculation of the virus, but they could not contract the disease naturally from one another. Pigs suffered a relatively mild but highly infectious disease. Although the virus had never been found naturally in American pigs, it seemed to Shope, who did all this work, that the indications pointed strongly towards the pig as the natural subject of the disease. It was known that after infection swine developed antibodies in their blood which could inactivate the virus. As in many similar problems, the easiest way to tell whether pigs were infected with the virus was not to look for the virus, but to see whether the pigs had developed antibody to it. Thirty or forty samples of blood from pigs killed in Iowa were tested, and all were found capable of rendering the virus harmless. Extending such work, Shope found that while pig farms in the eastern states were not infected, the majority of pigs in the middle west had passed through the infection apparently without any obvious symptoms.

Mad itch in cows only appears when cattle and swine occupy the same enclosures. Shope suggests that the common sequence that leads to infection is a cow resting on the ground; a pig infected with the virus nuzzles around, and its slobber infects either an existing scratch or a little abrasion made as the pig tries to push the cow out of the way. From the point of inoculation the virus spreads up nerves toward the brain. On its way it infects especially the ganglia of the nerves of sensation, and by its action on these nerve cells produced the intolerable itching around the point of entry of the virus.

In this example of an infection passing from its natural host to other species we have the same difference in virulence which characterizes the earlier examples mentioned, but an additional important point appears. The virus can spread easily only in the normal host species; infection occurs in other species only by abnormal and exceptional methods. It is much easier for a pathogenic microorganism to multiply in an alien host when it reaches its internal tissues directly than when it has to make its own way into the tissues. A highly specialized adaptation of virus to host cells seems to be necessary for simple contact infection to occur, using this term to include any form of infection of unbroken surfaces, either by droplet infection or by physical contact. It is particularly striking that of the virus diseases spread in this way hardly any can be caused to infect animals of another species by natural contact. Many are incapable of being transferred even by inoculation. Of human diseases in this group only influenza is infectious in the strict sense for any other animal, and here the susceptibility of the ferret must be regarded as something of a lucky accident. The same holds for animal infections spread in this fashion, rinderpest and foot-and-mouth disease in cattle, sheep-pox, and swine fever are all highly infectious, but strictly limited in their infectiousness to their normal hosts. The diseases spread by vectors which penetrate the skin with their bite are much more liable to infect unusual host species, and most of our examples of transfer between species have naturally been of this type.

CHAPTER XIII

THE GENERAL CHARACTER OF EPIDEMICS AND PREVALENCES OF INFECTIOUS DISEASE

When we come to study the actual occurrence of infectious disease in the community, there is an immediate and obvious distinction to be made between those diseases which are always present and those which appear in the form of isolated epidemics. In Australia, for instance, we have always present such diseases as influenza, measles and tuberculosis. Now and again we have a small outbreak of typhoid fever, and at long irregular intervals some exotic disease like plague or smallpox gains a temporary foothold. The ever-present infections are referred to as endemic diseases. It is usual to contrast endemic and epidemic diseases, but since seasons of greatly increased prevalence, popularly called epidemics, are characteristic of almost all endemic diseases, the distinction is a confusing one. It is more satisfactory to refer to diseases which visit the community only on isolated occasions simply as non-endemic diseases.

We might define an endemic disease as an infectious disease present in a community in which the social circumstances do not offer any effective barrier to its spread. Typhoid fever is not endemic in Melbourne or London because effective sanitation and good water supply allow no opportunity for extensive spread, but it is endemic in most Indian cities, which lack such facilities. In many tropical countries malaria is endemic simply because there is no check on the breeding of mosquitoes, and no practical way of protecting the population from their bites. So, while in civilized countries the only endemic diseases are those which pass readily from person to person either by droplet infection or by transfer of highly infective material by direct or indirect skin contact there is no necessary limitation to these. The venereal diseases have their own special epidemiological characters, which cannot be usefully discussed along with the diseases spread by other methods, but excluding these, we find that all endemic diseases, irrespective of their mode of spread from person to person, show certain features in common.

The most satisfactory way to elucidate the difference in behaviour between non-endemic and endemic infectious disease would be to follow the history of a single disease which had manifested both types of activity. Although a number of infections are known to have done so, it is difficult to find a satisfactory example for discussion, principally because no disease has shown both phases in a civilized community in recent times. In every available instance we have to be content with scrappy information about one of the phases, either because the account is a century or two old, or because the outbreak in which we are interested occurred in some remote savage community and was only casually reported.

In 1957 we experienced what seems to have been a genuine emergence of a new infectious disease in the form of Asian influenza. For a time there were serious forebodings that this might grow into something as disastrous as the great epidemic in 1918–19, but though the virus swept around the world within a year, its impact everywhere was that of ordinary influenza and nothing more. It did show some interesting features but these are best deferred to a later chapter.

With the development of much more convenient methods for the isolation and study of the viruses concerned with the more trivial human diseases, a number of 'new' diseases have been reported. The only one we need mention is the 'ECHO 9' epidemic which swept through Europe in 1955–6 and flourished in America in 1957. It was a very mild disease with only one established fatality (in an infant) amongst many tens of thousands of cases. The symptoms included fever, rash and some evidence of mild damage to the nervous system. It affected both children and adults but there are no statistics of relative age incidence.

Perhaps the most important finding about infectious disease in recent years has been the recognition of the immense variety of trivial infections that are always current in a large city. In the days when bacteriology was taken seriously—in the pre-antibiotic era—many investigations showed how frequent were invisible epidemics of streptococcal infection of the throat, particularly in orphanages and similar institutions. Nowadays the spread of antibiotic-resistant staphylococci has become the most popular type of epidemiological investigation for bacteriologists with much the same picture emerging. Some of the infections produce conditions dangerous and difficult to treat but most are trivial.

The virologists, however, have found a much richer field of trivial infection in childhood. An orphanage outside Washington, D.C., had an average population of fifty young children with a rather rapid turnover which ensured the entry into the institution of most of the viruses circulating in the community. For a year each inmate was tested weekly for virus infection and more frequently whenever suspicious symptoms appeared. The results showed almost a continuous sequence of 'epidemics', most of them silent but with a proportion of respiratory or intestinal symptoms accompanying some. One of the most interesting was the spread of polio virus, Type III, to involve the majority of the current inmates without a sign of paralytic polio or any other of the standard symptoms in a single child. Every parent knows of the short-lasting minor fevers and upsets of young children. Recovery is complete in a day or two and except under very special conditions no real diagnosis is ever made. These can be regarded as the signs that the process of adjustment to the various microorganisms in the environment is proceeding, probably in the same way as it has ever since men lived in cities.

Epidemics that are recorded in history or in the foreign news in the newspapers are the rare exceptions in which microorganisms of undue virulence have flourished and particularly when a virulent strain has found a population without previous experience of less virulent strains of the same germ. It is by no means true that a 'virgin' population necessarily suffers a calamitous epidemic on its first encounter with a potentially dangerous virus or bacterium. An outbreak of polio Type III in the Aleutian Islands showed a number of persons with symptoms but no cases of paralysis, although the investigators could show that none of the population had had any previous exposure to this virus. Even in the classical instance of a virgin soil outbreak, the measles epidemic of 1875 in the Fiji Islands in which between 20,000 and 40,000 people died, the deaths were due largely to the complete social disorganization and shattering psychological effect of the epidemic rather than to the attack of the virus as such. There was no special racial susceptibility to the disease and since 1875 epidemics of measles in the Fiji Islands have been essentially the same as in any other parts of the world.

The special feature of any virgin soil epidemic by which it differs from a recrudescence of some endemic disease is that non-immune *adults* will suffer infection. Subject to a variety of exceptions we can say in broad terms that non-immune young adults tend to suffer more severely from a given infectious disease than non-immune children. It is common knowledge that when adults suffer measles or chickenpox they tend to be hit harder and take longer to recover than children. In many parts of the world during the First World War there was a significant mortality from measles plus bacterial secondary infection amongst recruits. Anyone who can remember the 1918–19 influenza will recall that the greatest mortality was amongst young adults. The interplay of physiological and immunological factors in determining the age incidence of infectious disease is a fascinating topic which will be developed in Chapter XV. Here we need only add that there are two other age groups that also show undue susceptibility to infectious disease when unprotected by immunity. As we might expect, these are the two extremes of life. Infants and old people are more susceptible to the impact of the environment than those in the middle ages between five and sixty. For almost every possible cause of death the child of ten or twelve is the least likely to suffer. Old people can usually count on being immune to all the common infections and it is only when a new or previously rare infection enters the community that their special vulnerability is seen. Such infections often show a sharply increasing mortality with advancing age. This is so marked in some prevalences that almost the whole incidence of death seems to be in the older age groups. Examples are psittacosis, the epidemic of encephalitis in St Louis in 1933, and the Liverpool epidemic of influenza in 1951.

At the risk of greatly oversimplifying the position we might say that when a 'new' infection enters a large community, the first impact will involve all ages and that any mortality is likely to show peaks in infancy and old age, with often a conspicuously high death rate in the young adult age group. With persistence of the disease in the community the situation will soon develop that the only susceptible non-immune individuals are those entering the community by birth. The incidence of both symptoms and deaths will then be highest in infancy and childhood. For obvious reasons the more readily transmitted the disease the younger will be the average age of infection. All actual infectious diseases show a recognizable approach to this behaviour, but all have their own peculiarities, and some, for example, tuberculosis and infantile paralysis, appear to behave, superficially at least, in very different fashions. We may next then discuss what are the factors which cause modifications from our type.

Perhaps the most important single factor is one which it is not easy to describe in a single word or short phrase. If we have a group of susceptible persons all of the same age exposed to infection by a microorganism, some, for one reason or another, may escape infection entirely. Those who are infected will not all show the same symptoms. If we take a hundred children infected with the diphtheria bacillus, it might easily happen that ten of them will have typical diphtheria with membrane over the tonsils and the general symptoms of fever and so forth. Unless properly treated, some of these children will die. Another dozen or twenty will have a slight sore throat, which is only likely to be diagnosed as diphtheria if attention is drawn to it by someone else in the family having typical diphtheria. The rest of the hundred will have no symptoms, but if swabs are taken from their throats at the right time, the diphtheria bacilli will be found to be present. In epidemiological discussions, we divide such a group into 'clinical cases', those in which a diagnosis can be made by a doctor's ordinary clinical examination of the patient, and 'subclinical cases' where the fact that the microorganism can be proved present by bacteriological methods is the only evidence of infection. Our first factor, which is responsible for the differences between epidemics, can now be expressed more concisely as the proportion of clinical to subclinical cases. This may range from 95 to 99 per cent of clinical cases in a measles outbreak to something as low as 1 : 5000 for infections by the virus of infantile paralysis in certain countries.

We do not know why some people have subclinical infections and others clinical ones. Probably inborn individual differences, genetically determined, play a major part but, in addition, we have to consider what is technically called the question of dosage. In all experimental infections, and presumably in all human ones, the dose of virus or bacteria which enters the body plays a large part in determining the outcome of the infection. We know, for instance, that a child whose brother has diptheria in the same house is very much more likely to develop clinical diphtheria than if he were exposed only to the casual contacts of the school and playground. All that any statement as to the proportion of clinical to subclinical infections can mean is that under the particular conditions of the community referred to this is the average result observed. In some other community the same type of infection might show quite a different proportion.

The next factor to be considered is the readiness with which transfer of infection is effected, and this in its turn depends on various subsidiary factors. Keeping to the endemic droplet infections, we must consider first the liberation of infective material from the patient or subclinically infected carrier. In measles the virus appears to be liberated into the secretions of mouth and nose for only a few days during the stage just before and just after the appearance of the rash, so that infection can be spread only during that period. In diphtheria the bacilli remain much longer in the throat, often for several weeks, while in tuberculosis a patient may be actively infectious for months or years. For every patient with an infectious disease we could, theoretically at least, prepare a graph to show how infectious he was for others at different periods of his illness. Most of these graphs would show a rather sudden rise from zero to a peak of maximum infectiousness usually a day or two after the beginning of actual symptoms, with a more gradually sloping line thereafter. The slope indicating the disappearance of infectiousness is on the whole much steeper for virus diseases like measles or influenza than for bacterial infections like diphtheria. The virus diseases probably make up for this by liberating more infectious material during the brief period of their infectiousness. Other things being equal, if one microorganism is liberated in greater amount than another, there will be a corresponding difference in the ease with which infection spreads.

Then there may be all sorts of variations in the intermediate stage of transfer when the virus or bacterium is actually in transit from one person to another. We often find that 'close contact' is necessary for the easy spread of infection, i.e. that people must be intimately associated and not just come near one another in public conveyances and the like. It does not necessarily mean that we can say in any given instance just what close contact signifies from the point of view of the actual mechanics by which the infection passes. In both World Wars, crowded camps and barracks showed high incidences of some of the typical 'droplet' diseases, especially meningitis and the streptococcal throat infections associated with rheumatic fever. In the First World War it was shown that the intensity of meningitis was directly related to the degree of crowding in army huts used as sleeping quarters, and it was thought that the reason was simply that the infectious droplets had to pass a shorter distance from carrier to new susceptible host. In the Second World War the most popular interpretation of the spread of infectious disease in sleeping quarters was quite different. The floating droplet was regarded as of minor importance in comparison with contaminated bedclothes and floor dust. By one means or another saliva and nasal secretion can easily contaminate blankets or other textiles, and when these are shaken clouds of bacteria are liberated into the air and eventually settle as dust. The inhalation of dust raised during bed-making and sweeping was the important factor, and special techniques for oiling floors and treating bedclothes were being rapidly extended at the end of the war.

At the present time there is a somewhat similar difference of opinion as to the means by which the poliomyelitis virus spreads by close contact between children. According to one school it is by droplet infection, according to the other, faecal infection is transferred via fingers and playthings.

Finally we come to factors involving the recipient of the infection. By far the most important are the interrelated conditions of age and past immunity which will be discussed in a later chapter. But even if we take a group of individuals all of the same age and all without previous experience of the disease concerned, we will still find differences in what results from similar exposure to infection. Some of the differences are constitutional, determined by inheritance. A few years ago there was published from New York an account of an investigation of tuberculosis in twins. As most people know twins are of two sorts, identical and non-identical. A pair of identical twins arise from the same fertilized egg and have an identical inheritance; non-identical twins come from two separate eggs and need be no more alike than other brothers and sisters. In the New York investigation, the records of tuberculosis in the State were combed for the names of patients with tuberculosis who had a twin brother or sister. Whenever possible both twins were located and carefully examined from two points of view, first to discover whether they were identical or non-identical twins, and secondly, as to whether the 'other' twin also suffered from tuberculosis. The results were very striking. Of the thirty-nine pairs of identical twins no less than thirty-four showed both twins infected with tuberculosis, and in most cases the disease was of similar severity in each. In contrast to this 87 per cent correspondence in identical twins, the incidence in non-identical twins was 25 per cent, almost exactly the same as in non-twin brothers and sisters in the same families. The latter will of course have many genetic characters in common with the 'index' case of tuberculosis, and be exposed to much the same chance of infection so that a high incidence might be expected. Finally, when husbands or wives of tuberculosis 'index' twins were examined, the incidence of tuberculosis was 7 per cent. Here there were no genetic factors necessarily concerned, but a high exposure to infection. The only conclusion possible was that inheritance plays by far the major part in determining the clinical result of infection with the tubercle bacillus.

There are hints that the result of infection with the virus of poliomyelitis is also influenced by the genetic make-up of the child concerned, and here and there we come across stories of twins showing remarkable resemblances in their response to some infection. In the experimental field, too, there are strains of laboratory mice which differ sharply in their response to the same infection. One strain is much more susceptible to tuberculosis than any others. There is another which is quite insusceptible to several viruses which in ordinary mice produce regularly fatal brain infections.

It is almost humiliating to have to confess that we have as yet no clues as to how genetic factors can influence the resistance of the body to disease. The fact is unassailable, but there is hardly even a hypothesis to account for its mechanism.

Then there are minor physiological factors, some of them with a genetic background which may influence the result of infection. The strength of the acid in the stomach varies with the phase of digestion, and it is reasonable to believe that when cholera or dysentery bacilli are swallowed they are unlikely to reach the intestine if the stomach contains food undergoing active digestion in what is normally a highly acid fluid. On the other hand, dangerous bacteria swallowed with a drink of water on an empty stomach are almost certain to pass rapidly into the intestine without coming under the antiseptic action of the gastric acid. The variability of the typical respiratory infections, influenza and the common cold is notorious, and it has been suggested that the amount of mucus secretion on the respiratory surfaces may have much to do with this. Influenza viruses have what might be called an ambivalent attitude to mucus. They enter the cell through mucus-like substances in its surface layer, but they are blocked temporarily at least by mucus outside the cell. There are possibilities here of some finely balanced situations which may be tilted toward infection or failure to infect by small general or local changes in mucus secretion.

One of the major achievements in the medical laboratories during 1959–60 was the isolation of several types of virus from patients with common colds. The viruses grown in tissue culture could be shown to produce typical colds in a significant proportion of human volunteers. It was perhaps a little disappointing to find out there was no single 'common cold virus' and most of those concerned with the new work are pessimistic about making practical use of these isolations to prevent colds. It may be that colds will eventually be prevented by some discovery in regard to why only a proportion of people deliberately infected with virus show any symptoms. Ordinary experience embedded in the very name suggests that we catch a cold as a result of infection with a virus at a time when the nasal mucous membranes are in an abnormal condition as a reflex response to chilling in some part of the body. There may be some truth in this, but what experiments have been done in recent years have failed to prove that cold has anything to do with colds.

It can be taken as broadly true that under-nourishment of any sort, undue fatigue, and bad environments prejudice the chances of the body overcoming the infection. Poverty and war are the two most potent helpers of infectious disease. Both, of course, act in many different ways, almost all toward the same unfortunate result. In the slums, overcrowding and personal uncleanliness favour the spread of infection, under-nourishment increases the severity and the chance of death. All that can be said for a slum environment is that, if children survive to ten or twelve, they will usually have acquired a very substantial immunity to all the current diseases.

With so many complex and variable conditions to be considered, it is no wonder that the only practicable method of treating the available data about the prevalence of disease is statistical. Detailed investigation of particular instances of infection may often provide information of much value, but chance plays so great a part in determining whether, when, and how severely any individual is attacked that any general conclusions must be based on large numbers of experiences, treated according to proper statistical methods. In most civilized countries statistics are available as to the numbers of deaths from all the infectious diseases, and for the numbers of cases notified of certain scheduled diseases, usually the more serious infections. As a rule, the age and sex distributions of cases or deaths are also available. For particular outbreaks which have aroused public interest, it is generally possible to obtain weekly totals of cases or deaths, and to ascertain in what municipalities or other administrative districts they occurred. In general, this information is the raw material from which the epidemiologist must draw his generalizations and hypotheses.

For those who are interested in the historical and statistical aspects of epidemiology, there is available an unrivalled semi-popular account in Greenwood's *Epidemics and Crowd Diseases.* Our object here is quite distinct from his. It is to touch on epidemiology only as exemplifying the general biological processes of interaction between living species, and in particular to demonstrate the significant influence of the immunity reactions which we described in earlier chapters, on the large-scale phenomena of infectious disease.

CHAPTER XIV

EPIDEMICS OF ENDEMIC DISEASE

The first general characteristic of endemic disease which we will touch upon is the distribution of cases according to time. Everyone knows that the childhood infections occur in epidemics or prevalences with intervening periods in which the disease is either absent or at least significantly rarer. When the data are arranged in the form of a graph with time along

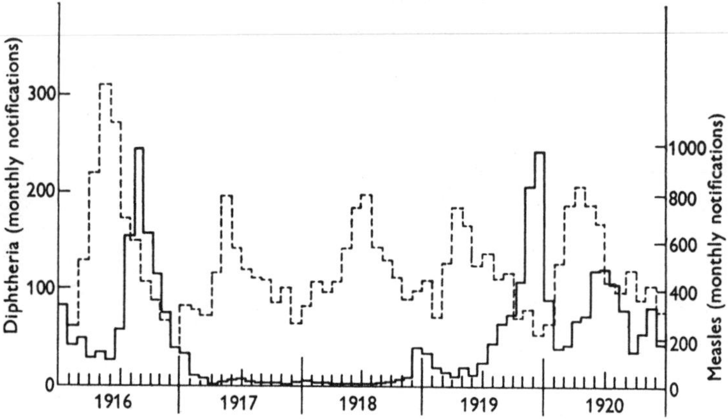

Fig. 5. Waves of prevalence in two endemic diseases, measles and diphtheria. The monthly notifications of measles (heavy continuous line) and diphtheria (broken line) in South Australia over a period of five years.

the horizontal direction and the number of cases or deaths shown vertically, we have for nearly every endemic disease a more or less regular wave form, the crests of the waves representing the times of epidemic. The graph (Fig. 5) shows examples of such wave-like curves for measles and diphtheria in an Australian community.

In these oscillations we have an example of the general biological principle that really stable equilibria between species are never attained. There are always short-period variations in favour of one or the other, and only by using relatively long periods as our units of time is it possible to say that a real equilibrium between the species exists. Except for such very slowly acting infections as tuberculosis, an infection can never keep spreading at just the rate necessary to infect as many susceptible individuals each month as are entering the community by birth or immigration. When we have an epidemic at its height there are large numbers of individuals who can serve as sources of infection, and there is a high probability that any susceptible will contract the infection. With exhaustion of susceptibles, the epidemic dies down rapidly, and what cases occur will have little chance of passing on their infection. The rate of spread of an epidemic at any moment is not only a function of the number or density of susceptible persons available, but of the number of sources of infection as well. An epidemic will affect some of even a small proportion of susceptibles if the number of infecting individuals is large, but if there are very few sources of infection, the chances of the same small number of susceptibles escaping infection are more than proportionately increased. Perhaps a diagram will make this clearer. In Fig. 6 are shown the lines of infection from one case to another at various stages of a hypothetical epidemic, starting in a wholly susceptible population. The incubation period is taken as a week, and three four-weekly periods are shown. It is assumed that once an individual has been infected he becomes immune, and underneath are shown the proportions of susceptibles and immunes at each period. In the first month, one case at the beginning gives rise to ten at the end of the period; at the peak of the epidemic many cases have no opportunity of infecting others, but there are still the same number of cases at the end of the period. As we approach the end of the epidemic, very few lines of infection can be continued, for all the contacts of most cases are already immune. If the epidemic is one like measles or influenza in which the infective period of any infected individual is limited to a few days, the disease will die out completely in a community when the proportion of susceptibles reaches a certain low level.

Occasionally an opportunity arises by which this process can be followed in detail. This happened in Melbourne when a new type of influenza appeared in 1957. Each week over the whole duration of the epidemic Keogh arranged for random samples of blood to be put aside from 100–200 blood donors. Subsequently the serum was tested for antibody against the new virus. There were no positive results in the first week, but thereafter the percentage rose regularly in the expected fashion but flattened out when approximately 45 per cent of donors had acquired the new antibody. There was evidence that a much higher percentage could be infected in schools, but it was of considerable interest to find that what we regard as a highly infectious virus can die out when less than half the community has been infected and immunized.

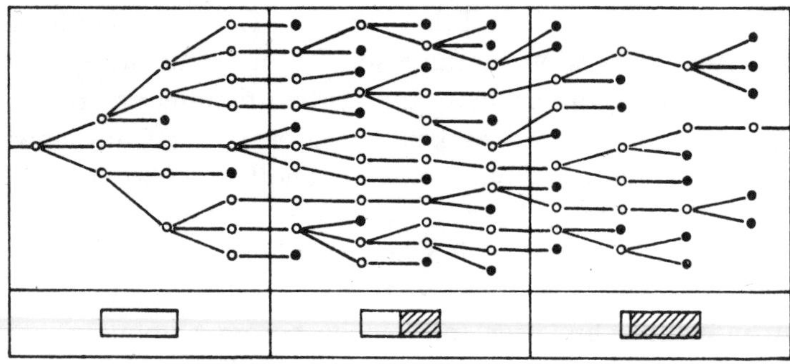

Fig. 6. A diagram to indicate the course of a typical epidemic. Each circle represents an infection, and the connecting lines indicate transfer from one case to the next. Black circles represent infected individuals who fail to infect others. Three periods are shown, the first when practically the whole population is susceptible, the second at the height of the epidemic, and the third at the close, when most individuals are immune. The proportions of susceptible (white) and immune (hatched) individuals are indicated in the rectangles beneath the main diagram.

It is quite possible for a large city like Melbourne to be completely free from epidemic influenza or measles for two or three years. Of course, epidemics of such diseases do not all occur simultaneously in different places, and what happens is that there is a kind of irregular peregrination of the infection around the various communities of a country, or, now that all countries are linked by rapid transit, of the world. By the time it returns to our original community, a fresh population of susceptibles has arisen, and the process is repeated.

When there is not the same limited period of infectivity, a different state of affairs develops, and carriers play an important role. In diphtheria, for instance, the bacilli may persist for months after infection, particularly if the nasal cavity becomes infected. If a few such carriers persist during the period following an epidemic prevalence, even if the proportion of susceptibles is low, a few cases will keep on occurring; there will therefore be no such striking ups and downs as there are with measles and influenza, and no periods in which a large community is free from infection. Carriers are nearly always found in bacterial or protozoal infections, much less commonly in those due to viruses.

So far we have ascribed the waves in intensity of endemic diseases only to the variations in the number of susceptible individuals in the community. There is only one disease whose epidemic behaviour may be determined almost wholly by such variations in the number of susceptible individuals. This is measles, when it occurs in such a large, densely populated area as London. There is an almost regular two-yearly cycle of measles in London with the highest incidence in the spring of one year. This is followed by a virtual disappearance of the disease till next spring when there is a smaller rise in the number of cases. Then there is a short-lasting fall in autumn with a steady build up of cases during the winter to the next spring peak of measles. There are, of course, variations from year to year but the general picture is consistent. In smaller communities, however, the regularity disappears and all one can say is that measles outbreaks occur at intervals of a few years. In country villages in Yorkshire the intervals tended to be about nine years, and in all Australian states the epidemic prevalences have been at very irregular intervals. It is self-evident that an epidemic cannot occur unless there are sufficient susceptible individuals available, but the mere accumulation of susceptible persons is not sufficient to ensure that an epidemic will at once arise. For such diseases as measles and influenza, which will frequently disappear completely from even large communities, the virus may need to be reintroduced from outside for an epidemic to occur. Other infections like diphtheria, scarlet fever and whooping cough are always present to some extent, and their prevalences are determined both by the accumulation of susceptible children and by seasonal factors. Some particular types of weather seem to favour the spread of one or other infection. We might expect that all droplet infections would respond similarly to weather changes, and we should be inclined to think that winter would be the season of greater incidence for all of them. Actually there are considerable variations from one type of infection to another.

When diphtheria was prevalent in Australia, its incidence was highest in late autumn and early winter (April to June): scarlet fever shows some tendency also to be more frequent in winter, but there is no regular prevalence at this time. Measles epidemics occur at very irregular intervals, but when the disease persists for a year or two its highest incidence is in spring. Whooping cough has well-marked spring and early summer prevalence in all the states of the Commonwealth. Infantile paralysis used to be equally regular in its concentration on the months of late summer and autumn just as it does in the northern hemisphere.

After 1937, however, the seasonal distribution of poliomyelitis in Australia became irregular and there were several long-lasting epidemics running through the winter.

The reasons for these seasonal prevalences are still largely matters for conjecture. In all probability, season may affect both the ease with which infection is transferred and the susceptibility of the recipient. Colds, feverish colds and influenza are largely concentrated on the winter months. Though it is perhaps no more than an intelligent guess to do so, we may ascribe this to the combined action of a heightened susceptibility of the lining of the nose and air passages to infection in cold and changeable weather, and to the greater crowding indoors with increased opportunity for the transfer of infection. On the whole, changes in the susceptibility of the individual are probably more important than changes in the degree to which he is exposed to infection. In most instances consumption is a result of the flaring up into activity of a tuberculous infection of the lung which has been initiated years before. It is not a result of a new infection by the tubercle bacillus. It necessarily follows that the well-known tendency of tuberculosis to show increased activity in spring is wholly due to changes within the patient. Similar seasonal changes in the functioning of the body may possibly be responsible for the seasonal variation of other infectious diseases, the real variation being not in the ease with which infection is spread but in the changing ratio of clinical to subclinical infections. The influence of weather and climate on the human body is probably far more important than is generally realized, and there is a big field available here for future research.

If we go beyond the diseases spread by droplet infection, we will usually have to go to the tropics to find them endemic in the sense that diphtheria and influenza are in the temperate zones. Plague in India has a sharp seasonal incidence, most of the cases occurring in the north-west in March, April and May. Since human plague is, as it were, an overflow via the flea from endemic plague in rats, the periodicity of human outbreaks depends on the influence of climate on the complicated interaction of rat, flea and plague bacillus. In the Punjab the bacillus gets the upper hand during the hot season. When plague was endemic in England from the fourteenth to the seventeenth centuries, the outbreaks were also always during the summer. Any disease which, like plague, depends on the transference of infection by some insect or tick will obviously have its seasonal incidence largely or wholly determined by the life history of the insect responsible.

In temperate climates and civilized communities the more serious gastrointestinal infections are now rare, but mild dysentery due to the Sonne bacillus and a variety of short-lasting diarrhoeal infections, possibly of viral origin, may be expected to take on local epidemic proportions occasionally. In England and Australia such outbreaks are not limited to any one season. Early in the century summer diarrhoea of infants, usually bacillary dysentery, was important. Its disappearance has been ascribed both to the general improvement of personal hygiene and the progressive elimination of the horse by the motor vehicle. The dysentery bacilli were probably spread largely by domestic flies and the removal of their favourite breeding ground, horse manure, may have been an important factor in the disappearance of infantile dysentery.

Waves of any sort need more than just the interval between their crests to describe them fully. We must also know the height of successive waves above the troughs and something about the shape of the wave. This applies just as much to the conventional waves which appear in a graph of the prevalence of an endemic disease as to the waves of the sea. We have discussed why increased prevalences occur periodically, and what factors influence the times at which they occur. We have yet to deal with what determines how big the epidemic will be when it does occur.

One of the important factors will obviously be the number of susceptible individuals present at the beginning of the prevalence. If instead of coming every second year measles remains absent for four or six years, when it does recur the number of susceptible children available and hence the number of cases, will be proportionately greater. During the earlier history of Melbourne, measles recurred at rather long and irregular intervals, and the number of deaths in each epidemic showed a rough proportionality to the length of the interval during which the virus had been inactive.

Table I. *Measles epidemics in Melbourne*

Epidemic	1866–7	1874–5	1880	1884	1887	1893	1898	1900
Previous free interval (years)	6	7	4	3	2	5	4	1
Number of deaths	433	733	174	176	64	386	403	95

As we have frequently had to remark, other infectious diseases are not so easy to understand as measles. We can by no means ascribe all the variations from epidemic to epidemic of diphtheria or scarlet fever to mere differences in the numbers of susceptible children available. When a particularly large or severe epidemic of diphtheria occurs, it is usually found to be due to the activity of a strain of the bacillus different from those previously in the community. Diphtheria and scarlet fever are both what may be called composite diseases. Each is caused by a number of recognizably different bacteria, all producing the same toxin, and therefore the same general symptoms, and all stimulating the production of the same type of antitoxin. Immunity developed against one strain is therefore effective against any other strain.

When a new, more virulent strain appears in a community, the increase in the number of cases is chiefly due to an increase in the ratio of clinical to subclinical cases. Similar numbers of susceptible children are infected, but a greater proportion of them show recognizable symptoms of disease. In all such outbreaks due to a more virulent type of microorganism already endemic, the age incidence of disease remains much the same as previously. Even the sudden widespread appearance of diphtheria in many parts of the world around 1858 affected almost entirely young children. So did the severe epidemics of scarlet fever which occurred ten or twenty years later.

The story of scarlet fever is more complicated than that of diphtheria. The various types of diphtheria bacilli have more in common than the streptococci responsible for scarlet fever. The exact quality which allows some streptococci and not others to produce scarlet fever has not yet been identified.

With scarlet fever now a trivial disease we may have lost our opportunity to analyse the factors that made it so lethal for children in the second half of the nineteenth century. Streptococci have always been present in the throats of scarlet fever patients and in at least one experiment such streptococci proved capable of causing typical scarlet fever in two non-immune volunteers whose throats were sprayed with a pure culture of the germs. There is no doubt that there are very many sore throats, mild and severe, which are caused by streptococci, but which are not accompanied by a scarlet rash and are only very slightly infectious for others. To produce scarlet fever, a *Streptococcus* must have both a high infectiousness and ability to produce toxin in large amounts. These two qualities may not necessarily go together. There is a third quality of great importance in determining the result of streptococcal infections which is in its turn independent of these two. This is the invasiveness of the germ, its power to multiply in the tissues and to spread to other parts of the body.

All sorts of combinations of these qualities may be found in streptococci, and the results which follow infection of the throat are correspondingly varied. A realization of this variability makes it much easier to understand, in general outline at least, the very complicated and obscure history of the epidemics of severe throat infections before the period of bacteriology. Scarlet fever in its uncomplicated form is nothing more than a fairly severe form of poisoning by toxin produced by streptococci in the throat. There need be only a mild degree of local invasion and no serious spread to other parts of the body. The scarlet rash which allows the diagnosis to be made is wholly a reaction of the skin to toxin in the blood. It is clear that those who have developed antitoxin in their blood as a result of previous contact with toxin-producing streptococci will not have scarlet fever. The presence of antitoxin will not, however, protect against invasion by virulent forms of streptococci, so that a strain which produces scarlet fever in a susceptible child may produce a severe sore throat without a rash in a person who is immune to scarlet fever by virtue of his antitoxin. To become immune to the invasive power of such a *Streptococcus* requires the assistance of antibodies against the surface antigens of the microorganism as well as antitoxin. Unfortunately, while there is only one scarlet-fever toxin, there are at least twenty different sorts of antigen which may compose the surface of scarlet fever streptococci, each needing a different type of antibody to check invasiveness.

With all these complications one cannot be surprised that, more than any other infectious disease, scarlet fever has shown wide differences in severity at different periods. In the eighteenth century there were serious epidemics which were probably due to streptococci of high infectiousness and invasiveness, but with little power to produce toxin. Ordinary mild scarlet fever was also prevalent.

There were fluctuations in the early nineteenth century, then a steady increase in severity which culminated in a period of thirty years from 1850 to 1880 when scarlet-fever epidemics were frequent and severe both in England and Australia. The streptococci active then combined high degrees of infectiousness, toxin production and invasiveness, and the death-rate amongst children rose tragically. After 1880 the severity of scarlet fever diminished, and at the present time it is on the average probably milder than at any time in its history.

The common virus diseases, which in addition to measles include german measles, chickenpox and mumps, all behave as if the only important factors were the ease with which the virus passes from person to person and the proportion of susceptible people in the community at the time of its activity. There is no evidence of any significant variation in the virulence or other characteristics of the virus from one epidemic to another. With influenza and poliomyelitis the conditions are more complex, and these two important diseases are best left for individual discussion later.

The Australian experience of rubella (german measles) during this century offers some interesting evidence of the constancy of the virus concerned. Until 1940 german measles was universally considered to be the mildest of all infectious diseases. Complications were unknown and no treatment was necessary. Then in 1940 an Australian ophthalmologist (Gregg) reported that he had seen a large number of cases of congenital cataract (opacity of the lens of the eye) in babies whose mothers had suffered from german measles during their pregnancy. It rapidly became clear that, in addition to these eye changes, other babies were being born deaf or with congenital malformations of the heart as a result of infection in the uterus during the early months of their mother's pregnancy. In Australia during the years 1939–42 there were probably 400 to 500 infants born with congenital damage of one sort or another resulting from german measles infection. Elsewhere in the world sufficient similar cases were discovered to make it clear that the Australian experience was not unique, but nowhere else was there evidence of a virtual epidemic of congenital infection such as occurred in Australia. The question was raised as to whether this capacity to produce ante-natal infection was a new property of the rubella virus first manifested in the Australian wartime epidemic. Why otherwise had so common a disease as german measles never shown this frightening ability to invade the embryo before? A wholly convincing answer has recently been provided by Lancaster in Sydney by the simple procedure of tabulating the birth dates of all persons listed as deaf-mutes on census and other records. He has found that in Australia there have been several periods where many such birth dates are concentrated within a few months. In 1900, for instance, the graph of births of people subsequently registered as deaf-mutes provided a typical epidemic curve whose peak was six or seven months after that of the rubella epidemic responsible. The answer then is simply that congenital damage by german measles in pregnancy had been occurring for at least forty years before Gregg recognized it in 1940. There had been no change in the virus. It was simply that nobody in Australia had been interested enough to wonder why so many deaf-mutes seemed to have been born about the same time.

It may well be that Australia has differed somewhat from more populous parts of the world in having longer intervals between successive rubella epidemics. There had been very little rubella in Australia between 1925 and the wartime epidemic, so that an unusually large number of young women had had no opportunity of developing immunity during their childhood. In wartime of course there was far greater opportunity for the rapid spread of any disease of this type amongst young non-immune adults than in peace time. Both measles and german measles were rife in the camps and in the civilian population. This time the toll of damage on the unborn children could not escape notice.

CHAPTER XV

THE AGE-INCIDENCE OF INFECTIOUS DISEASE

We have already indicated the importance of the age-incidence of infections in relation to the degree of immunity in the community, and given an outline of the general situation in relation to diseases which had not previously been experienced in the community. Special emphasis was laid on the frequency with which disease appeared to be more severe and mortality higher in young adults than in children. This is by no means universal, but there is a paradoxical flavour about the assertion that calls for its expansion and justification. Most people would probably consider that children are more prone to the common infections than adults because they are weaker, with more delicate tissues, and unable to respond so effectively to the attack of disease germs. The thesis that children may be more resistant to infectious diseases of which they have had no previous experience than are adults in the same condition, requires to be established by an adequate amount of evidence.

In any discussion of the age-incidence of infectious disease, it is very important to be clear about the nature of the information we are attempting to study. There is first the statistics of mortality from a given disease. In many ways this is the most useful and least equivocal of all the information we can obtain. The fact of death is incontrovertible, and the diagnosis of a fatal case of infectious disease is with some qualifications likely to be relatively accurate. The age of the victim will always be known in any civilized community as well as the size and age distribution of the administrative unit being studied. The incidence of disease, irrespective of whether it is fatal or not, is much more difficult to be sure of. There are several difficulties. Except under exceptional circumstances, infectious disease is reported by doctors on the basis of patients they are called on to visit and on their opinion of what the patient is suffering from. Where, as is so often the case, a given infectious disease can give rise to conditions of widely varying severity, the criterion for reporting will often be very poorly defined. Whether or not mild cases are reported will depend very largely on the interest of doctor or patients at the time. If it is known that an epidemic of polio is in progress, many cases of minor feverish upset with headache and stiff neck will be diagnosed and reported as polio which at other times would be lumped with other trivial undiagnosed infections. A rather similar difficulty arises in regard to dysentery. From 1934 onwards there was a steady and large increase in the number of cases of dysentery notified in England and Wales, reaching a peak in the last years of the War. The annual numbers of deaths from dysentery, however, hardly varied over the period and most authorities believe that what had happened was simply that facilities for the bacteriological testing of cases of diarrhoea were being steadily improved at that time and doctors were making greater use of them.

If a disease like smallpox, measles or mumps has well-marked clinical symptoms in the great majority of cases we are on surer ground, but even with these there will be a proportion of patients who do not see a doctor and are never reported.

If we bear in mind these difficulties, we can usefully look at the changes in age-incidence of two important and interesting diseases, smallpox and poliomyelitis.

The history of smallpox in England is illuminating. Before the Stuart period, smallpox appears to have been rare, the first considerable epidemics in London being in 1628 and 1634. These attracted notice largely on account of the number of young adults attacked. This characteristic of the disease continued for some years. Shortly after the Restoration in 1660, a brother and a sister of Charles II died of smallpox, and other deaths of notable persons are mentioned in memoirs and diaries of the period. Smallpox in children was said to be mild and rarely fatal. From the Stuart period onward, smallpox prevalence in London increased irregularly but consistently, and throughout the eighteenth century an average of about 1500 deaths per annum were ascribed to smallpox. By the middle of the century, practically every child born in London or in one of the larger provincial cities must have been exposed to infection early in childhood.

Smallpox now was almost entirely a disease of early childhood, over 90 per cent of deaths occurring under the age of five. In the figure are shown the distribution of smallpox deaths in Manchester 1769–74, according to age. This concentration on childhood was not, however, an intrinsic characteristic of eighteenth-century smallpox. In small country towns, there were frequent cases amongst adults, and records are available of an outbreak in a small Northamptonshire town in 1723–4 where the mortality was about 30 per cent in those aged twenty to forty, about 23 per cent in infants under five, and only 8 per cent for the ages five to twenty. It was only in country areas of course that we could expect to find a significant proportion of cases in non-immune adults. The important finding is the low mortality in children beyond the years of infancy as compared to adults.

During the nineteenth century, smallpox became steadily less prevalent in England. Widespread vaccination probably played a large part in its disappearance, but it was not the only factor at work. As the disease diminished in frequency, the curves of age-incidence of deaths from smallpox showed a characteristic change, with a progressive diminution of the peak in infancy and an associated rise in incidence in young adult life. This change was by no means wholly due to vaccination in infancy protecting the younger children. In the same figure (Fig. 7) is shown the curve of age-incidence amongst unvaccinated individuals who contracted smallpox in the mild Sydney epidemic of 1913–14. In this epidemic,

39 per cent of cases fell in the age group twenty to thirty. Here we can be reasonably certain that the great majority of cases were recognized and this concentration in the young adult has never been fully explained. If we eliminate as very unlikely the suggestion that there was a high proportion of subclinical or unrecognized smallpox in children, we must assume either that young adults were more exposed to infection or that with equal exposure they were considerably more likely to contract infection. The last alternative seems to be most likely.

In smallpox, then, we see a complete cycle. Starting as a sporadic disease with its most serious incidence on young adults, it increases in prevalence and becomes more and more a disease of childhood—at its most intense, of infancy—then as it dwindles, the proportion of cases in childhood diminish and those of young adults increase, until in the early twentieth century it had almost the same epidemiological character as at its first appearance.

The behaviour of poliomyelitis—once called infantile paralysis, now almost universally spoken of as polio—has been particularly illuminating. Until 1954 polio was the one important infectious disease of advanced countries which had failed to respond to the general improvement of medicine and standards of living. It had, in fact, increased in incidence and severity *pari passu* with those rising standards. To sort out why it did so is an absorbing exercise in epidemiology and incidentally one that exemplifies particularly well the way a disease differs in age-incidence according to the circumstances of the population it attacks.

Poliomyelitis was recognized as a distinct disease fairly early in the nineteenth century, but it was always rare and was not considered an infectious disease. The first *epidemic* of the disease to be described occurred in Sweden in 1887. Since then there has been an irregular but consistent extension of epidemic poliomyelitis to other countries. In general, the more advanced a country in its standards of hygiene and

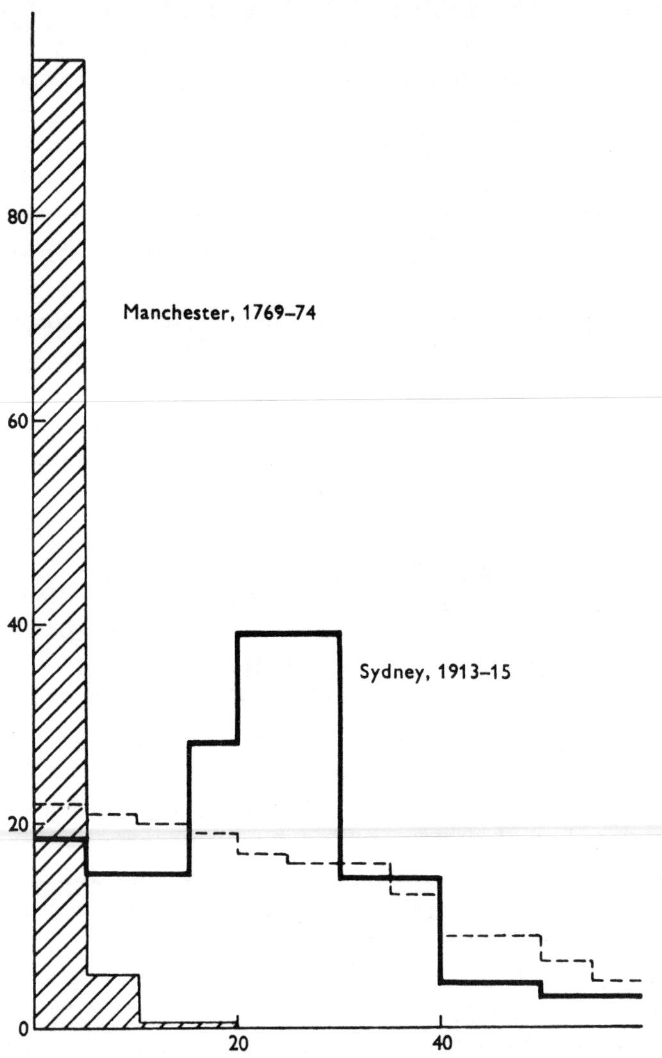

Fig. 7. A comparison of the age-incidence of smallpox in unvaccinated persons (*a*) in Manchester in the eighteenth century, when smallpox was endemic, (*b*) in Sydney, 1913.

general living, the earlier did it experience epidemics of poliomyelitis. For thirty years epidemics were almost confined to Scandinavia, north-eastern United States and Canada, Australia and New Zealand. In recent years epidemics have been more widely distributed, but there is still a general correlation between high-living standards as evidenced, for example, by a low infantile mortality and the frequency of poliomyelitis. There is, however, one striking set of exceptions to this rule: the epidemics which have occurred amongst people in remote island or Arctic communities. Such outbreaks have been observed in Guam, Samoa, New Guinea, St Helena and the Hudson Bay Arctic. The last of these, in two isolated Eskimo communities, was investigated in great detail by Canadian epidemiologists. In these epidemics the brunt of the disease is borne not by infants and young children but by adolescents and young adults. In the Arctic epidemic of 1949 the small Eskimo community concerned was devastated over its whole age range except that *there were no cases of paralysis in infants three years of age or under*. The paralysis rate was 40 per cent, the mortality 14 per cent of the whole population. The only large epidemic of this type which has been accurately reported is one which occurred in St Helena in 1946. A graph showing the age-incidence of diagnosed cases by five-year intervals in the St Helena epidemic may be contrasted with two similar graphs, one for the 1942-43 epidemic on Malta and the other for a typical epidemic in an Australian state (Fig. 8). These three types of age-incidence broadly cover all the epidemics of which we have records.

The first epidemics in Scandinavia, North America and Australia all showed the typical 'infantile paralysis' picture with the major incidence in children under five—the graphs would be almost the same as that of the Malta epidemic. Since about 1920, however, polio epidemics in the advanced countries have always involved older children, especially the five to ten age group, and with the years there has been an increasing proportion of young adults, a group which everywhere shows an abnormally high death-rate. In Scandinavian epidemics in 1950–2 the outstanding feature was the large number of adults with severe paralysis requiring respirator treatment.

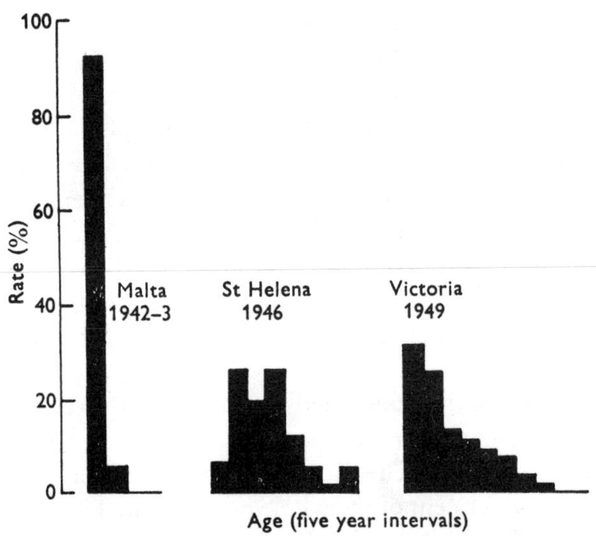

Fig. 8. The age-incidence of poliomyelitis in three epidemics, Malta 1942–3, St Helena 1946 and Victoria 1949. The percentage of the total cases falling in successive five-year age groups is shown.

In many ways the epidemiology of poliomyelitis is the most interesting and illuminating of any infectious disease. To understand it we must first say something about the way infection occurs and how symptoms are produced. The polio virus is far commoner than the paralytic disease that is its most important manifestation. In any large American city the virus can usually be shown to be circulating through the community during the late summer months even when there is no frank epidemic. By appropriate tests evidence of infection in the intestine can be obtained from a small percentage of children—but the percentage is large enough to make it likely that by the time they are ten to eleven years of age almost all children have been infected at least once by the virus. When one considers the difficulty of isolating the virus, it is an extraordinary fact that in any summer when poliomyelitis is present in New York or Chicago, polio virus can be isolated from a few cubic centimetres of city sewage from any of the main out-fall channels. It gives a very vivid realization of the wide extent of invisible infection that goes on in the presence of relatively few cases of paralysis. Since studies on polio infection have been extended to crowded cities of warm climates and low standards of child care—Cairo, Bombay, the native 'locations' in Johannesburg—it has become even clearer how widely the virus spreads amongst infants with a minimal number of paralytic cases.

In Western countries infection is most commonly transferred from child to child at the age when they first tend to mingle in play or other activities with children from other families than their own. Close association between children is necessary, but it is still a matter of some controversy as to the common means of transfer.

Most epidemiologists would probably agree that unnoticed minor contamination of fingers with excreta is the most important factor, with a host of other ways by which food can be contaminated directly or indirectly with faeces occasionally playing a part. The possibility of transfer of the virus by air-borne droplets of saliva is still upheld by some. An episode that strengthened our belief in the 'dirty fingers' theory in Australia was associated with the visit of Queen Elizabeth II to Western Australia in 1954. A polio epidemic was in its early stages and public health authorities were faced with the dilemma of forbidding children from taking part in all public gatherings or running the risk of an explosive flare-up of the epidemic. Their decision was to allow the children to attend the appropriate festivities but insisting that both families and teachers in charge of groups of children should make certain that every pair of hands was washed with soap and water after any visit to the toilet. Many of us were impressed that the incidence of new cases fell during and immediately after the Queen's visit.

Primary infection of human cells may take place either in the throat or in the lining of the intestine. In the majority of children the virus multiplies in one or both of these situations and the body is stimulated to produce antibody against the virus. In a week or two multiplication and excretion of the virus ceases and the episode is over without the child or its parents having noticed any ill effect. In less-fortunate children the virus passes into deeper tissues of the body and if it reaches the nervous system, infection will produce effects ranging from simple headache and fever with some changes in the spinal fluid—non-paralytic poliomyelitis—to paralytic disease which in its severest manifestations may be rapidly fatal.

Once infection has occurred the resulting immunity will ensure that if further infectious material is swallowed there is a much smaller likelihood of its becoming implanted on the intestinal wall, and an even smaller one of its producing paralytic infection. This immunity resulting from *subclinical* infection is the first important key to the behaviour of poliomyelitis as a disease. The second key is the influence of age on the likelihood that infection with the virus will result in paralysis. Closely related to this is the third key, the realization that the type of virus concerned in one epidemic may have a higher intrinsic capacity to produce paralysis than another type of virus. (There is a fourth factor, the existence of three immunological types of polio virus, which may become important but which can be neglected at present.)

If we were to take a whole community of people of all ages, none of whom had ever met the virus of poliomyelitis, and in some way arrange that they were all infected with a single type of virus, we should find that only some of them became paralysed. The highest proportion both of paralysis and deaths would probably be in persons between the ages of fifteen and twenty-five, the smallest would be in infants. We can extend this experiment in imagination to do the same thing with several different types of polio virus, types which differ in their capacity to invade the nerve cells. The expected results can be depicted as a family of curves *A*, *B*, *C*, etc., in Fig. 9.

This graph will allow a simple explanation of the changes in the age-incidence of poliomyelitis. When the common virus in the population has the character depicted by curve *C*, and when the living standards of the community are such that infection spreads easily at an early age, most infections and immunization occur before children are more than three or four years old. All that will be seen is a case or two each

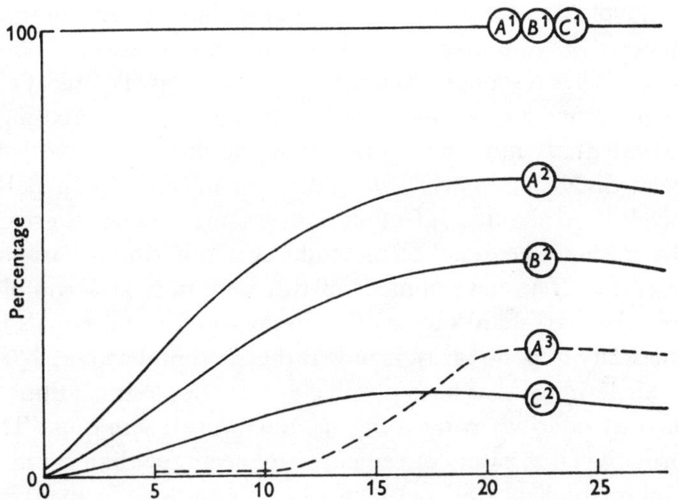

Fig. 9. A graph to indicate the influence of age on the result of infection with poliomyelitis viruses of different invasiveness. If all members of the community are infected (line $A^1B^1C^1$) the incidence of *paralysis* might be as A^2, B^2, C^2 for strains of decreasing invasiveness, while the incidence of *death* at each age for the most invasive strain might be as line A^3.

year in unlucky unusually susceptible infants. When a highly invasive strain of virus like *A* is brought in, a higher proportion of paralytic infection occurs in those individuals who have not previously been immunized by contact with a milder strain of virus. In any community that has been heavily infected with low-grade virus for years, the only susceptible persons are the infants, and we see the Malta type of epidemic.

With every improvement in the standard of living, in cleanliness and toilet training in children, and in housing and sanitation, the proportion of children who escape infection in the 'safe' period of infancy increases. They meet their first infection predominantly just before or just after commencing school and the proportion of paralytic cases—the visible part of the epidemic—is correspondingly increased. Special local features crop up in many, perhaps most, epidemics, but there is no escaping the general over-all character of the picture. Only the explanation we have given can make it clear why, unlike every other infectious disease, poliomyelitis has responded to improving standards of comfort and hygiene not by disappearing but by becoming increasingly prevalent. It must be stressed that the differences we have been discussing concern only the first infection with poliomyelitis. Once first infection is overcome there is a greatly diminished likelihood of the child ever suffering a paralytic infection. The development of this immunity is a complex process that, thanks to the development of new methods for the study of polio virus, is now rather well understood.

Since 1952 it has been possible to carry out tests of antibody against polio virus by using tissue culture techniques. This provides far greater convenience and accuracy than could be obtained when all experiments had to be done in monkeys. Polio virus growing in tissue culture rapidly damages the cells in an easily recognizable fashion. If sufficient antibody is added to the virus the cells go on growing normally. This allows us to tell in regard to each of the three types of polio virus whether or not antibody is present in any human serum in which we are interested. If antibody is present this is presumptive evidence (*a*) that the person providing the serum has at some time been infected with polio virus and (*b*) that he is now relatively or absolutely immune to infection with the corresponding type of polio virus. For the present we can consider only populations in which no vaccination against polio has been carried out. Using such tests it has been found that the proportion of children with antibody increases with age, but the speed of that increase varies greatly from one place to another. In tropical areas with low standards of living, Guam, Mexico, Egypt and India, for example, antibody against all three types of virus was present in 90 per cent of children by the time they were three years old. In North American cities the process of natural immunization was much slower and tended to vary from one type to another.

Such work on natural immunity pointed clearly to the necessity of developing an effective method of vaccination against polio that could safely imitate the dangerous natural process. Very soon it was recognized that virus grown in tissue culture and killed by formalin could be used as a vaccine to protect monkeys against experimental polio. In principle, therefore, it would also protect children against paralysis. Before such a vaccine could be ready for human use, however, many technical problems had to be solved. Obviously the three immunologically distinct types of polio virus had to be included but there was still the question, not yet fully resolved, of which was the best strain of each type. Most important of all was the method to be used in making certain that the vaccine contained no living virus and, on the other hand, in proving that the dead virus had the potency to produce an effective immune response. In one way and another these problems have been solved, and in 1954 the Salk vaccine successfully passed a large-scale experimental trial in the United States. Since then immunization against poliomyelitis has become a standard procedure in most advanced countries throughout the world. It has been highly effective in some countries, notably Australia, Sweden and Denmark, but others have been worried by the occurrence of paralytic polio in a proportion of immunized children. In 1960 there were a number of countries, notably the U.S.S.R., which preferred to use the Sabin live virus vaccine.

Smallpox and polio are only two of the many infectious diseases which have been studied either currently or in the past in relation to age-incidence of infection and death. It is impossible to generalize without bringing in many qualifications, but our two examples at least point the way toward some general principles. The first is that when a disease spreads in a community whose members have not previously encountered it the highest proportion of mild and invisible infections is found during childhood (two to fifteen); infants and older people are more severely affected but in many, perhaps all, infections there is another peak of severity in young adults (fifteen to thirty-five years). The relative importance of the three periods of danger varies with the disease. For reasons which have already been hinted, the workings of immunity make it difficult to compare the mortality from infection in infancy with that in unprotected young adult or elderly subjects. The special vulnerability of the old can, however, be seen in some of the rarer diseases. Psittacosis is very rarely fatal in persons under forty, while in the outbreak of mosquito-borne encephalitis in St Louis (U.S.A.) in 1933, fatal cases were virtually all in the elderly.

There are two groups of infectious disease each due to a wide variety of bacteria with viruses often playing an initiating role. These are the respiratory infections which, when fatal, appear on death certificates as pneumonia, bronchitis and influenza and the various diarrhoeas and dysenteries. If deaths from these are sorted out by ages from some satisfactory set of vital statistics, an interesting regularity emerges. It is evident to everyone that 'physiological time' is not the same as ordinary time. The rate of growth of a human being is highest early in embryonic life and, with some minor oscillations, slows down progressively till it stops about the age of twenty. One can allow for this in a crude way by using a logarithmic time scale from conception to twenty years and thereafter using the fifteen to twenty year value as the standard unit for each further five years of life. Deaths from these 'non-specific' diseases pile up at the two ends of life and to make the numbers tractable it is convenient to use a logarithmic scale. If now we plot deaths from respiratory infections on a graph of this type, we get the form seen in Figure 10. Mortality

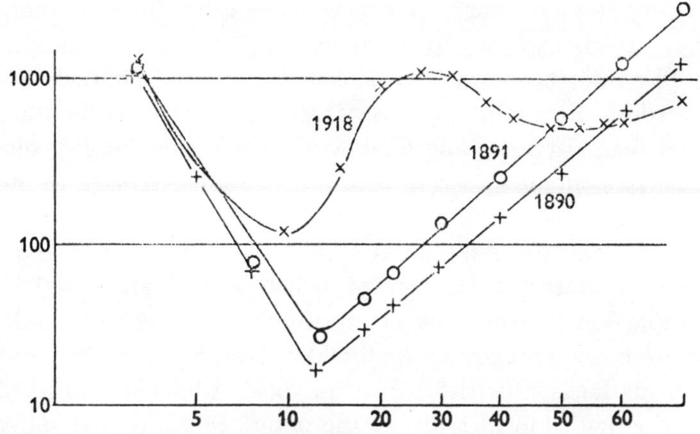

Fig. 10. Mortality rate by ages from respiratory disease in England and Wales—(*a*) In a normal year—1896, (*b*) in an 'ordinary influenza' year—1891, (*c*) in a pandemic influenza year—1918. Mortality rate on logarithmic scale; time in childhood on a logarithmic scale changing to a normal scale at twenty years.

lies along two straight lines which slope down to a minimum at the age of ten to twelve. If there is a real 'prime of life' it must lie in those magic years. There has been only one serious exception to this regularity. In 1918–19 respiratory disease was dominated by the onslaught of a new type of infection, and the graph shows how the resulting young adult peak of mortality is superimposed on the basic pattern.

The second general rule may be put as follows: endemic diseases show a high preponderance of infections in early childhood; the greater the ease with which the infection spreads the younger will be the age of maximal incidence.

The converse is also necessarily true that any infection with its highest incidence in infants is caused by a microorganism widely spread throughout the community. Examples that come immediately to mind are infantile meningitis due to meningococci or influenza bacilli and the staphyloccal skin infections which may be very dangerous amongst premature and newborn infants in hospital nurseries. These are all due to very common bacteria which in the adult have no more than trivial capacity to do harm.

The influence of age on the incidence and character of infectious disease has been very little studied in species other than man. In searching for information on the subject one must be content as a rule with an occasional remark to the effect that calves (or foals) appear to be more (or less) susceptible to some infection than adult animals. It is usually impossible to find definite figures which would allow a real comparison between the susceptibility of young and adult. There is one group of cattle diseases, however, for which the information is sufficient and unequivocal. Adult cattle infected for the first time with any of the pathogenic protozoa suffer much more severely than calves. The best known of these protozoal infections is Texas fever, the American form of an infection by a protozoon (*Babesia*) which, like the malaria parasite, lives in the red cells of the blood. Texas fever received its name, not so much because Texan cattle suffered from it, but because when they came north and were grazed for a week or two with northern cattle the infection passed to these with much more serious effects. It was the northern cattle that suffered from Texas fever, not those from Texas. The disease no longer exists in the United States but in the 1890's it was an important economic problem. Theobald Smith's investigations of this disease is one of the classical pieces of bacteriological work, for his discovery that the cattle tick was responsible for transmitting the infection was the first demonstration of an intermediate vector of disease. He showed that in Texas the disease was endemic and ticks numerous. Calves were inevitably infected within a few weeks of birth, and as a rule they recovered without serious symptoms. In most such diseases recovery does not mean elimination of the parasite from the blood. The calves recovered and remained immune to re-infection and without symptoms, but the protozoa were still in their blood and capable of infecting ticks. When the cattle were brought north for final fattening and slaughter, the infection spread to locally bred animals which had not suffered a mild infection as calves. A high proportion of deaths was the result. In this example economic circumstances demanded exact observations on the mode of infection and the relative susceptibility of different ages. There is no similarly detailed knowledge available about most of the other protozoal infections of cattle, but there are sufficient data to show that the same relative insusceptibility of calves holds for them all.

Several workers consider that the harmlessness of trypanosome infections in wild African antelopes is due, not so much to inherited resistance, as to this quality of youthful insusceptibility. They assume that the young antelope is infected soon after birth when its blood still contains some of its mother's antibody. The combined effect of this antibody and of the natural insusceptibility of the young results in any symptoms being trivial. A partial immunity develops and persists through life. Attempts to imitate this natural process in domestic stock have been partially, but only partially, successful. If there is not to be a high mortality, the calves must be inoculated with a strain of the infection carefully chosen for its low virulence. French veterinarians working in northern Africa have made much use of this method with excellent results.

Although the relative insusceptibility of the young is often important, it is only one aspect of the resistance of native animals to endemic infections. Inheritance undoubtedly plays a major role. Increased capacity to survive infection is of obvious evolutionary advantage and there is both field and experimental evidence that inheritable resistance can emerge rapidly in a susceptible stock. We have already told the story of myxomatosis and the Australian rabbit, while laboratory experiments with mice have pointed in the same direction. By suitable tests and breeding techniques it is possible to derive from a given stock of mice, races with increased resistance or undue susceptibility to some chosen infection. Just what genetic and physiological changes are responsible for increased resistance is unknown, but the experimental observations are indisputable.

It must not be assumed either that all infections are normally milder in young animals. Some, in fact, show quite the opposite. Infections of the intestinal tract seem to show a predilection for the young which is not to be explained solely by their absence of immunity. Diarrhoeal diseases of calves and chickens provide examples similar to infantile dysentery in human infants, and there is a respiratory infection of pigs which is said to produce symptoms only in very young animals. Perhaps the nearest approach to a satisfactory generalization is to say that infective microorganisms find it easier to get into the tissues by natural routes in the young, but that this does not necessarily imply that the resulting infection will be more severe.

We may conclude this chapter with an attempt to interpret these differences in the susceptibility of children and young adults to diseases with which they have not previously come into contact. This problem, like so many others in biology, can be considered from two aspects. One is to look at it from a physiological point of view, and ask whether there is any significant difference in the actual bodily reactions to infection of children and adults. The other is to think along broader lines and inquire whether the differences are indicative of some adaptation directed toward more effective survival in the environment in which man has evolved.

On the physiological side there is very little experimental work to help us. A hint may be drawn from some studies made rather a long time ago on the histamine content of tissues.

The amount of histamine in the lung of the cat increases steadily as the cat becomes older; concomitantly, the reaction of the cat to poisons such as snake venom, which produce much of their effect by the liberation of histamine, becomes more severe as its age increases. For obvious reasons, we cannot obtain the same sort of evidence about children of various ages as about cats, but there are hints that similar results would be obtained. For instance, the lung of a human embryo contains no histamine, that of an adult contains much. Then we have the fact that one of the commonest human manifestations of what we may call 'unnecessary liberation of histamine', hay fever, practically never starts until adolescence, and is most marked as a rule in young adult life. If we may attempt to combine these hints into a rather speculative generalization, it would be to the effect that an adult reacts too effectively against any infection which involves the whole body. In a lesser degree, it is the story of anaphylaxis over again. Histamine liberation, and the whole train of reactions of which it is only one easily recognized index, is very valuable as a response to a localized infection, but when the invading organism or its poisons spread through the body, the response may be excessive and damage rather than aid the tissues in their struggle with the invader. The opposite condition is seen in infants. Surgeons with experience of osteomyelitis, a severe *Staphylococcus* infection of bone, usually occurring in childhood, will tell us that in a baby a severe osteomyelitis may cause very few local symptoms until a large portion of bone has been destroyed. In older children and adults there is fever, pain and all the signs of local inflammation. In the infant, the inflammatory response is too weak, in the adult it is too active for general infections, in the child it is at its best. That, in essence, is our physiological interpretation of the problem we have set.

Whatever may have been the significance of disease for animal evolution in general, there is no shadow of doubt that for the last two or three thousand years man has evolved in an environment saturated with infection. An intense selection of those best fitted to resist disease has been constantly in progress. Only in the last century has it been in any way diminished in severity. We can feel reasonably certain that those characteristics we find in human beings now are the best practical compromise for dealing with infection which lay within the species' power to develop. In all probability the pattern developed was broadly similar to that of other mammals, but ever since urban life developed there must have been a more stringent selection for survival in the presence of a variety of infections than was ever experienced by our prehuman ancestors. If the species was to survive, it was necessary that children should be able to overcome these diseases and develop immunity against them. In a constantly infected environment it was not so necessary that the adults, immune from childhood against the common diseases of their herd, should be relatively insusceptible to diseases they had not previously met. Probably it was more important in the long run that they should possess high resistance to local infections of wounds and abrasions suffered in hunting, fighting and the like.

From both the physiological and the evolutionary point of view we reach the same general picture of what may be called the five ages of man. First the infant, needing protection both by the antibodies transmitted from its mother and by a diet which is uncontaminated by bacteria. Then the child, easily infected, but dealing effectively and rapidly with most infections, and during this period building up a basic immunity to common infections which will last through life. The young adult in full physiological vigour is less easily infected and deals rapidly with local infections, but in the absence of a pre-existing immunity is liable to be overwhelmed by his own too vigorous reactions to general infections. Then when the prime of life is past, immunities persist and the unduly vigorous response to generalized infection disappears. Acute infections are much less frequent and there is usually a long period when, barring accident, the individual is free from anything but minor illness. Finally the gradual degeneration of all bodily function is associated with an increasing susceptibility to non-specific respiratory or gastrointestinal infection in old age.

This is an unduly simplified picture, but the general trends of evolutionary adaptation can only be based on what is on the average good for the species as a whole, not on the detailed experiences of individuals or small groups. What appears a naive simplification may, nevertheless, be a better description of the trend of evolutionary development than any attempt to qualify and particularize. At least it provides a frame within which can be fitted both the epidemiological and, as far as they go, the physiological facts.

CHAPTER XVI

IMMUNITY AS AN EPIDEMIOLOGICAL FACTOR

We have seen that the characteristic age-incidence of an endemic disease is mainly determined by the fact that, after a child has once been infected, he remains almost completely immune so long as he remains in the community. It does not necessarily follow that the first infection alone is sufficient to confer lifelong immunity. There is the important alternative that the first infection supplies a basic immunity which requires to be periodically reinforced by slight reinfections if it is to remain effective. The duration of immunity following a single attack undoubtedly varies very greatly from one type of infection to another. The most clear-cut evidence on the matter is obtained from the experience of isolated island communities. The Faroes in the North Atlantic have been inhabited for some centuries by a civilized Danish community. It was always clear to their physicians that the behaviour of infectious disease in these islands was very different from the usual European experience. The epidemiological happenings tended to be much more dramatic, and it was natural that they should be carefully described. These records, extending over a century and a half, have provided much valuable information for epidemiologists. They showed unmistakably, for instance, that the immunity conferred by an attack of measles was of lifelong duration. After a widespread epidemic in 1781, there was a complete absence of measles from the islands for sixty-five years. When it returned in 1846, the whole population, except for a few greybeards who had been infected in infancy, went down with the infection. The next epidemic appeared in 1875, and on this occasion accurate records showed that only persons who had not been affected by the previous epidemic, i.e. persons under thirty, were susceptible, and that approximately 99 per cent of these had typical measles.

We can hardly call measles a typical infectious disease. It is almost the only one in which, with insignificant exceptions, every susceptible person, irrespective of age, who becomes infected shows the typical symptoms of the disease. The permanent immunity which follows infection with measles is not unique, but it is much commoner for immunity to be temporary and to disappear almost entirely after a variable period if it is not occasionally reinforced. Isolated communities offer many examples of this state of affairs. It can be stated almost categorically that any community which is cut off from the rest of the world for periods of a year or more will, on the arrival of visitors, suffer an epidemic of illness of the feverish cold-influenza type. A detailed study of this phenomenon was made at Spitzbergen in the years just before the Second World War. On the island there was a moderately large resident population engaged in coal mining who, for approximately nine months of the year, were completely isolated from the outside world. During the height of the winter the three communities were also isolated from each other for approximately three months. Soon after the arrival of the first ship in summer an epidemic of respiratory infection, always colds, sometimes 'influenza', would appear and move through most of the population before fading away in the late autumn. During the winter night the population remained free from colds and other infections. With the spring the mutual isolation of communities on the island was broken down and with the mingling of the groups minor outbreaks of mild colds sometimes appeared, but no serious prevalence until the next ship from the outside in July or August.

Such occurrences were naturally commoner in days when rapid transport was less universal. The 'stranger's cold' which affected the islanders of St Kilda off the west coast of Scotland whenever a ship touched the island was commented on by Dr Johnson, and was observed by medical writers several times in the nineteenth century. Similar phenomena are on record about the Faeroes, Tristan da Cunha and others of the proverbially lonely spots on the globe. Antarctic expeditions have suffered similarly with the arrival of a relief ship or on their return to civilization.

These outbreaks of mild infections occur even when the people who bring them appear to be perfectly healthy, and it is characteristic that the strangers are themselves always unaffected. The only possible interpretation is that in any large community there is a constant interchange of bacteria and viruses of low virulence. Apart from an occasional 'cold' they produce no obvious effect. With the discovery in 1960 that a number of different viruses can be responsible for common colds and that these can be cultured by a special technique, we should soon know a good deal more about susceptibility and immunity to colds. There are hints that immunity to any given virus is fairly long-lasting, but there are so many others that any clinical immunity appears to last only a very short time. Undoubtedly a large proportion of infections are subclinical but there is very little to tell us what other factors than partial immunity are concerned in this. During and after the International Geophysical Year 1958–9, a detailed study of respiratory infections in the Antarctic was undertaken and it is to be hoped that the results of this work will be helpful in this field.

In the history of epidemics there is a particularly interesting series of outbreaks which created great alarm and excited much interest in England during the Tudor period—the English Sweats. Although the nature of the microorganism causing the disease is unknown, we can feel reasonably confident that it was a virus, and probably one spread by droplet infection. The behaviour of the disease exemplifies a number of interesting epidemiological points, and it is worth while giving a fairly full account of the five outbreaks. The information is taken almost entirely from Creighton's *History of Epidemics in Britain*, which is the classical and almost the only account of the history of disease in Great Britain.

The disease appeared suddenly in London in 1485, a fortnight after the arrival of Henry VII fresh from his victory over Richard III at Bosworth Field. The symptoms were highly characteristic, a sudden onset with 'great swetying and stynkying with rednesse of the face and all the body and a continual thirst with a great heat and headache.' Death might occur within one or two days from the onset, but many, probably the great majority of those infected, recovered after a brief illness. The infection attracted particular attention by its tendency to affect members of the upper classes of society rather than poorer folk. On its first outbreak in London, two successive Lord Mayors died of the Sweat within a month, as well as several aldermen. In 1517, during the third epidemic, Cardinal Wolsey suffered a severe attack with relapses, but recovered, while in the course of the next outbreak (1528) Anne Boleyn was infected, but apparently had only a mild attack. Although little or no mention is made in contemporary writings of the incidence of the disease on the lower classes or on children, there are distinct implications that both groups were little affected in comparison with adults of the wealthier classes. During the epidemic of 1528 the disease spread to the Continent, and showed a curious tendency to avoid the French and spread freely amongst the German kingdoms. It is said that when the Sweats broke out in Calais, then an English possession, only the English were affected, the French were untouched. Even if the effect of these differences of race, class and age on the incidence of the disease had been exaggerated, there can be little doubt that they were in the direction indicated.

In his discussion of the nature of the English Sweats, Creighton put forward a theory which, with slight modifications, appears to provide an adequate account of the happenings. Henry Tudor invaded England in 1485 with troops, nearly all of whom were French mercenaries drawn from the valley of the Seine. From this region there are records of occasional outbreaks, particularly in the eighteenth century, of a relatively mild infectious disease with symptoms resembling those of the Sweats. Some of the French soldiers were apparently carriers of the virus responsible in France for these mild endemic infections. Most of the others must have been immune.

In England the virus appears to have been present, but in a less virulent form, and spreading easily only under crowded and filthy conditions. When Henry VII's troops reached London, carrying what was for England a particularly virulent strain of virus, two more or less distinct populations were exposed to its attack. On the one hand were the poorer classes, amongst whom there was a high incidence of all infectious disease and an enormous infantile mortality. On this section of the community the Sweats made little impression. No doubt there were fairly numerous cases, but there was a sufficient degree of immunity to prevent the disease being severely felt. The immunity may have resulted from past infection with weakly active strains of the same virus, or possibly with other viruses, having some antigenic similarity to that of the Sweats.

Infectious disease was prevalent enough amongst the upper classes, but there was not the same constant exposure to all sorts of infections as amongst the less fortunate. No immunity was apparently present against the virus, and for this part of the population the Sweats represented a new disease. As far as can be ascertained, the incidence of the Sweats fell chiefly on adults, children being very little affected. Probably adults of all ages were more or less equally liable to the disease, but the chief mortality was amongst those past middle life.

The apparent insusceptibility of the French to infection is obviously to be explained by the supposition that the virus, apparently in a relatively non-virulent form, was widely endemic through the country, but had not previously found conditions suitable for spread outside of France. Whether or not the so-called 'Picardy sweats' of the eighteenth and early nineteenth centuries were the lineal descendants of this endemic French virus will probably never be known. At the present time there are no known infections which can be regarded as of the same type.

If this interpretation of the English Sweats is correct, we have a striking example of how in one country a disease may be endemic and produce a widespread immunity with a minimum of visible disease, while in another country, where such immunization has not occurred, its introduction results in outbreaks of serious and often fatal disease. On a more dramatic scale, it is merely the story of the 'stranger's cold' again.

Of course there is also the converse of the picture by which the stranger coming from a non-endemic region falls an easy victim to diseases which seem to have no effect whatever on the natives. The story of yellow fever in the West Indies or on the West Coast of Africa is the classical example, but that is best left for a chapter of its own. The history of military operations by European powers in the tropics contains many other instances of the same general type right down to the 1939–45 war. In New Guinea malaria and scrub typhus were the two important medical diseases amongst Australian and American army personnel. Neither caused any evident effect amongst the adult native population provided they had been brought up in the endemic areas. Malaria, however, was just as serious for Melanesians from the non-malarious highlands brought down to the coastal regions as for the white Australians in the army.

An interesting wartime episode of similar character took place not in the tropics but in southern Europe. Q fever is a relatively mild disease due to one of the rickettsiae. It is a subject in which I have a close personal interest because after the disease was first defined by Derrick in Queensland the rickettsia responsible was isolated in my laboratory in 1936. The microorganism differs somewhat from typical rickettsiae such as those responsible for classical typhus fever and scrub typhus but like them has the nasty habit of infecting those who work with it in the laboratory. Our five cases (my own attack spoilt a New Zealand holiday!) were the first of a long series of laboratory infections in all parts of the world.

In 1939 it was believed that Q fever was an Australian disease not occurring elsewhere in human beings, though it was known that the same rickettsia had been isolated from ticks in western United States. Then when the Germans gained control of the Balkans in 1941, their troops experienced numerous cases of a fever which they called 'Balkan *grippe*'. During the conquest of Italy by British and American forces they too were afflicted with many cases of a mild fever resembling a typical pneumonia in often showing patches of partial consolidation in the lungs. Eventually it was established that both Balkan and Italian cases were due to Q fever, and since 1944 there has been a steadily increasing list of countries in which the disease is endemic.

The main interest of the disease in the present connexion is that in the areas of Italy where most American cases occurred, most of the local inhabitants showed by blood tests that they had already been infected. The clinical disease was not known amongst the Italians, most of whom had probably had many opportunities to become immunized from childhood onwards.

Another wartime experience that teaches the same lesson was the relatively high incidence of poliomyelitis in British and American troops in the Middle East and in the American occupation forces in Japan. Both regions were reputed to have virtually no poliomyelitis amongst the native populations. This, of course, meant merely that there was almost universal dissemination of infection by polio virus amongst young children with a consequent high degree of immunity. The virus was constantly circulating, and the occasional non-immune soldier from Britain or America was likely to go down with a severe attack when he became infected.

Any practising physician will agree that more than half the minor febrile illnesses which occur in his own family cannot be diagnosed at the clinical level. With the new methods of studying viruses by tissue culture most of them can be shown to be due to infection by viruses involving either the respiratory or the intestinal tracts. The great majority clear up in a day or two and their serious study is only called for as part of an epidemiological research. It is quite unnecessary to know exactly what type was involved as far as care of the patient is concerned. There is one group known as the Coxsackie viruses which are characteristically found in the intestine without producing symptoms, but which may be responsible for a variety of minor illnesses from sore throat to the acutely painful muscular affection called Bornholm disease. In the field of short-lasting intestinal upsets occurring often in small epidemics, a definite bacteriological diagnosis can often be made, the Sonne dysentery bacillus being one of the commonest causes. Most of these outbreaks are not important enough to justify extensive investigation, but from the studies that have been reported one judges that there are still many that are of unknown origin. Some are undoubtedly due to viruses of the so-called ECHO group.

The 'feverish colds' have been more difficult to identify. A limited amount of work with human volunteers carried out during the war indicated that at least three types of viruses were concerned, and in recent years the general adoption of tissue culture methods has greatly clarified the position. A dozen or more virus types have been isolated from such cases, most of them in a group called the adenoviruses. In ordinary medical practice there is no particular need why a definite name should be given to these minor illnesses. They cure themselves in a few days, and if any signs of more severe infection appear one of the sulpha drugs or penicillin will probably deal with the possibility of secondary bacterial infection which is the only danger to be feared. An old-fashioned physician will probably continue to lump these nondescript respiratory infections with influenza, a more up-to-date one will be aware that true influenza can be clearly differentiated, but the knowledge will make no difference to his management of the case.

If we exclude the bigger epidemics of respiratory infection which are mostly due to one of the true influenza viruses, we can feel certain that the trivial fevers are the occasional, clinical manifestations of viruses which normally pass invisibly from person to person, producing a temporary immunity as they do. It is these viruses which provoke the 'influenzas' on isolated islands when ships arrive, and probably the virus of the English Sweats behaved in the same fashion in central France for several centuries. The limitation of this last virus to a single country could probably find modern parallels. Any Australian who arrives in London in winter is very likely to go down with 'influenza' soon after his arrival, even when there is no particular prevalence of influenza in England. Despite increasing speed and frequency of travel, it is probable that each country still has its own pattern of endemic infections, most of them common to other countries, but some with sufficient local individuality to make them mildly dangerous for the foreigner. In regions where the possibilities of intestinal infection exceed the civilized standard, we find mild gastro-intestinal upsets playing the same roles as the catarrhal fevers. The local inhabitants are immune: the stranger suffers.

CHAPTER XVII

THE GENERAL PRINCIPLES OF CONTROL FOR INFECTIOUS DISEASE

It is natural that every community should endeavour to diminish the incidence of infectious disease within its boundaries. Enthusiasts have claimed that it needs only genuine international co-operation and concentrated work to eliminate all serious infectious diseases from the globe. So much has been achieved in this direction even since the first edition of this book was being written in 1937, that something very close to this could now be formulated as a realistic and attainable goal. The advanced countries of the World have already eliminated every one of the plague diseases, plague itself, cholera, typhus, smallpox, malaria and yellow fever. Infantile dysentery, scarlet fever and diphtheria which were responsible for most of the childhood deaths in the nineteenth century are now rare and usually extremely mild. Some of these changes have occurred without any deliberate human action, but well-directed public health action has played a steadily increasing part. Today the principles of control for infectious disease are soundly based on fifty years' experience and can be applied almost as a routine.

Broadly speaking, the endeavour is to protect the *community* against sporadically occurring diseases by measures designed to prevent their transmission, and to protect *individuals* against endemic diseases. The two aims may overlap, especially if a long-term effort is being made to eradicate an endemic disease, but the difference needs to be kept more clearly in mind than it often is.

As examples of the prevention of sporadic infectious disease, we may take one or two examples from Australian experience. There is no plague, cholera, rabies or smallpox in Australia, and the one necessary measure to prevent their occurrence is an efficient quarantine service. On one or two occasions plague has got past the quarantine restrictions, and infected the rats of Sydney or Brisbane. The remedy has been to institute active rat-catching and poisoning measures, with regular bacteriological examinations and to educate the public about the danger of rats and the necessity for grain and food stores to be made adequately rat-proof. So far, such action has been sufficient, although in the case of the New South Wales outbreak it took ten years to eliminate all plague-infected rats.

Typhoid fever still occurs in all states, though it is much less prevalent than in former years. In Australia the 'gold rushes' have always resulted in serious prevalences of typhoid as a natural consequence of the extremely primitive sanitary arrangements which are inevitable in the early 'canvas town' days of a new goldfield. Nowadays, in addition to organized removal of excreta either by water carriage or, in smaller towns, by the most satisfactory method which is within the economic ability of the community, control is exercised over the sanitation of temporary or permanent camps involving more than a small number of habitations. A clean water supply and the prevention of known carriers of the typhoid bacillus being employed in any trade involving the handling of food, complete the defences of the community against typhoid.

As one other example which has not yet been dealt with by the Health Authorities, we may mention psittacosis. In Australia the most important source of infection, young wild parrots, could easily be removed by a simple prohibition of the sale of such birds. In California it was found possible to eliminate psittacosis from the budgerigar-breeding establishments by making bacteriological tests compulsory, and prohibiting breeding from any but healthy birds.

Every disease will present its own problems, but if it is not endemic, then an adequate knowledge of its method of transmission should always allow its virtual or complete elimination from the community—always supposing that an energetic public health service with adequate finance and a sympathetic educated public opinion is available

From both the theoretical and the practical points of view, the control of an endemic disease is much more difficult. The fact that it is endemic means that the social and economic structure of the community is such that no serious barrier to its spread is present. It may be possible when circumstances demand it and finance is available, to produce such a barrier. A classical example was the way in which a serious typhus outbreak was cut short when Naples was occupied by allied troops in December 1943. It was the first great demonstration of the large scale use of D.D.T. as a 'delousing' measure. Naples had been heavily bombed and a large proportion of the population had been living under crowded and insanitary conditions in caves and other types of air-raid shelter. Conditions for the spread of lice (and the typhus *Rickettsia*) were ideal. The problem was to free half a million people of lice within the shortest possible time. The old methods of providing a bath and local treatment for each individual while his clothes were being heat sterilized would have been physically impossible in the time available. Fortunately new techniques for handling D.D.T. to the best advantage had just been developed. With proper equipment a mixture of D.D.T. powder and an inert dust could be blown into the clothes in a matter of seconds and, in the great majority of instances, all body lice would be killed in an hour or two. The American army personnel applying the method were immunized against typhus. Some tons of D.D.T. dusting powder and the necessary blowers were available and for the first time in history a menacing typhus epidemic was abruptly terminated.

Another example of this type of approach was the cleaning up of the Panama Canal zone. Malaria and yellow fever, both mosquito-borne diseases, were the chief hindrance to the construction of the canal. By intense attack on the breeding-places of mosquitoes, by universal screening of houses and by the isolation and treatment of all malaria and yellow-fever patients in mosquito-proof hospitals, both diseases were practically eliminated. In the last ten years new and potent weapons have been developed against malaria in the form of D.D.T. to kill mosquitoes, and new drugs like paludrine and chloroquin to protect people exposed to infection. Since the war indigenous malaria has been eliminated from the continental United States and from the whole of the once notoriously malarious island of Sardinia. In fact, it can be said that nowadays only intelligently directed human effort with adequate financial support is needed to rid any area of malaria.

In 1959 the World Health Organization announced that it was now a realistic objective to aim at the complete elimination of malaria from the world. This may be over-optimistic, especially since the discovery in 1960 that there are probable reservoirs of malarial parasites in the monkeys of south-east Asia, but the extension ofcontrol in South America, India and Africa since 1946 has been very striking.

As long as an area from which malaria has been eliminated adjoins an uncontrolled area, constant vigilance will be needed to maintain a satisfactory control. If, for instance, all sanitary control were withdrawn from the Panama Canal zone, we should probably see malaria rampant again within a few years. In the population who had grown up in the region without experience of infection and with no immunity the intensity and mortality of malaria would almost certainly exceed that of a district which had never been controlled.

This is the great limiting factor in such attacks on endemic disease. Unless a disease can be exterminated from the whole globe, the precautions necessary to prevent its spread must be permanently maintained and incorporated into the social life of the community. If a population has been freed from any disease still prevalent in a country with which it communicates, it is in a peculiarly dangerous position should control ever break down. In the absence of constant immunization by clinical or subclinical infections, a highly susceptible population will arise, and if the infection re-enters at a time when the measure that eliminated it have become ineffective, the resulting epidemic will be abnormally severe.

Under the ordinary circumstances of endemic disease, usually the most that can be done is to provide some measures of individual protection to those who can afford them. When protection from mosquitoes is impossible, prophylactic doses of an appropriate drug will prevent any symptoms of malaria. Venereal disease can be prevented by those who will take the necessary disinfecting precautions after exposure to infection. If only cooked food and boiled water are taken, it will usually be possible to avoid cholera in the most heavily infected region. Other examples will suggest themselves, all on one of two principles, either to take some extra precaution to prevent infection reaching its usual point of entry into the body, or to apply some medicinal remedy which is capable of dealing with the infection before it develops far enough to give symptoms.

Since potent anti-bacterial drugs became available the method of chemoprophylaxis has been widely tested. The use of quinine to prevent malaria had been common practice for many years. During the war quinine was replaced by atebrin with vastly better results and, just as the war ended, two new drugs of extraordinary effectiveness, paludrine and chloroquin, were introduced. A weekly dose of one-tenth of a gramme will protect against infection. This is the only type of chemoprophylaxis that is in wide general use. It might be thought that penicillin or one of the sulpha drugs could be used to prevent all the common bacterial infections, and in one sense this is true. All attempts to do so have, however, encountered important difficulties, and it will be the best to leave their discussion for a separate chapter. In general, we may say that the use of chemoprophylaxis is only applicable to protection of individuals who are known to have been exposed to danger of infection by some specific episode. The pathologist who pricks his finger while doing a post-mortem examination, the patient who is having a severe operation on his lung, the doctor who has examined a patient with pneumonic plague or the sailor who has exposed himself to the danger of venereal disease—any of these can be protected by appropriate treatment with one or other of the modern antibacterial drugs. Widespread protection against the possibility of infection over long periods is not a practical proposition.

If we cannot eliminate a disease or prevent it by suitable drug prophylaxis, as is the case with most of the endemic diseases of civilized countries, the most logical approach is to attempt to develop immunity against the microorganism without the necessity of illness. In a great many diseases, tuberculosis, diphtheria, scarlet fever and infantile paralysis being the most important, the majority of individuals manage normally to acquire immunity by natural infection without symptoms. The logical aim of public health measures should be to ensure that such immunity is obtained by all. It is the most important task of childhood to do so, because, as we have seen, childhood from the ages of two to fifteen is the period at which infections first met are likely to be least dangerous. Unfortunately, we cannot as yet say what determines whether or not an infection takes a clinical or a subclinical form. Common sense, plus a little, but only a little, relevant evidence, suggests that subclinical infections are most liable to occur in children who are well nourished and healthy at the time of infection, and who receive only a small dose of the infecting agent. Such a point of view provides us with certain practical rules for the upbringing of children. From the age of six or even earlier all children should mix freely with others, but in the open air or in well-ventilated school rooms. The aim to be kept in mind is that in the period from six to twelve years children should be infected with and overcome without damage each of the common endemic infections, meeting them in small amount and as far as possible at times when the infective agents are not of abnormally high virulence. Unless this is done in childhood the individual will reach adult life without immunity, and will be more liable to be severely infected when he eventually meets the disease.

Since we cannot ensure that any given child will develop only mild or subclinical infections, attempts have been made to develop an immunity by artificial methods. Such methods are even more urgently called for when adults from one country have to live in another where a disease which they have not previously met is endemic. Actually the greatest stimulus to develop methods of immunization has been military necessity. When European troops were needed in countries where infections like typhoid fever and cholera were endemic, it was necessary to find some means of protecting them.

When it was believed that the development and persistence of antibodies in the blood were wholly responsible for recovery from disease and subsequent immunity, the requirements for prophylaxis seemed to be obvious. What was needed was to provoke the body by some harmless method to produce the proper type and amount of antibody. Even with a more sophisticated view of the complexity of the immune response, it should still be possible to induce the essential features by something less than actual disease. In the most general terms the way in which this is attempted is to prepare antigenic material from the corresponding microorganisms in some non-infectious and non-poisonous form and inject this under the skin. There are two difficulties: on the one hand we must avoid using anything so like the causative microorganism as to be dangerous to the person inoculated, and on the other we must be sure that in preparing the artificial antigen we retain all the qualities which are needed to produce an effective response. It is not infrequent to find that when a bacterium or virus is killed by heat or antiseptics it loses just those antigenic qualities which are required to produce real immunity.

The most effective but also the most dangerous way to produce immunity is to inoculate with living germs whose virulence has been reduced to below the danger level by some suitable method. The very first method used to protect children against smallpox was by the inoculation of virus of undiminished virulence in the form of matter from a natural smallpox pustule on another child. Actually this was probably not quite so dangerous as it sounds, and the results obtained were good enough to make the method relatively popular for fifty years. The inoculation was made into the skin, and an infection starting here was much less likely to be severe than one contracted naturally by inhalation of the virus into the nose or throat. This 'variolation', as it was called, was eventually replaced by Jenner's method of inoculation with cowpox—vaccination. The history of vaccination is full of controversy and misunderstanding; neither Jenner and his supporters nor his opponents showed much of the scientific attitude in their endeavours to prove on the one hand that vaccination was an absolutely certain protection against smallpox, or on the other that it was harmful and dangerous. There is even considerable doubt as to what sort of virus was actually used for vaccination in the years immediately following Jenner's discovery. Recent comparative studies of the viruses of smallpox and cowpox with the standard vaccine virus now used for vaccination show that vaccine virus more closely resembles smallpox than cowpox. We can feel reasonably certain that vaccine virus is a lineal descendant of true smallpox virus which has lost most of its virulence and all its contagiousness, but is still able to provoke the appearance of the same type of antibody.

Vaccination against smallpox can be taken as type of those methods by which living but only slightly virulent germs are inoculated into the body. Methods based on this principle are in rather general use by veterinarians to protect domestic animals against their infectious diseases, but they have not yet been widely applied to the prevention of human infections. In recent years, however, there has been an increasing tendency to make use of such methods. Immunization against yellow fever with living virus is now a widely used and successful procedure. By 1960 other living virus vaccines were being tested on a large scale against polio, measles, mumps and influenza.

The use of a live vaccine against polio was first suggested in 1950 and by 1960 over sixty million persons had been immunized in this fashion, most of them in the Soviet Union. Even in 1960 there was still some reluctance in Western countries to admit the complete safety of the new Sabin-type vaccine. In particular there were lurking doubts on three matters: Could a live vaccine be made quite safe from accidental contamination during manufacture? Could the living virus find ways of mutating to a virulent form? And finally was there any possibility that a strain of virus proved to be harmless to children, might still be capable of provoking paralysis in a few specially susceptible adults? Supporters of the Sabin vaccine have a strong case for saying that these fears are groundless and have been proved so by experience.

No one would doubt that where the objective is to prevent polio in a country of relatively low hygiene where the paralytic disease is confined to children, the live vaccine is ideal. In Russia the vaccine is incorporated into a small sugary confection—the Russian name is translated into American as 'candy pills'—in which the live virus survives indefinitely. Children swallow the sweets with enthusiasm and even theoretically there should be no danger if a child gets away with a bottle of pills and eats them all!

When the vaccine virus reaches the intestine it infects the cells of the bowel wall, concentrating probably on the lymphoid tissue accumulations we call Peyer's patches. Here and in the abdominal lymph glands and spleen, antibody is produced and new lines of lymphoid cells that can react sharply to renewed contact with the virus, laid down. In one way or another, most probably by leakage of antibody and lymphocytes into the bowel, the intestine develops a local resistance to any fresh implantation of virus, a resistance which is not produced by Salk vaccination.

There is abundant evidence that the method is effective in preventing paralysis but not that it is any more effective than the standard three doses of properly prepared Salk vaccine. Cheapness of production and ease of administration are the major advantages of the live vaccine.

Living measles virus can be attenuated by growth in tissue culture of chick embryo cells. In 1959–60 such vaccines were successfully tested in pilot scale experiments sufficiently to justify its use as a practical vaccine. The vaccine is injected under the skin and in seven to ten days' time the child has a minor rise of temperature and usually a scattering of spots if one looks closely enough but no significant symptoms. So far, when such immunized children have been re-exposed to contact with measles patients, they have proved to be completely immune. The only query that needs answering is how long the immunity will last. The vaccine would not be of much real value if its effect waned after a few years and left adolescents and young adults fully susceptible. However, there are now extensive programmes of immunization under way and time will soon give us our answer.

Amongst bacterial diseases, living attenuated cultures have been used for immunization against plague in Indonesia and Madagascar with considerable success. In a later chapter we shall mention the BCG vaccine against tuberculosis, now being very widely used but still not universally acceptable to epidemiologists.

The use of living organisms for immunization on a large scale is always liable to occasional disasters. It may be possible to be quite certain that the germ we intend to inoculate is harmless, but there is always a possibility of some unwanted and harmful microorganism finding its way into the material. Cultures or tissue extracts containing living microorganisms to be used for inoculation cannot be sterilized, so there is no automatic method by which their safety can be assured. In any reputable laboratory every safeguard will be taken to eliminate any possibility of danger from contamination, but all these precautions depend ultimately on human vigilance, which is never infallible. There was a strong prejudice in favour of using immunizing preparations which could be sterilized by some reliable method and therefore were necessarily free from any living microorganisms. History, however, suggests that accidents can happen with either type. On the one hand with live vaccines we have the Lubeck disaster with BCG and the enormous number of American servicemen who developed hepatitis after yellow fever immunization in 1941–2. Killed vaccines produced the 'Cutter episode' when virulent polio virus was somehow present in a Salk-type vaccine and the Bundaberg tragedy referred to earlier where diphtheria toxin-antitoxin became contaminated with *Staphylococci*. Whatever type of vaccine is to be used, it must be prepared and administered with care and precautions that will cover extraordinary accidents as well as routine dangers.

Most killed vaccines in common use are suspensions of killed bacteria in some suitable antiseptic fluid. Vaccines against typhoid and paratyphoid fever and cholera are still in general use, but few people now regard such vaccination as an effective substitute for environmental hygiene. When the British Army was in occupation of the Canal Zone in the post-war years, typhoid fever still produced cases in troops properly vaccinated with the best typhoid vaccine in the world.

A notable development during the 1939–45 war was the use of a typhus vaccine prepared with killed *Rickettsiae* that had been grown in chick embryos. This vaccine plus the use of the new insecticides kept the Allied troops in North Africa almost wholly free from the typhus which at the time was widespread among the civilian populations.

The best known of the killed virus vaccines is the Salk vaccine against polio which has been discussed earlier. This is essentially a solution of the three types of polio virus rendered non-infectious by treatment with formalin. After five or six years of practical experience it is evident that the Salk vaccine properly made is both safe and effective in preventing polio. For some time, however, manufacturers found considerable difficulty in producing vaccine with full immunizing power and particularly in the United States there were some disquietingly large numbers of cases of paralysis in children who presumably were immunized with substandard vaccine.

Killed influenza virus vaccine, the only other commonly used virus vaccine of this type, can best be discussed in a later chapter.

In civil life the only bacterial disease which calls for prevention by vaccines of this type is whooping cough. It took many years of work to produce a really effective vaccine, but there is no doubt that modern vaccines confer a high degree of resistance for several years. Unfortunately it is moderately toxic and very rarely a child may suffer severely as a result of vaccination.

The final type of immunization to be mentioned is that directed against infections which produce symptoms by the liberation of bacterial toxins. Diphtheria is the best-known example but tetanus (lockjaw) which results from infection of wounds with tetanus bacilli is today at least as important. As we have already discussed, immunity to these infections is almost entirely a matter of antitoxic immunity. In the absence of their toxins the bacteria would be harmless. Artificial immunization is therefore logically directed toward provoking the appearance of antitoxin; antibodies against the bacteria themselves are not required. Methods of preparing the toxins of these bacteria have been known for many years, but the toxins themselves are too poisonous to be injected as such. Fortunately there is a simple method by which any bacterial toxin can be rendered non-poisonous, but still capable of provoking the formation of antitoxin. Treatment with formalin will convert the toxins of diphtheria or tetanus bacilli into 'toxoids' with these desirable qualities. The use of tetanus toxoid has been standard military practice for many years and in view of the fact that tetanus, though rare, is also important in civil life, there is a strong trend of opinion that immunization against tetanus should be a standard procedure. Probably the best current practice is to combine diphtheria and tetanus toxoids with whooping cough vaccine as a triple antigen for immunization in infancy. Some laboratories also include Salk polio vaccine in the same mixture.

Amongst these methods of artificial immunization two are of outstanding importance for civilized communities. Vaccination was probably the most important reason for the disappearance of smallpox as an endemic disease from Europe during the nineteenth century. Now that smallpox occurs only on rare occasions, universal vaccination is hardly called for. When smallpox was endemic, a child vaccinated in infancy would probably come into contact with smallpox on several occasions during childhood and reinforce the basic immunity acquired by vaccination. In the absence of such reinforcement either by contact with the disease or by revaccination, immunity fades and vaccination in infancy is of little significance when first contact with smallpox occurs thirty or forty years later. Under modern conditions, vaccination is best regarded as an emergency measure to be used whenever danger from smallpox threatens, not as a semireligious ritual to be performed on every infant.

Immunization against diphtheria has been just as effective and seems likely to remain necessary indefinitely. It will be best, however, to leave its story to a later chapter.

CHAPTER XVIII

THE ANTIBACTERIAL DRUGS

When the first edition of this book was being written the first news of the sulpha drugs had just appeared in the medical literature. At the time it appeared that this discovery, however important from the point of view of treatment, would have no significant bearing on the natural history of infectious disease and no mention was made of the sulphonamide drugs. Since 1940, however, the whole approach to infectious disease has been dominated by successive chemotherapeutic triumphs. It is not too much to say that at the present time no acute infection occurring in a previously healthy individual will result in his death if he reaches a well-equipped hospital before irreparable damage has been done to his tissues. The only exceptions are the two virus diseases, smallpox and yellow fever, and a rare bacterial disease, melioidosis. The future of infectious disease will be in an environment where sulphadiazine and penicillin are important factors influencing the survival of the microorganisms—a new ecology opens up, and it is from this point of view that this discussion of the new drugs will be undertaken.

Domagk discovered prontosil, the first sulpha drug, by following an idea that was a guiding principle for Ehrlich, that dyes stain living cells by much the same process as certain drugs kill them. Prontosil was a red dye that killed streptococci, but it was soon found that the effective part of the compound had nothing to do with its colour. The modern sulpha drugs, sulphadiazine, sulphamezathine and the rest, are all derivatives of sulphanilamide, which to a near approximation is the uncoloured half of the protonsil molecule.

Penicillin came into practical use in medicine by a rather roundabout route. In 1922, Fleming saw a mould colony on a bacteriological plate that appeared to be dissolving adjacent colonies of staphylococci. Following up this chance observation he showed that this particular mould, a species of *Penicillium*, produced something which diffused into surrounding fluids and had a very strong action in preventing the growth of certain bacteria. Only half-hearted attempts were, however, made to use this substance for the treatment of human infections. For several years it found a technical use in bacteriological laboratories as an aid to the isolation of bacteria like the whooping-cough bacillus which are insensitive to its action. Most bacteria in the mouth are incapable of growing in the presence of penicillin, and the standard method for confirming a diagnosis of whooping cough depends on the use of a plate of nutrient medium containing an appropriate amount of penicillin. If a child with suspected whooping cough is allowed to cough on to the surface of such a plate, thousands of bacteria of various sorts will be showered on the plate. The whooping-cough bacillus is, however, almost the only type capable of growing into visible colonies, and even if only a few are present they will be readily recognized.

An important stimulus to the further study of penicillin was probably provided by Dubos's work in America. He was a French bacteriologist who conceived the idea of using bacteria from the soil to destroy disease-producing bacteria. His early training had been as an agricultural chemist and he had an intimate knowledge of the enormous variety of bacteria in ordinary soil. By a special technique he isolated a bacterium from soil dug from a cranberry bog which produced something that destroyed pneumococci. Then he went on to isolate the responsible chemicals, gramicidin and tyrothricin. These were extremely active in killing pneumococci and other bacteria in the test-tube, but they were too toxic to be of much use in treating human disease. Dubos's experiments created great interest amongst bacteriologists, and suggested that other products from microorganisms might be even more effective. At the beginning of the 1939 war, Florey at Oxford was looking for a project that might offer a significant contribution to the war effort. He knew that in addition to Dubos's substances, anti-bacterial agents had been observed in cultures of Fleming's mould and of the bacterium *Pseudomonas pyrocyaneus*. He almost literally tossed up to decide on which to study, and chose penicillin with the result that is known to everyone. A method of producing and purifying penicillin was worked out and its effectiveness in treatment demonstrated. The technical problems of large-scale production were sent across the Atlantic for solution, and penicillin in quantity was ready to play its part in the liberation of Europe.

Once penicillin had proved its quality a furious search began for similar products of fungi and bacteria which might have a wider range of action. Most of the significant discoveries have been made by the American drug firms or by workers closely associated with them. About twenty of these 'antibiotic' drugs have come into use in medicine and there are hundreds more which for one reason or another have been judged unsuitable for practical use.

Practically all have been discovered by purely empirical means but as they became available, biochemists and bacterial physiologists found much to interest them in trying to elucidate their structure and mode of action. In the case of penicillin, the first and still the best of the antibiotics, a great deal is known and without going into details of chemistry, it is possible to describe the process in a way that exemplifies some of the general principles of drug action on bacteria and allows us to see the sort of problems that are going to arise in the new natural history of infectious disease.

Bacteria are living organisms whose substance and chemical activities are very similar to those of animal cells. Nevertheless, on top of this background of similarity every type of cell has individual qualities and processes of its own. An antibiotic is essentially a substance which will interfere seriously with some vital function of the bacterial cell which is either not present in or of much less importance for human cells. It must not attack any of the processes common to all living cells but only something that is special to one or other group of disease-producing microorganisms. Only with such substances are we going to be able to give doses sufficient to kill or 'paralyse' bacteria in the body without producing serious damage to the patient's cells.

Penicillin affects only the processes that are concerned in building the cell wall of those bacteria, like pneumococci and staphylococci, against which it is effective. The cell wall, as was mentioned earlier, is a very important part of the bacterium and only under special highly abnormal conditions can a bacterium remain alive without its rigid support. The bacterial wall contains several components not found in any animal body including abnormal amino-acids, right-handed in structure instead of left-handed, and a compound, muramic acid, which in some ways resembles a common component of mammalian cells. Penicillin interferes with the process by which these and some other compounds are brought together to make the essential fabric of the cell wall.

One of the most interesting aspects of penicillin to those who worked with it in the early days was that it had no action on a bacterium that was not growing, only when growth commenced did it become susceptible. The concentration of action on the cell wall supplies the answer. If growth occurs and the cell wall cannot be built, the bacterium must either burst or be exposed to harmful influences of the environment without its normal protection. The other unique quality of penicillin, its harmlessness—at least when first administered—to all the cells of the body is also readily understood since it interferes with a bacterial function quite unlike anything that occurs in the human body.

Not all antibiotics act in this fashion. Chloramphenicol and the tetracyclines interfere with protein synthesis generally, but apparently at some points in the process that are characteristically bacterial and absent or unimportant in human cells. A good antibiotic must necessarily have this specialized type of action and herein lies its major weakness. Bacteria are labile organisms capable of mutation in many directions and since an antibiotic is never directed against any of the basic living processes but against some specialized aspect thereof, there must always be the possibility of a variant appearing which has some alternative way of fulfilling the same chemical requirement.

The story of what has happened to the common staphylococci since the advent of penicillin is enlightening. Nowadays it is rare for staphylococcal infections arising in hospitals to be due to organisms sensitive to penicillin. Most of them are due to staphylococci which can produce an enzyme destroying penicillin and so are relatively immune to its action. It is something of a mystery where these organisms come from. In all probability they have always been present as a small proportion of the population of staphylococci but only found an opportunity to flourish when the environment in which a hospital *Staphylococcus* had to live contained penicillin almost as a matter of course. If one 'trains' a *Staphylococcus* to grow in gradually increasing amounts of penicillin, the descendants will eventually become highly resistant to its action. This is not due to production of the enzyme which splits penicillin but to some type of modification of the wall-building process in the organism. Conceivably such resistant strains could be a danger in hospital practice but in fact they are rarely observed. The important danger is the *Staphylococcus* that produces the enzyme penicillinase capable of breaking down the drug and so rendering it useless as a thereapeutic agent.

There are two ways of dealing with the situation. The first is to find or synthesize a penicillin which is not destroyed by penicillinase. In 1960 British chemists reported a successful move in this direction. Penicillin is not a very large molecule but its construction is complex and subtle. Its formula is known and very small amounts have been synthesized by a rather inefficient process that could never be a commercial proposition. Short of complete synthesis, however, there are two ways by which penicillin can be modified. As produced in culture 'penicillin' is a mixture of substances with a common chemical nucleus whose name can be abbreviated to 6–APA with one or other of several possible side chains. By incorporating appropriate chemicals like phenyl-acetic acid in the culture fluid we can ensure that the great bulk of the penicillin produced has that particular side chain which experience has shown to give the most active penicillin. This has been standard practice for many years but in 1959–60 a more directly chemical approach has appeared in the form of a method of producing the nucleus 6–APA itself. This could then be united to chemical groups of many different types. Amongst these is the side chain 2–6 dimethoxybenzoic acid, which gives rise to a penicillin that is resistant to penicillinase. As penicillins go this is a rather weak antibiotic which must be used at about twenty times the concentration of standard penicillin that is adequate to prevent growth of a non-resistant *Staphylococcus*. Even so it is a highly active therapeutic agent and already accounts of its successful use in otherwise intractable cases of infection by resistant staphylococci have been reported in the medical journals.

The older approach was to treat such infections by some other antibiotic such as tetracycline which is not susceptible to penicillinase and which influences some other aspect of bacterial chemistry. These substances can, however, also produce or uncover resistant types and probably the commonest test called for in a hospital bacteriology department today is to find which of the available antibiotics a given culture of *Staphylococcus* is sensitive to. Fortunately the manufacturing drug houses have managed to stay just one or two steps ahead in this race and it is still almost unknown to find a *Staphylococcus* that is resistant to *all* the antibiotics.

Development of resistance to an antibacterial drug is not confined to staphylococci or to the antibiotics.

Around 1944 some very large groups of men in American

Navy establishments were given a daily dose of sulphadiazine with the object of preventing meningitis and streptococcal infections during the winter. In the 1943–4 season the results were most encouraging—there was a marked reduction in the rates for both types of infection. Next winter the use of sulphadiazine was extended to cover many more groups of men. Soon it became evident that something was going wrong, there were many more severe streptococcal infections than there ought to have been, and had it not been for the availability of penicillin there would have been a considerable number of deaths. These streptococcal quinsies and the like were due to streptococci resistant to sulphadiazine. In fact there was evidence that they produced more harm in people taking the supposed prophylactic course than in those who had not.

Findings of this sort indicate the nature of the dangers of mass chemoprophylaxis referred to in the last chapter. Obviously we must avoid converting a microorganism that we can readily handle with available drugs into one which is still a disease-producer but insusceptible to control by standard measures. The conditions under which this change is likely to occur are worth thinking about. In the first place we can feel certain that the drug does not in any strict sense *cause* the appearance of resistant variants. Microorganisms are constantly undergoing mutation. If we take an ordinary culture of bacteria, the turbid fluid that results from the growth of a single parent individual, we can show that it contains in each cubic centimetre about a thousand million bacteria. By suitable methods we can find that say twenty only of those thousand million bacteria are resistant to an amount of penicillin which will prevent the growth of all the others. If we now grow some of these few resistant bacteria in the presence of that amount of penicillin and again analyse the thousand million descendant bacteria, we find amongst these perhaps a hundred or so which can withstand a much larger amount of the drug. By this method of growing bacteria with progressively increasing amounts of penicillin, we favour the multiplication of those variants which, essentially by chance, happen to be resistant to penicillin. Resistant variants are always appearing but they can only replace the ordinary type of the species when there is some special *survival value* in that resistance.

If in the course of treating a patient with penicillin the original infecting organism is replaced by a resistant variant, this is no more likely to spread to another person than the original form. On the other hand, suppose that everybody in the community is sucking penicillin lozenges and a highly resistant *Streptococcus* initiates a throat infection. This organism will obviously be at an immense advantage over an ordinary *Streptococcus* as far as spread through this particular community is concerned. If it has any capacity at all to spread and induce throat infections it will become the dominant epidemic type. So far no such appearance of penicillin-resistant streptococci in epidemic form has been described, but something of the sort has occurred in regard to staphylococci in hospitals where many or most surgical patients receive penicillin either for curative or prophylactic reasons.

It is a good general rule that chemoprophylaxis should never be used on a universal scale unless we are quite certain—and in fact we never are certain—that the microorganisms concerned cannot develop resistance to the drug. Prophylactic use of antibacterial drugs is wholly legitimate when it is designed to protect an individual for a short period against a specific hazard. One of the great advances made possible by the advent of antibiotics has been in the surgery of lung tuberculosis. It is now common practice to remove a diseased lobe of the lung under protective cover of streptomycin and penicillin injections. Twenty years ago the operation was technically possible, but would often have been followed by fatal tuberculous and septic infection of the region involved in the operation. Now any bacteria liberated from the infected tissues during handling by the surgeon are dealt with by the antibiotics circulating in the blood and do no harm.

Another important practical application of the same principle is seen in the penicillin injections which are, or should be, always given when a person with rheumatic heart disease is having teeth extracted. A heart valve damaged by rheumatism is liable to be infected by an otherwise harmless *Streptococcus* that tends to lurk around the apex of an unsatisfactory tooth. Extraction will nearly always result in a little flush of streptococci into the blood, harmless in a healthy person, but if some of them lodge on a chronically injured heart valve a fatal disease, subacute bacterial endocarditis, may be initiated. The risk can be obviated by an injection or two of penicillin on the day of the dental operation.

There are circumstances when it is practical and necessary to use large-scale chemoprophylactic measures. If a few cases of meningococcal meningitis appear in a military establishment or a residential school, investigation will almost certainly show that many other members of the community are carrying the organism in their throats. If every person is given a daily dose of sulphadiazine for a period of two or three weeks, actual experience in the past would indicate that the carrier rate will fall and cases cease to appear. The *Meningococcus* is one of those organisms which always produces many harmless throat infections for every instance in which it invades the body and produces illness. If the proportion of carriers can be reduced below 5 per cent of the population concerned then we can be reasonably certain that no frank cases of disease will arise. Ideally it would be desirable to keep a constant watch on the carrier rate and provide short prophylactic courses whenever a significant rise became evident. So far there has been no record of any variant of the *Meningococcus* resistant to sulpha drugs appearing in the course of an epidemic. If we were concerned only with the *Meningococcus*, sulphadiazine tablets could be given indefinitely, but other organisms like the streptococci we have already mentioned have to be considered, and like all measures of this sort it should be continued only long enough to procure the desired result. It is an excellent rule in practical epidemiology, as in clinical practice, to adopt the motto: 'When in doubt, don't do it.' In other words, the conditions are so complex that any action to affect one aspect of the situation may have unexpected results on other aspects. If some procedure has been thoroughly tested in the past, it must be used as circumstances require, but any new procedure must for some time at least be applied only in the form of the *controlled trial*.

The controlled therapeutic trial is perhaps the most practically important aspect of modern medical science. In principle the approach is simple. Experiments in animals or some accidental observation in human patients, suggest that some drug or other treatment would be of value to patients with a certain disease. To test it we collect a group of patients, treat half of them with the new drug, half with whatever is the best current treatment of the disease. We tabulate how many die in each group and how long it takes the survivors to get well. The answer should then be obvious.

In fact, things are vastly more complex and very special caution is needed in designing, carrying through and interpreting such trials. No two patients with a given disease are wholly similar unless they are two identical twins. In general they will differ in sex, age, bodily build, past or concurrent illnesses, intelligence and personality. The statistician will insist that the two groups to be compared must be similar in every relevant quality except for the actual procedure under test. In practice this means a large number of patients and allocation to test or control groups by some completely unbiased method.

Where a drug is being tested for its action in controlling some acute infection, a trustworthy answer can usually be obtained without much difficulty. The time taken for the patient's temperature to return to normal is probably the usual criterion. It is objective enough to be trusted and suitable for statistical analysis when the groups are being compared. When penicillin first became available, very few controlled tests were needed to show that it was supremely effective in dealing with streptococcal or pneumococcal infections. The greatest difficulty in such tests was often the ethical one that as soon as a doctor in charge of desperately ill patients is convinced that his new drug is effective, he will naturally wish to give the drug where it is most likely to save life, without regard to whether it will ruin his trial or not.

In many clinical trials the result is not a matter of life and death and there is less difficulty in adhering to the planned design. A new difficulty also involving the doctor-patient relationship however emerges. It is not always easy for a patient to be sure whether he feels better than he did a week ago, or for a doctor to judge whether his patient is improving or not. If either patient or doctor is enthusiastic for any reason about a new treatment both are likely to be more definite about its benefit than if they were sceptical. To avoid this possibility the 'double-blind' therapeutic trial is now almost standard for any comparison which is expected to show relatively small differences between the new treatment and the old.

As before the available patients are divided into two randomly selected groups. If the drug to be tested is to be given in the form of a white tablet taken three times a day, a large supply of these tablets, sufficient to cover the whole trial, is prepared. An equally large supply of identical appearing white tablets, *without* the drug, is also prepared. The statistician in charge of the trial arranges with the dispenser that each patient receives a regular supply of tablets of the right type—with or without the drug—but that neither the patient nor his doctor knows which he is receiving. It is the doctor's business simply to put on record his observations or impressions of each patient at appropriate times throughout the trial period. His ignorance of what is being taken will eliminate any bias for or against the drug. Only when the trial is finished is the code broken and doctor and statistician together can assess the results and their significance.

An almost identical procedure should also be used when a new method of preventing disease is being tested. Here the difficulties may be even greater than in a therapeutic trial. On more than one occasion we have mentioned vaccines which are widely used but which have never been rigidly proved to be effective. The largest scale trial of a method of prevention that was ever made was the controlled test of Salk vaccine during 1954 in the United States. In the 'double-blind' section of the trial, 200,745 children received the vaccine and 201,229 were given tissue culture fluid without vaccine. When the results were sorted out and all the diagnoses checked, there were 88 cases of polio in the control series (0.044 per cent) compared with 19 (0.009 per cent) in those vaccinated.

An immense effort was put into this particular test because of the certainty that once it was believed by people generally that the Salk vaccine was effective it would never be possible to organize a further trial. This holds to some extent for all types of preventive or curative procedures which are directed against fatal or crippling conditions. It is all-important that no new vaccine or drug should ever come into use without a trial which is so designed as to give an answer that is unequivocally acceptable to any competent medical statistician and to any physician experienced in the disease being treated.

Trials are concerned only with short-term results. Sometimes the long-term effects may be quite different. The first trials of isoniazid in tuberculosis gave dramatically good results, but the rapid appearance of resistant organisms required a new assessment within less than a year. There is much discussion in 1960 as to whether or not Salk vaccination will influence the movement of poliovirus through the community and whether and when booster injections should be given to children immunized in infancy. Everything effective that we do in medicine will in one way or another have a repercussion on our daily lives.

We are moving into a new world in which the old natural

history of disease is being rapidly distorted, and we must be always alert to look beyond the immediate effect of some new procedure to see what the logical outcome of its large-scale use will be. Antibacterial drugs, like measures to prevent the spread of infection or immunization procedures, are potent weapons, but to the biologist they are merely new factors introduced into the environment within which the micro-organisms of infection must struggle to survive. We must never underestimate the potentialities of our enemies.

Part V

SOME IMPORTANT INFECTIOUS DISEASES

CHAPTER XIX

DIPHTHERIA

It is appropriate that we should take diphtheria as the first infectious disease for a more detailed discussion. Other diseases are more important causes of death, and some have been just as carefully and extensively studied as diphtheria, but no other common disease has been so successfully studied. From research on diphtheria there have been developed a satisfactory method of treating the disease and an even more effective way of preventing its occurrence. In the course of research directed towards these ends, a third important gain has been made, perhaps of more real significance than these spectacular successes. We have gained a relatively detailed knowledge of the epidemic behaviour of the disease. Studies on diphtheria have in fact done more than anything else to provide a scientific basis for epidemiology. For other diseases we have to work largely on indirect evidence if we are to provide a connected account of their behaviour. For diphtheria direct evidence is available.

The history of diphtheria is of great interest. Until we reach the beginning of the nineteenth century it is practically impossible to diagnose the nature of the various throat infections which are mentioned in medical writings. The great majority of them were probably of streptococcal nature, including typical scarlet fever and all the various forms of tonsilitis and quinsy. Children certainly died of 'croup', a general term for any form of obstruction to breathing, and according to modern experience the only commonly fatal form of such obstruction in the larynx is laryngeal diphtheria. One can justifiably assume that diphtheria was present, but was usually mild and unrecognized except when the infection spread into the larynx and produced fatal 'croup'.

Early in the century definite epidemics of what we can recognize as diphtheria occurred on the Continent, especially in France, Norway and Denmark. The disease was recognized as an infectious one and given its present name by Bretonneau in 1826, but no more than a few stray cases were recognized in England for thirty years. In 1858 there was a sudden widespread appearance of severe diphtheria in England, and within the year it had spread to almost every part of the globe. Even Australia was infected before the end of 1858. The first Victorian cases were in October 1858, and Tasmania experienced the epidemic in January 1859. The small and isolated settlement in Western Australia remained free from diphtheria until 1864, when numerous cases occurred.

Wherever it appeared at this time, diphtheria was recognized as something outside the previous experience of physicians. The spreading grey membrane on the throat, the high fatality and the common appearance of paralysis of the muscles of the palate some time after infection were all new. Nevertheless, if our criteria for deciding whether a disease is endemic or non-endemic are correct, diphtheria in 1858 was not a new disease. From the beginning it was a disease of childhood, not of adult life. The Australian statistics show that diphtheria was more exclusively a disease of young children in the 1860's than in the 1920's. Even before diphtheria appeared, children must have been developing immunity against the responsible germ, and in 1858 those over ten years were nearly all possessed of sufficient immunity to avoid infection. Since 1858 typical diphtheria has been present in all the civilized communities of temperate climates. Its incidence and severity have shown the inevitable ups and downs. There was a second period of high mortality in Europe around 1890, then a steady fall for about thirty years with a distinct recrudescence of activity in Europe at least, in the period 1927–31. A very sharp increase in the incidence and severity of diphtheria occurred in Germany and the European countries under German occupation during 1941–5, Norway and the Netherlands being particularly affected. This contrasted sharply with the steady fall in diphtheria in Britain during the same period that was associated with, and probably resulted from, a strenuous effort to immunize all children in the country. Since the end of the 1939–45 war immunization has been almost universal practice, and few reports of serious outbreaks of diphtheria have appeared.

As soon as the foundations of bacteriology had been laid by Pasteur and Koch, attempts were made to isolate bacteria from the throats of patients with diphtheria. In 1882 it was observed under the microscope that there were numerous bacilli of an easily recognized shape in the grey 'false membrane' which forms on the tonsils in diphtheria. Cultures of these bacilli were isolated without much difficulty a year later. It did not take very long to show that the diphtheria bacillus was the immediate cause of diphtheria, but there was still much to be done before any possibility of controlling the disease could be thought of.

As soon as a bacterium has been shown to be responsible for an infectious disease, it is natural to ask: 'How do the infecting bacteria make the patient sick?'; and it is equally natural to answer: 'By setting free some poison into the blood or tissues.' So Roux and Yersin at the Pasteur Institute set about to look for such a poison from the diphtheria bacillus. They kept cultures growing in a nutrient fluid mixture for a week or more in the hope that any poisonous substances would pass from the bacteria into the fluid. To get rid of living bacteria they then passed the fluid through a filter of fine unglazed porcelain. The clear liquid from the filter contained no bacteria, but if they injected some of it into a guinea-pig the animal died with symptoms almost the same as those which followed an injection of living bacteria. Diphtheria toxin had been discovered.

The next step, the preparation of antitoxin which could render the toxin harmless, was made by a German and a Japanese bacteriologist working together in 1890. We have already discussed the relation between diphtheria toxin and antitoxin in chapter VIII. There we were concerned only with the general nature of the immunity responses of the body, and diphtheria antitoxin provided a useful example of a well-studied antibody. To those concerned with diphtheria as a disease, these discoveries were of much more immediate practical importance. Their problem was to interpret the significance of toxin in causing the symptoms and complications of diphtheria, and to assess the value of antitoxin as a means of preventing the action of the toxin on the body. We shall not go into the history of how these things were done. It is simpler to take the long process of investigation and discovery for granted, and give a brief account of the accepted present-day views in regard to the part played by toxin and antitoxin in diphtheria. It is always dangerous to think that knowledge about any subject is almost complete. There are probably surprises in store for us even about diphtheria, but it is almost unthinkable that the main outlines of our present teaching about diphtheria will ever be seriously changed. Put as concisely as possible, this teaching is that the local and general symptoms of diphtheria are all due to the action of the toxin, and can be prevented by antitoxin given early enough in the disease, and further that individuals become immune to diphtheria only by the development of antitoxin in their blood and tissue fluids. At one period it seemed that we might regard the diphtheria bacillus as just something which produced diphtheria toxin. Any other properties it might have were of no practical importance. We shall see later that there are some important aspects of diphtheria unrelated to the action of toxin or antitoxin, but for the present we shall keep to the main theme of the importance of toxin and antitoxin.

When the problem of how diphtheria could be controlled was being studied from 1920 onwards, it was necessary to determine the natural history of diphtheria bacilli within the human community, what proportion of children carried the germs without symptoms and to what extent children of different ages had already developed immunity. That stage has been passed in most countries, but essentially similar information is needed whenever an unexpected outbreak of diphtheria occurs. 'Swabbing' and 'Schick-testing', two terms not now so familiar to newspaper readers as they were thirty years ago, are the two methods mainly used to obtain such information. Swabbing merely means the taking of a sample of mucus from the back of the throat on a piece of sterile cotton wool. The material is then suitably cultured to see whether virulent diphtheria bacilli are present. Swabbing is mostly carried out when diphtheria is prevalent, and under these conditions it is usual to find from 2 to 5 per cent of apparently healthy children with bacilli in their throats. In normal times, the proportion may be smaller, but even so, when we consider that these 'carriers' probably retain the germs in their throats only for a week or two, it seems likely that practically all schoolchildren have diphtheria bacilli in their throats during at least one period each year.

Even in the days before immunization not more than 5–10 per cent of children ever suffered from clinical diphtheria, so that we can feel sure that on most occasions the presence of diphtheria bacilli in the throat does not produce the disease. If we are to understand the results of these repeated harmless contacts with the germ, we must consider what is found by the use of the Schick test. The Schick is merely the simplest method of finding out whether or not there is diphtheria antitoxin in the blood. A very weak solution of toxin is infected into the child's skin. If there is sufficient antitoxin in the blood, the toxin is neutralized and produces no result. The Schick test is negative. In the absence of antitoxin, the injected toxin damages the skin cells, and a deep red patch of superficial inflammation appears after two or three days—a positive Schick test.

In Fig. 11 is a graph of the results from a famous investigation made in New York before the widespread use of artificial immunization. This is what could normally be expected from the natural spread of diphtheria bacilli in a crowded city area. It shows the proportion of individuals at different ages who are Schick negative, that is, whose blood contains antitoxin. It will be seen that in infants the proportion is very low and steadily increases with age. This gradual appearance

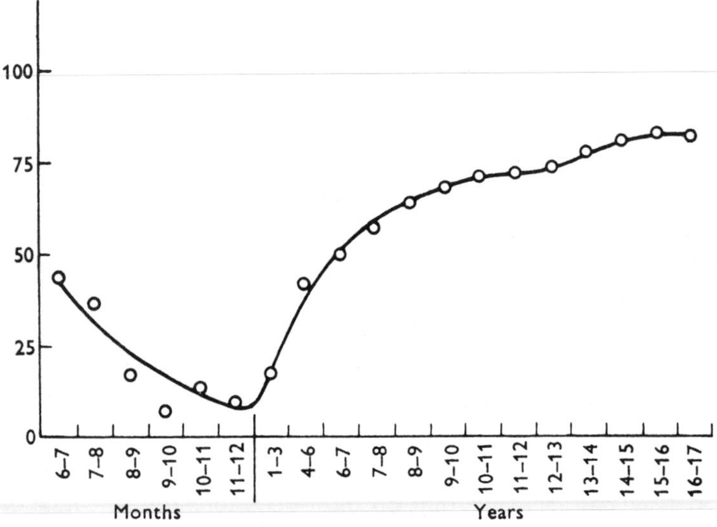

Fig. 11. The development of immunity to diphtheria during childhood. The percentage of infants and children at various ages who are Schick-negative, i.e. immune to diphtheria. The immunity of infants is derived from their mothers, and disappears during the first year of life.

of antitoxin is the commonest result of the entry of diphtheria bacilli into the throat. With each contact the bacilli liberate a little of their toxin and the body responds by the formation of antitoxin each time a little more efficiently than the last. In all probability diphtheria results only when a child receives either a very large dose of bacilli or a particularly virulent strain before he has had an opportunity to develop an adequate degree of immunity by more harmless contacts. Very wide experience has shown that children who are Schick negative practically never develop diphtheria. They have already developed sufficient antitoxin to render even a large dose of bacilli incapable of doing any serious damage. It is amongst the children giving a positive Schick test that diphtheria occurs.

It will be easier to understand why there is this difference in susceptibility if we look into what happens when a large dose of virulent diphtheria bacilli lodges on the tonsils of a susceptible Schick-positive child who has not previously developed antitoxin. The germs multiply first on the surface, but very soon they get into the lining membrane of the throat. Toxin is produced, whose first action is to kill the adjacent cells and any phagocytes in the vicinity. This provides dead tissue in which the diphtheria bacilli can grow and produce more toxin. More and more damage is done, and soon there is a grey patch of dead tissue over the tonsils and spreading over the palate. There are millions of bacilli here actively producing toxin which now leaks into the blood, causing the general symptoms of diphtheria. To overcome the process, antitoxin is required, either produced by the body or provided by the doctor's injection of ready-made antitoxin.

In a Schick-negative child the diphtheria bacilli may invade the tissues to a certain extent, but the damage they can produce is trivial. The antitoxin in the blood is there to protect the tissues from toxin, so that no convenient mass of dead tissue is produced in which the germs can multiply freely. With the toxin rendered impotent, it is usually easy for the ordinary tissue defenders, the phagocytes, to deal with the invasion. Even if with particularly virulent diphtheria bacilli a local foothold is established and the available antitoxin overcome, the partially immune child can very rapidly produce more antitoxin in response to the stimulus of infection, and only a mild attack results.

If this is true, it follows that to prevent diphtheria all we have to do is to make certain that each child develops antitoxin before it comes into contact with a large dose of bacilli. We have to find a way of imitating nature's method of harmless contact and immunization, without the liability to serious infection which is inherent in it. The closest imitation would be to inoculate many very tiny doses of toxin under the skin, but this would be impractical when large numbers of children had to be treated. Fortunately, it is possible to treat toxin in such a way that it loses all its poisonous properties but still retains its power to produce antitoxin. By the action of formalin on toxin, a harmless but still antigenic substance, toxoid, is produced. Large amounts of toxoid can be injected with complete safety and with the certainty that if a proper course of injections is given, any child will develop sufficient antitoxin in his blood to ensure almost complete immunity against diphtheria.

The value of immunization against diphtheria is now fully established, and the only aspects under discussion at the present time are the most appropriate preparation of toxoid and the best age for children to be immunized. In the earlier years of the work, between 1920 and 1930, many papers were published to show that immunized children were far less severely hit by diphtheria than unimmunized children in the same environment. With the general adoption of immunization first in some of the larger American cities like New York and Toronto and then progressively in other countries, evidence of its efficacy on a much larger scale could be provided. In Fig. 12 is shown the trend of mortality from diphtheria in New York City and in England and Wales since 1900. A semi-logarithmic scale is used to give a clearer indication of how great the fall in the death-rate has been. Both curves show first the gradual fall in mortality that resulted from improving living standards and the increasing effectiveness of medical care. Then in New York about 1929–30, and in England and Wales about 1941–2, the line turns sharply downwards. The turning point in both cases is at the time when the proportion of school children who had been immunized against diphtheria reached 50 per cent or more. Immunization is not a complete protection against diphtheria nor even against death from diphtheria, but the overall effect shown in the figure and paralleled in many other countries must mean that in Britain and North America alone about 20,000 children each year survive who, in the absence of immunization, would have died from diphtheria.

Research at the present time is directed mainly towards preparing the ideal immunizing agent. In general, the aim is to have the toxoid as free as possible of other products of the diphtheria bacillus and to mix it with an inert substance which will enhance its capacity to produce antitoxin. Probably most immunizations nowadays are done by giving two injections of alum-precipitated toxoid (A.P.T.) with an interval of three weeks between injections.

There has been a steady tendency over the years to immunize at progressively earlier ages. Where immunization is done by public authorities the rule is to concentrate on the youngest available groups in primary or nursery schools. Where the parent takes the responsibility the best current advice is to give combined immunization against diphtheria and whooping cough when the baby is four to six months old. There is much to be said for combining these with tetanus toxoid and polio vaccine and in 1961 such quadruple antigens were coming into use.

We mentioned earlier that there were certain aspects of diphtheria which were important, yet which had nothing to do with toxin or antitoxin. So far we have referred to the diphtheria bacillus as if it were a single distinct species of microorganism. This is what was generally believed for many years, but in 1931 it was suggested that there are at least three important types of the bacillus. Around 1929 and 1930 diphtheria in the north of England appeared to be more severe than it had been for the previous twenty or thirty years, and a disquietingly high proportion of children were dying, despite antitoxin treatment. Bacteriologists at Leeds, in searching for the cause of this apparent change, observed that cultures from the severest cases had some unusual qualities. The colonies had a distinctly different shape when cultures were grown on a special solid medium, and the strains could cause starch to ferment, a quality lacking in

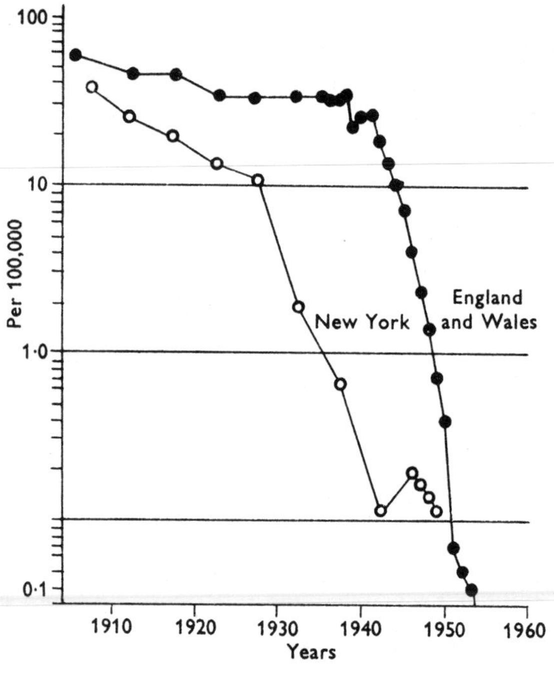

Fig. 12. The death-rate per 100,000 from diphtheria in New York and in England and Wales over the last sixty years. Deaths are shown on a logarithmic scale. The arrows mark the year when immunization of 50 per cent or more of children against diphtheria was first attained.

ordinary strains of diphtheria bacilli. These were easily recognized objective differences, and all the cultures obtained from patients in Leeds were classified according to these criteria. Then the results were considered in relation to the severity of the disease in the patient from whom the culture was obtained. In Table II are shown the figures they obtained. Since this new type of diphtheria bacillus they had found was apparently responsible for most of the severe cases, they called it the *gravis* type, while the other they called *mitis*. After further work, it was found that a third type, *intermediate*, could be differentiated.

Table II. *The severity of diphtheria in relation to the type of bacillus responsible*

	Type of bacillus		
Severity of disease	*Gravis*	*Intermediate*	*Mitis*
Mild	189	11	74
Moderately severe	151	10	31
Very severe	81	3	5
Deaths	50	2	0

The figures show the number of patients in each group out of a total of 555 cases.

These studies on diphtheria cultures were taken up all over the world. In every city there are bacteriologists whose chief routine work is to examine diphtheria cultures, and here was a very welcome opportunity to add interest and additional value to what can become a rather boring task. For a time nearly all diphtheria cultures were classified into the three groups, and there are now sufficient data to allow us to see something of their significance. First of all, we must summarize the facts. These are first, that the three types, *gravis*, *intermediate* and *mitis*, are easily recognized and are found in varying proportions all over the world. Serious outbreaks of diphtheria with high mortality are always due to *gravis* or *intermediate* strains, not to *mitis* strains. The converse is not necessarily true—*gravis* and *intermediate* strains may, under certain conditions, give rise to epidemics of quite ordinary mild type. *Mitis* strains produce usually mild diphtheria; when they cause death it is nearly always due to blocking of the larynx, and rather curiously, the great majority of cases of laryngeal diphtheria are due to these relatively weak *mitis* strains. We may picture conditions fairly accurately if we think of diphtheria as made up of a steady stream of mild *mitis*-type infections, only a few seriously ill, plus irregular epidemic waves due to the appearance of one or other of the more active types.

Those are the facts of the matter, perhaps a little over-simplified. Next we want to know why there is this difference in virulence. Why do *gravis* strains, which produce the same toxin as *mitis* strains, produce on the average much more serious infections? Analysis of the difference by bacteriological methods makes it reasonably certain that the *gravis* strains are more invasive than the *mitis* ones. Like streptococci and pneumococci, they multiply readily in the tissues, and are only properly dealt with by phagocytes when the appropriate antibody is present. In discussing recovery from pneumonia, we described the antibodies which assisted phagocytosis by coating the surface of the bacterium with protein. Similar antibodies are probably needed to deal with invasion by *gravis* diphtheria bacilli. We must make it clear that the antibodies needed for this purpose are not the same as antitoxin. The phagocytosis-helping antibodies correspond to the antigens which make up the actual surface of the bacterium. Antitoxin corresponds to toxin, which is something set free by the diphtheria bacillus, not part of its substance. We may put it concisely by saying that the *gravis* type of diphtheria bacillus has two weapons to assist its attack, its invasiveness and its toxin, the *mitis* strain only the toxin. Diphtheria bacilli are sensitive to penicillin and, although penicillin has no action against the toxin and cannot be substituted for antitoxin, it is a valuable adjunct to antitoxin treatment in serious cases. Bacteria producing toxin on the surface of the throat and tonsils are relatively shielded from the action of penicillin, but those that invade the deeper tissues and produce the swollen 'bull-neck' of a severe *gravis* infection are nearly as susceptible as streptococci in a similar situation. The toxin still remains the important feature of diphtheria, but the high invasiveness of some strains of bacillus makes it desirable to use penicillin in all serious cases as well as to give antitoxin at the earliest possible moment.

However, the rule that prevention is better than cure holds particularly for diphtheria, and now that fully effective methods of artificial immunization are available to replace the risky and uncertain process of natural immunization, they should be used for all children.

We may finish this section by returning to the history of diphtheria in order to see whether our modern knowledge can throw any light on its sudden appearance (or at least greatly increased activity) in most parts of the world around 1858. Any attempt to give a bacteriological explanation of epidemiological happenings before the 1880's is necessarily pure conjecture, and since it cannot be experimentally proved or disproved, is unscientific. So all that we can justifiably say is that if, after a long period in which only *mitis* strains of diphtheria had been present in the community, one or more virulent *gravis* or *intermediate* strains had appeared, then the results would have been of just the same general character as actually happened in 1858. With only *mitis* present in the community, the only recognizable result in the days before bacteriology would be the occurrence of numbers of cases of laryngeal diphtheria (croup) amongst children, but, except in rare instances, no indication that this croup was an infectious disease. Nevertheless, nearly all children would be lightly infected and develop immunity to diphtheria in general, so that when the new virulent strains arrive only the younger children, who had not become immune, would on the whole be affected.

It is impossible to know whether this hypothesis is correct in detail, but unless all our epidemiological reasoning is wrong, its general principles are sound. Diphtheria and scarlet fever are two diseases which resemble one another in being caused not by a single type of germ but by a group of closely related microorganisms with the common quality of producing a single toxin. Diphtheria may be caused by any of eight or ten different types of diphtheria bacilli (for we can further subdivide the three main types of *gravis*, *intermediate* and *mitis*), all producing diphtheria toxin just as scarlet fever may be due to a considerable number of streptococci whose common feature is to produce the toxin responsible for the characteristic scarlet rash. In both diseases immunity is mainly a matter of immunity to the toxin, not to one particular type of the germ. Infection with a mild type of bacterium is almost or quite as effective in producing immunity as a severe infection.

The history of these two diseases is what would be expected from this character. They have both varied greatly in virulence (because of the large number of different types which can cause disease) from period to period, but throughout their history they have always been diseases of childhood and infancy (because immunity to their common toxin is developed during childhood, irrespective of the type of disease). Neither, in the period over which knowledge is available, has shown the characteristics of a really 'new' disease.

CHAPTER XX

INFLUENZA

Amongst the important infectious diseases, influenza holds a rather special interest for the average man. It is the one disease of which he is almost certain to have had personal experience during adult life. And nine times out of ten it has been a mild, almost pleasurable experience, an opportunity for an unexpected fortnight's holiday from work. At the end of the First World War, influenza was responsible for what was probably the worst plague in history, yet despite that calamity, its name still remains something of a jest. In previous centuries, influenza presented an even sharper contrast to the other prevailing infections. When smallpox, typhus, typhoid fever and the like were ever present and often fatal, the sudden appearance of influenza which, as a rule, killed only infants and old people, was almost a relief. Influenza was always referred to in a flippant fashion, and Creighton has collected some of the facetious names which have been applied to it in different periods. In the sixteenth century we find it called 'the new acquaintance' or 'the gentle correction'; in the next century 'the new delight' or 'the jolly rant'. In Horace Walpole's letters he speaks of 'these blue plagues'. It was much the same on the Continent. In Germany, one writer referred to it as the 'Galanterie-Krankheit', while the French name still in use, 'la grippe', appears to have had the same meaning as the German—disease *à la mode.* The term 'influenza', which reached England from Italy, with the epidemic of 1782—the influence—had probably something of the same significance.

For us the chief interest lies in the great epidemic of 1918–19, but to understand how this differed from influenza before and after, it is necessary to say something about the history of the disease. Until 1933, when the virus responsible was first isolated, it was just as easy to diagnose influenza from sixteenth- or seventeenth-century descriptions as it was to say whether a current epidemic was or was not influenza. The disease had to be diagnosed not so much from the symptoms of the patients, but from the characteristics of the epidemic. Other infections might produce the same symptoms of a few days' fever with catarrh and a tendency for pneumonia to follow in old people. But only influenza resulted in a sudden appearance of many such cases with, after a few weeks' prevalence, an almost equally sudden disappearance of the epidemic. Such qualities are not difficult to recognize in old writings. For instance, there is a contemporary description of an epidemic of influenza in Edinburgh in 1562 which included Scotland's most famous queen amongst its victims. It shows clearly how little ordinary influenza has changed through the centuries.

> Immediately upon the Queene's arrivall here she fell acquainted with a new disease that is common in this towne, called here the newe acquayntance, which passed also throughe her whole courte, neither sparinge lordes, ladyes nor damoysells, not so much as ether Frenche or English. It is a plague in their heades that have yt with a great cough that remayneth with some longer, with others shorter tyme as yt findeth apte bodies for the nature of the disease. The Queene kept her bed six days. There was no appearance of danger, nor manie that die of the disease except some olde folkes.

From such lay descriptions as this, as well as from medical writings, it has been possible to compile a fairly complete list of influenza epidemics in Europe since 1500. There are also scattered earlier accounts of the disease, the earliest recognizable reference in English records being to an epidemic in 1170.

The most striking feature of this historical record is the irregular appearance of universal epidemics or pandemics involving the whole of Europe, or in more recent years the whole civilized world. In between these pandemics every country has experienced lesser epidemics, often at two-, three-

or four-year intervals. There were several earlier pandemics, but the first one to which we need refer is that of 1781–2. This appeared in Asia in the autumn of 1781 and spread through Siberia to Russia, which it reached in December. Finland and Germany were attacked in February, Denmark, Sweden and England in April, while France and Italy, with most of the rest of Europe, felt its effect during the early summer. In London there was a sharp epidemic, limited to the month of June, and probably responsible for 200–300 deaths. This pandemic was not a particularly fatal one, but had one characteristic which is of interest in relation to the great pandemic of 1918–19. It spread rapidly, affecting three-fourths of all adults but a much smaller percentage of children, only 2 per cent of the boys at Christ's Hospital being ill. Another comment by a medical writer of the time is significant: 'Children and old people either escaped this influenza entirely or were affected in slight manner.'

We can pass over the fairly severe epidemics of 1803, 1833 and 1837, and come to the pandemic of 1847–8. This, like that of 1782, came from the east, being active in Russia in March 1847 and spreading westward reached England in November. This winter epidemic in England caused a large increase in deaths, particularly amongst the elderly. During the six weeks it lasted there were about 5000 deaths which could be ascribed to influenza, including not only those attributed directly to influenza, but also the excess of deaths registered for pneumonia and bronchitis during these weeks. Creighton makes the interesting remark in regard to this epidemic that it had the usual effect of an influenza epidemic in lengthening enormously the obituary columns of *The Times*. The elderly rich, protected from the stresses which sent the old folk of poorer classes to their graves in a fairly steady stream, were liable to die in relatively large numbers when something as unavoidable as influenza appeared. It was the one physical danger to the old against which wealth and position could afford no protection.

From 1848 to 1889 there was a rather extraordinary absence of influenza from England. A small number of deaths each year were registered as due to influenza, but no epidemics are on record. One can hardly imagine that the virus was absent from England for forty years, and it is probable that the minor outbreaks which must have occurred produced few deaths and passed unrecorded simply because of lack of interest by the doctors concerned. During this period there were four active prevalences of influenza on the Continent which failed to reach England. The pandemic of 1889 showed the usual spread across Europe from Russia, and reached England in the first week of 1890. This first wave was relatively mild, but was followed by three other waves of influenza at short intervals. The four waves had their 'peaks' in January 1890, May 1891, January 1892 and December 1893. The second and third waves showed relatively high mortalities, each being responsible for more than 2000 deaths in London. As in previous epidemics, except for that of 1782, the deaths were predominantly amongst infants and old people.

The year 1890 initiated a period of activity of influenza in England, which, after four waves of the primary onslaught, remained always present with exacerbations in 1895, 1900 and 1908, until it culminated in the great pandemic of 1918–19. Like the previous pandemic, this one came in waves. The number and time of the waves varied in different countries. In England, there was a relatively mild but almost universal summer epidemic, then a lull until the main wave rose in October, reaching its highest mortality in November and December. Then came a diminution in deaths, but another serious rise occurred in February and March 1919. In England there were approximately 150,000 deaths from influenza in this period. The rest of the world, with the exception of St Helena, New Guinea and a few other isolated places, suffered at least as heavily. Most countries populated by western Europeans had a death-rate of three to five per 1000. Non-Europeans, on the whole, showed a much higher mortality. South African natives lost twenty-seven per 1000; in India there were over five million deaths, with rates per 1000 varying in different parts of the country from four to sixty. The highest mortality of all was recorded in Samoa, where a full quarter of the native inhabitants died.

Such mortalities from influenza were everywhere unprecedented, but an even more remarkable feature was the

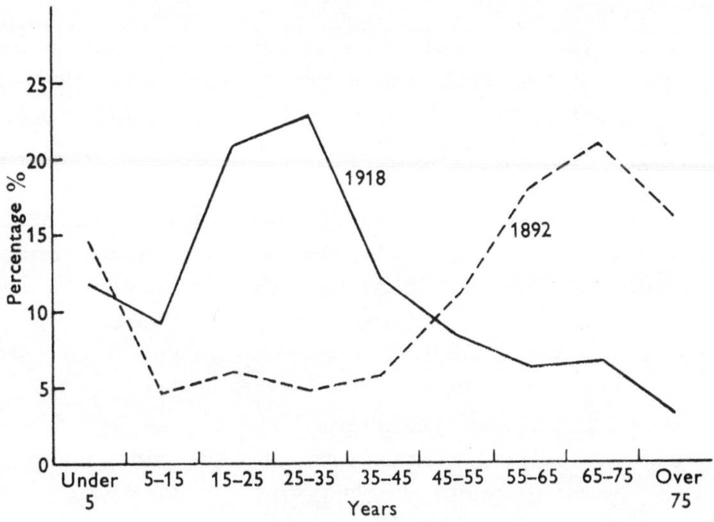

Fig. 13. The change in the age-distribution of deaths from influenza in the 1918–19 epidemic. The percentages of deaths falling in the successive age groups is shown for the 1892 and 1918 epidemics of influenza. In 1892 the chief incidence of death was on old people, in 1918 on young adults.

change in the ages of the people most severely affected. Everywhere the incidence of death fell most heavily on young adults. There were many deaths amongst infants and old people, but the former predominance of these groups in the death-roll had completely vanished. The difference can be strikingly seen by comparing the graphs of age-incidence for the 1890 pandemic with that of 1918–19 (Fig. 13). This characteristic age-incidence was seen in each of the three waves and in all the countries struck by the pandemic. It had not been observed on any previous occasion, unless we can assume from the brief accounts of the 1782 epidemic that this much less fatal outbreak had a similar age-distribution of deaths. As far as they go, these accounts suggest that the 1782 prevalence was extremely similar to the 1918 summer wave, but was not followed by any severe winter epidemic.

Since 1919 influenza has continued to recur irregularly in much the same fashion as it did in the earlier years of the century. It seems probable that for a few years the pandemic type of virus was responsible for some further outbreaks but by 1929 it seems likely that it had either changed into or been replaced by another type. The pattern of illness and death reverted to the earlier form and has not seriously altered since then. The English outbreak in early 1951 was the most severe that had occurred since 1919, and in Liverpool there were actually more deaths in the worst week of the epidemic than in the worst week of 1918–19. The distribution according to age was, however, totally different; in 1951 deaths were almost wholly over fifty-five, and became increasingly more frequent in the older age groups.

The great pandemic left bacteriologists and epidemiologists with several important problems to solve. Why was it so much more widespread and fatal than any previous epidemic? Why did three successive waves occur? Why did the first of these waves not render those attacked immune to the second and third waves? Why did the age-incidence of deaths differ so remarkably from that of former epidemics? And, finally, why did European peoples escape more lightly than most coloured races?

No attempt could be made to answer these questions until the cause of influenza had been discovered. This discovery might have been made in 1918 or earlier, but only by some lucky accident. At that time the methods for research into virus diseases were undeveloped, and most bacteriologists were content to look for a bacterial cause of the disease. By

1933 great advances had been made in the technical side of virus research, and the time was ripe for the discovery of the influenza virus. Most people have heard the story of how it was found by three English scientists that ferrets were susceptible to influenza. They probably do not realize that this was not a chance discovery, but one carefully planned beforehand. If influenza was a virus disease, it could only be investigated by finding an animal susceptible to infection. So when influenza appeared in England in the winter of 1932–3, it was decided to take material from the throats of patients with the disease, filter it through membranes which would hold back bacteria but let any virus pass through, and then test the power of the filtered material to infect all the species of animals, which could possibly be used for laboratory work. Rabbits, guinea-pigs and mice refused to show any symptoms at all, so more out-of the-way animals were tested. The first to be tried was the ferret, because it was known that this animal was highly susceptible to distemper, the virus disease of dogs which has a considerable resemblance to influenza. The ferrets were inoculated into their noses, and two days later they looked miserable, ran high temperatures, developed running noses and sneezed. There was no doubt that they had influenza. That day opened the new epoch in the story of influenza. Now it was susceptible to experimental study, and no longer a nebulous entity that could only be defined by the fact that it occurred in epidemics of a particular type. Since then there has been steady progress in the development of technical methods for handling influenza viruses, so much so that we can say today that influenza virus A is not only the most adequately studied of all the viruses but that we probably understand its activities at least as well as those of the diphtheria bacillus.

The first technical advance was to transfer the virus to a much more convenient experimental animal than the ferret. The white laboratory mouse is not readily susceptible to infection with the virus but by a process of 'training', i.e. by transferring the virus rapidly from one mouse to another, the disease becomes evident as a form of rapidly fatal pneumonia. For several years most experimental work on influenza was carried on by this method, but since 1940 the mouse has been to a very large extent replaced by the chick embryo.

I can remember well the days when the nature of influenza was the biggest mystery still to be solved in the field of infectious disease and I can imagine how incredulous we should have been if we had been told how fantastically simple it is to study influenza virus today. To grow influenza virus we merely inoculate a minute amount of virus into a fertile egg that is halfway through incubation. The virus lodges in one of the cavities or water sacs of the embryo and multiplies in the surrounding cells. After two days' incubation we can withdraw the fluid from the cavity and find that it now contains a million times as much virus as we put into it. To measure the amount of virus is equally simple. We merely mix graded amounts with a suspension of red blood cells in salt solution. If virus is present in sufficient amount the cells will be clumped or agglutinated and settle to the bottom of the tube in a characteristic pattern.

For twenty years, from 1935 to 1955, my own laboratory had influenza virus as its central interest and the chick embryo as its favourite experimental tool. With the steady move of virologists toward tissue culture techniques, the chick embryo may soon become outmoded, even for influenza virus studies, but up to 1960 it remained the most useful way to isolate and cultivate the viruses of the influenza group. By suitable experimental devices—tricks if you like—eggs and red blood cells can be made to tell almost anything one wishes about influenza virus and its activities.

The virus is isolated very simply from the throat of a patient in the early stage of 'fever, headache, general muscular aching and malaise'. The patient gargles a mouthful of fluid and returns it to a medicine glass. The throat washings are mixed with a little penicillin and streptomycin to kill the various bacteria present and a few drops of the mixture are implanted into an inner cavity, the amniotic sac, of each of six chick embryos. The virus multiplies in the cells lining the cavity and usually also in the lungs of the embryo which are directly accessible from the amniotic cavity. Five days later we can tell whether or not the virus has multiplied by mixing a little of the fluid from the amniotic cavity with red blood cells from a man or a guinea-pig. If the cells are clumped the virus is there and we can go on transferring it to further embryos. Once the virus has been induced to grow at all, it is possible to cultivate it in the more convenient outer (allantoic) cavity and to use the fluid from this for all types of work, such as vaccine production, for which virus is needed in quantity.

Influenza viruses are not all identical. With modern techniques at least a dozen characteristics in which they may differ can be defined. The most important difference is in regard to what we refer to as immunological or serological type. This refers to their capacity to produce immunity. A mouse will suffer a fatal lung infection if we cause it to inhale a suitable influenza virus but if we put large amounts of the same virus under its skin it will show no symptoms and survive. Within a fortnight it will in addition have become immune, in the sense that inhalation of the virus no longer produces pneumonia. If, however, a mouse immunized in this way with what we call influenza A virus, is tested—challenged is the laboratory term—with influenza B virus, the mouse goes down with pneumonia just as a normal mouse would. If we reverse the test we find similarly that influenza B will immunize against its own type but not against influenza A. Such immunological differences can be worked out in much greater detail by testing the power of serum from an immune animal to prevent agglutination of red cells by different viruses.

By these methods it has been shown that there are two wholly distinct viruses, influenza A and influenza B, which produce epidemics of generally similar character. The difference can be shown just as clearly in man as in the mouse.

As everyone knows it is most unusual for anyone to have two attacks of 'flu in the same epidemic. One attack provides immunity for at least two years against the same type of influenza. A few years ago we investigated a small epidemic in a school where three of the boys had two typical attacks within two or three weeks. In each instance one attack was due to A, the other to B. It was a case of two epidemics occurring concurrently.

Influenza A virus is responsible for more epidemics than B and the outbreaks tend to be larger and more severe. In the northern hemisphere the relatively severe epidemics of 1932–3, 1936–7 and early 1951 were all due to influenza A. Then in 1957 came the pandemic of Asian influenza, again a group A virus, but showing a sharp immunological difference from all previous types of this species. No one now has any doubt that the 1918–19 pandemic was due to influenza A and the experience of a new but much less lethal epidemic of the same general quality in 1957 has clarified our thoughts considerably about the sequence of influenza epidemics. We are primarily interested of course in the human disease and until very recently it seemed that animals played no significant part in the epidemiology of human influenza. Now we are not quite so sure and we should first say something about the influenza-like viruses of man and animals. Without going into technical detail we can say that viruses of the group Myxovirus are defined essentially by their power to agglutinate red cells but also have several other qualities in common. There are three influenza viruses, A, B and C in the group, and two para-influenza viruses which, like influenza A, produce mild respiratory infections in man. In addition the virus of mumps belongs here. From animals viruses identifiable as influenza A have been shown to cause disease in horses, swine, ducks and fowls. It is rather a paradox that away back in 1901 the virus of a fatal disease of poultry, fowl plague, was isolated and has been studied ever since, but not until 1957 was it recognized to be a variety of influenza A virus. The parainfluenza viruses are also to be found in animals, notably mice and cattle, and there is another important myxovirus responsible for Newcastle disease of fowls. This incidentally is responsible for a mild occupational disease of persons handling poultry. It takes the form of an acute conjunctivitis and interests me particularly because the first case to be reported in the medical literature in 1943 involved my own eye. It received a rather heavy splash of infected egg fluid and became acutely inflamed. Like almost all such cases it cleared up in a few days.

Swine influenza as it occurs in Iowa and other mid-Western states is of particular interest in relation to the 1918–19 epidemic. It is undoubtedly due to an influenza A virus and farmers in Iowa are confident that the disease they call, hog flu, was first seen in October 1918 when the great pandemic reached America. They believed that the swine had contracted the human disease and most workers on the subject would now agree that the farmers were probably right. There are probably other viruses of the group still to be found in domestic or wild animals but, having regard to the variability of influenza viruses, we already know enough to realize how complex the epidemiology of influenza may be.

With this background we may attempt to interpret what has happened in regard to human influenza during the twentieth century. Even before the days of intercontinental travel by air, human movement had made the whole civilized world a single epidemiological unit as far as influenza was concerned. Wherever there was a large human population susceptible to infection by an influenza virus active in some other part of the world, one could be certain that within a year the virus would produce an epidemic in that population.

A composite picture placed together from many observations in the past twenty-five years must be based on the changing immunological character of the influenza A viruses responsible for successive epidemics. Sometimes the difference from a previous epidemic is quite slight, at other times as in

1957 there is a more far-reaching change. We know that in the laboratory influenza virus is highly labile. If, for instance, we grow it in the presence of antibody at a level of concentration just below that needed to inhibit growth completely, we can confidently expect to obtain a variant or mutant that is resistant to the antibody that formerly destroyed its activity. Perhaps we can picture what is happening by looking at some large civilized country at a time when there are no influenza epidemics. Even in the warm months, however, careful and extensive scrutiny will uncover an occasional case. Influenza A is always present in every major area, but an epidemic arises only when three conditions occur together: first, suitable climatic conditions—influenza is a winter disease as a rule; secondly, a low level of immunity in large numbers of people; and thirdly, the presence in the country of a suitable type of virus. Once an epidemic of influenza A has passed through a district, the level of immunity is high, and it will be impossible for a similar type of virus to provoke another epidemic for about three years. If, however, the virus passing irregularly but persistently from one region of the world to another should undergo mutation to a partially new immunological character it will spread more readily. Two years after the last epidemic the new virus may be capable of overcoming a residual immunity that would have blocked any significant spread by the parent type. There is a constant premium for survival placed on the emergence of immunological novelty. So we find a progressive change in character of influenza A virus occurring since it was first isolated in 1933.

Here in Australia we are at the opposite end of the world from England with the winter epidemics coming in July and August instead of January and February. Since 1935 we have been 'comparing notes' about influenza with workers in England and North America, and on three occasions we have isolated 'new' variants of influenza viruses in our winter which about six months later were responsible for epidemics in the northern hemisphere. No more striking proof of the mobility of influenza could be given; all influenza epidemics nowadays are pandemics.

In 1957 the sequence changed more drastically. At the end of the 1956–7 winter, extensive influenza appeared in Northern China and a new type of influenza A virus was isolated in Peking. The western world only became aware of the new virus with the outbreak of influenza in Singapore and Japan in May. All who studied the virus agreed that although it was influenza A it was of completely new immunological type and that it would certainly spread throughout the world. The pandemic behaved almost precisely according to expectation. Epidemics occurred in the southern hemisphere in June and July and the northern winter showed a double peak of deaths due to influenza and pneumonia in October-November 1957 and February 1958. In both Australia and America there was the expected two years' interval before the next outbreak in May 1959 and January 1960 respectively. Also in line with past experience all epidemics of influenza A since mid-1957 have been of the new Asian or A2 type.

It is probable that most virologists will agree that there were some close epidemiological resemblances between the 1918–19 pandemic and that of 1957, despite the relatively insignificant mortality of the latter. Two questions are outstanding. Where did what was clearly a 'new' virus come from? and Why was 1918 so catastrophic in comparison with 1957?

If we accept the view that the 1918 influenza was of the same type as has persisted in American swine, we are naturally tempted to wonder whether it may not have arisen from an animal reservoir. It is, in fact, not wholly inconceivable that the pandemic was actually derived in the past from that same reservoir of infection in swine in the mid-West. The more usual hypothesis is that the new type arose by mutation from the pre-existent influenza A strains that had been producing moderately extensive epidemics in the armies of the First World War.

Similar alternatives have been raised for the origin of the

1957 virus but again there is no certainty. Did the virus emerge from some rodent reservoir in the Asian steppes or by mutation from the A viruses current in the preceding human epidemics? It is conceivable that extensive tests for antibody against Asian influenza in the mammals and birds of central Asia could provide a positive answer to the first question. In the absence of positive results we shall have to accept the second alternative as the more probable.

Direct and indirect evidence suggests that between twenty-five and fifty million people died of influenza in 1918–20. Probably a greater number of people were infected with influenza in 1957–8 than in 1918, but the deaths were no higher than those of any 'ordinary' influenza year. There has been much discussion as to the nature of the difference. There are still differences of opinion, but several authorities have been optimistic enough to believe that what made the difference was the advance of medical science in the intervening forty years. In their view we can feel reasonably confident that, provided our civilization persists, we need not fear that any lethal pandemic of influenza comparable to 1918 will emerge in the future.

There are those who believe that the Roman Empire fell primarily because of inability to deal with outbreaks of infectious disease. With movement of people in war or commerce from one end of the Empire to the other, recurrent epidemics were inevitable in the absence of any of the modern means of handling infectious disease. The development of modern western civilization went hand in hand with improving knowledge of hygiene. By 1918 the epidemic diseases that killed in classic and medieval times had been brought under control, but not the respiratory infections. War of 1914–18 type provided the best possible opportunity for airborne pathogens to flourish and to build up their virulence, and there was then no effective counter. In the opinion of most of those who discussed the matter at a special symposium in 1959, there is no reason for believing that the 1918 virus had any greater virulence than that of 1957. Both were 'new' viruses capable of spreading freely through the world's populations. When they killed it was because they were associated with the bacteria that also pass from person to person by the respiratory route. The difference we believe was in the bacteria that were current and in the methods available for dealing with bacterial infection. In 1918 the world was at war, bacterial infections were rife in camps and barracks, in the trenches and in areas of social disorganization. Soldiers with measles died of streptococcal pneumonia, meningitis epidemics were of an intensity never seen in civil life, and there were no drugs effective against bacterial infections. In 1957 the world was reasonably peaceful and reasonably prosperous. The sulpha drugs and the antibiotics were available everywhere and there was no opportunity for the rapid passage of specially virulent bacterial strains along with the virus.

As has happened so frequently in human history, we had stumbled into the last of the ecological traps laid by infectious disease in 1918 and by 1957 we had ensured that that particular trap would never be effective again. Perhaps there is a moral and a ray of hope here for the very different perils of the 1960's.

CHAPTER XXI

TUBERCULOSIS

Most of our discussion of the defence processes against infectious diseases has been concerned with the rapidly acting acute infections in which, as a rule, there is a short severe conflict resulting either in death or complete recovery. Tuberculosis is the great example of the chronic infections, and although the same general principles are involved, their application is greatly modified by the slowness of most of the processes concerned.

The tubercle bacillus is a very inactive organism compared, for instance, with the bacilli of typhoid fever or diphtheria. When a suitable supply of food material is provided, ordinary bacteria multiply rapidly; a single organism grows to double its original size and divides into two new bacteria every 30 minutes or thereabouts. The tubercle bacillus takes about a day to go through the process which takes the typhoid bacillus half an hour, and as we might expect, the rate at which it produces symptoms in infected animals or men is correspondingly slow. There is one important characteristic of the tubercle bacillus which is probably responsible for much of its behaviour. Its surface is very largely built up of a peculiar waxy material. This wax sheath largely replaces the polysaccharides and proteins of the ordinary bacterial surface, with three important effects: (1) it slows down the entry of food molecules into the substance of the bacterium, hence the slow multiplication of the bacillus; (2) it protects the bacillus to some extent from digestion when it is taken up by phagocytes in the body; and (3) it is less irritant to the tissues than the surface of rapidly multiplying bacteria, and produces a much more slowly acting inflammatory response, involving different cells from those which deal with acute infections. In addition to this waxy material, there is another substance of great importance in the tubercle bacillus, a protein which was first extracted in an impure form by Koch, the discoverer of the bacillus, and called by him tuberculin. There are of course many other substances which form part of the living material of the bacillus, but these two are the only ones whose importance in relation to disease has been shown.

Someone said that of all the millions of species of living organisms on the earth the two about which most had been written were man himself and—the tubercle bacillus. It is therefore no simple task to condense what is important about tuberculosis into a few pages, and for the most part we shall deal only with those aspects which bear on the natural occurrence of the disease.

There are two types of tubercle bacilli which may cause human disease. One is responsible for almost all cases of consumption, that is, tuberculosis of the lungs, and is called the human type. The other is primarily a parasite of cattle, and is mainly responsible for the tuberculosis of lymph glands and bones in children. This bovine type almost invariably enters the body in milk and infects by way of the intestine. On the whole, these infections of children with the bovine type are not highly fatal, although they usually result in prolonged illness, and they are not infectious for others. The lung infections with the human type of bacillus are much more important practically, and from our point of view much more interesting. We shall, therefore, say nothing further about the bovine form, and concentrate on the endemic disease, pulmonary tuberculosis.

Despite the superficial differences between tuberculosis and the more acute diseases, there are deep-seated resemblances in their behaviour within those communities in which they are endemic. Tuberculosis is no longer endemic in the cities of advanced western countries as it was thirty years ago. If we are to compare its behaviour with that of diphtheria, we have to go back to the classical epidemiological studies that were made on both diseases between the two world wars. In the first place there were many more infections with the tubercle bacillus than there were people showing symptoms of the disease. Even today a proportion of children are unfortunate enough to inhale infectious material probably in the form of tiny dried-up droplets of mucus loosed into the air by some infected person's cough.

In the lung a little spot of mild inflammation develops where the bacilli multiply, and from there some of them are carried to the lymph glands which are situated in the centre of the chest where the main air tubes and blood vessels enter the lung. The lymph glands also become inflamed and enlarged, but as a rule the child shows no symptoms and soon the little damaged patch in the lung begins to heal and the lymph glands to return to their normal size. Sometimes healing is delayed and an X-ray will show a shadow in the lung—the primary complex so-called—but even these mostly vanish under treatment or even without. Only a tiny proportion nowadays develop frank tuberculosis. In one careful study in midwestern America of 2,266 young people who were known to be infected, only fourteen developed recognizable disease and there were no deaths.

Recognition of the fact of infection depends on the development of a positive tuberculin test in a person who was previously non-reactive. To understand this we must look at some of the things which happen during the primary infection. Tubercle bacilli multiply and are broken down, liberating in the process the protein tuberculin which we have already mentioned in chapter IX. As the result of a complex process for which it appears that in addition to tuberculin, a waxy substance also produced by the tubercle bacillus and an accumulation of body cells (monocytes) are necessary, the body develops delayed hypersensitivity to tuberculin. It seems likely that in one way or another a considerable proportion of lymphocytes and monocytes come to carry something we could call fixed antibody, so that when they meet tuberculin molecules they are damaged. The damaged cells tend to 'stay put' where they were damaged and liberate soluble agents which in their turn damage blood capillaries in the neighbourhood.

The Mantoux test is a practical way of detecting whether or not a child or adult has ever undergone this process of sensitization by the tubercle bacillus. For the test a minute, carefully measured amount of purified tuberculin is injected into the skin. If the person has not been infected, nothing happens. If he has, the tuberculin and the 'antibody' in the cells unite and set going a rapid inflammatory change which shows itself as a red patch in the skin, bright and slightly swollen at twenty-four hours and slowly fading to a light-brownish patch in a few days. It is still routine in some hospitals to carry out such tests at yearly or shorter intervals on all the nursing staff. If a nurse gives no reaction at one test and at the next a typical positive red patch, we can be sure that between the two she has been infected with the tubercle bacillus.

By surveys of the results of such tests we know that in many parts of the world more than 90 per cent of people are infected before they are twenty. Around 1930 this held for most cities in the temperate zones as well. The present position is not so easy to assess because of the widespread use of BCG immunization. Before dealing with this, however, we should say something about what happens in the small minority of individuals who do not succeed in throwing off their infection.

First of all, there are those whose primary infection fails to heal. Infants born of tuberculous parents are very likely to be infected in the first months of life and die of a generalized tuberculosis in which the germs have passed to many parts of the body, especially the membranes covering the brain. In other children smaller numbers of bacilli get into the blood from the primary seat of infection and set up a new infection in one of the bones or joints, usually the spinal column or the hip.

In a proportion of infected children who have developed a

primary complex in the lung but who have made a good recovery, a new period of danger may start at adolescence. It may be that in the scarred relics of the primary spot of infection in the lung there are still some living tubercle bacilli. For some reason these are apt to show fresh activity in early adult life, and the scarred area may break down, liberating rather large numbers of bacilli into adjacent parts of the lung. The results of this spread will depend on many factors, but will certainly be influenced by the fact that all the lung cells have been rendered sensitive and reactive to the tuberculin protein by the primary infection. As we have noticed in a number of other connexions, the processes of immunity are on the whole much better adapted to deal with local invasions than with widespread ones. What is an appropriate protective response in a small area may become a fatal one if it takes place throughout a whole organ. When relatively large numbers of tubercle bacilli find their way into the lung of an individual sensitized by previous infection, irrespective of whether they come from an old area of infection or from outside, the reaction of the lung is much more violent that it would be in an unsensitized person. The blood-vessel walls let out cells and fluids into the tissue, which becomes swollen and airless; the pressure of the cells may close down many of the blood vessels, so leaving the area insufficiently nourished.

If, as most pathologists believe, the sensitization process is in part at least responsible for the damage that the tubercle bacillus can inflict in the lung, we may well ask whether this process of sensitization plays any useful part whatever in dealing with the infection. The question was once a hotly controversial one. Today's answer would probably be that conditions are far too complex to state dogmatically whether sensitization is 'good' or 'bad'. It exists and is important in many different ways. The doctor and the pathologist must understand and take account of its potentialities—but there is no call for either to regard the process of sensitization to tuberculin as 'designed' by nature to help cure tuberculosis.

It would be outside our field to go any further into the complicated details of the struggle with the bacilli in the lung of a tuberculous individual. If we realize that the tubercle bacillus multiplies only slowly, but on the other hand is difficult to kill and may remain present and alive in scarred lung tissue for years, and that the process of cell sensitization may sometimes prevent and sometimes favour the spread of infection, we can see how readily small factors might sway the balance one way or the other.

Probably the most important of these factors are in some way related to the genetic constitution, the inheritance of the person concerned. In fact there is a growing belief amongst those not directly concerned with the treatment of tuberculosis, that from the practical point of view there are only two things which are vitally important in determining the fate of an individual in regard to tuberculosis. These are (1) the fact of infection with virulent bacilli, and (2) his genetic constitution. If as happens now with increasing frequency in more favoured communities a person never becomes infected with the bacillus he will never suffer from tuberculosis. The importance of inheritance has been known for many years, but only in 1943 was its significance for tuberculosis given a quantitative statement. In a now famous paper, Kallmann and Reisner described their studies on tuberculosis in twins in New York State, using the only really effective method that is available for studies of inheritance in human beings. Anyone with a little general biological knowledge knows that there are two sorts of twins, identical twins which arise by the division of a single fertilized egg-cell and non-identical twins which represent fertilization of two egg-cells by two distinct spermatozoa. One-egg twins are identical in all genetic characters—they are the twins that only parents can tell apart. Two-egg twins are no more alike than any other two children of the same parents—they will show two distinct sets of combinations of actual and potential qualities derived from the parents.

In this study of tuberculosis in twins, as in all similar studies in medical aspects of human genetics, the method was to sort out from the register of cases of tuberculosis all those patients who had a twin. The families of these 'index cases' were then studied in regard to incidence of tuberculosis, not only the co-twin but father and mother, other children and marriage partners. The twin pairs were closely examined to decide whether they were one-egg or two-egg twins. There were thirty-nine pairs of one-egg twins in the series and, as is always the case, a much large number of two-egg twins. We can tabulate the results very simply in terms of the percentage of relatives of the index cases who had clinical tuberculosis:

Relation to index case	Percentage with tuberculosis
One-egg twin	87
Two-egg twin	25·6
Other brother or sister	25·5
Marriage partner	7

In addition to the 87 per cent correspondence in the fact of clinical infection, identical twins also showed a close resemblance in the type and progress of the disease.

One other factor requiring brief mention as perhaps influencing the course of tuberculosis is the time of life at which first infection occurs. There are hints that the safest time for first infection is around the age of ten and the worst, especially for women, between eighteen and twenty-five years.

There are hints too that in addition to the fact of primary infection the size and frequency of subsequent exposures to the tubercle bacillus may influence the extent to which a person's inherited vulnerability to tubercle will be manifested.

The decade 1950–60 was a turning point in the history of tuberculosis. In every advanced country of the world sanatoria for tuberculosis began to close their doors and public health authorities to feel that full eradication of the disease had become a legitimate objective. This was only the last step in a process that began about a hundred years earlier.

In 1850 the mortality from tuberculosis in England and Wales was about fifty times what it was in 1959. Roughly speaking, the rate has been successfully halved six times for females, five times for males, and the periods needed for each successive reduction to half are illuminating. They are

For females	40 – 30 – 22 – 8 – 4 – 4 years
For males	55 – 26 – 18 – 5 – 5 years

In every advanced country the fall during the period 1946–59 has been to unprecedentedly low levels. It is interesting to look at the possible reasons for these changes in mortality since 1850. In the light of present day-knowledge it is most unlikely that medical treatment as such had anything to do with the slow but persistent fall in mortality up to 1939. It is doubtful whether treatment ever did more than delay the fatal event in those who would have died without treatment. The steady fall shown in nearly all western countries must have been due to other factors. There is no reason to believe that any changes have occurred in the tubercle bacillus itself. The improvement must be sought in social or biological factors on the human side. In all probability the diminution resulted mainly from the steady advance in the standard of living over the period. By 1939 the average person in a civilized community was eating more and better food, was housed in greater comfort, had more opportunity for fresh air and sunlight, and was more cleanly in his habits than in the nineteenth century. A higher proportion of people with active tuberculosis were being cared for in sanatoria and those under ambulant treatment had been given enough training in elementary hygiene to diminish their likelihood of infecting others. The net result was probably that on the whole children when they were infected received a smaller dose of bacilli on the average and could deal more effectively with the primary and any subsequent infections.

Perhaps the most important factor of all was a genetic one. We have indicated how the ability of a person to deal effectively with tuberculous infection is very largely an inherited quality. The child of a tuberculous parent is not born with the disease, but he may inherit a relative inability to resist infection when he comes in contact with it. It is natural to think therefore that some of the improvement in mortality is due simply to the fact that, particularly in the earlier years of the nineteenth century, there was an intense 'weeding out' of people with an inheritable tendency toward tuberculosis. A much larger proportion of these would die before they could have children, and the average resistance of the community would rise with each generation.

A good deal of light is thrown on these questions by the facts which have been accumulated about tuberculosis in peoples who have not previously been exposed to infection. Research on this question became a matter of economic importance with the increasing exploitation of African natives either as soldiers or mine labourers by Europeans. During the war of 1914–18 very large numbers of West African troops and labourers were brought to France, forced to live in a crowded and totaly alien environment, and exposed, most of them for the first time, to the tubercle bacillus. The death-rate from tuberculosis was enormously higher than amongst white troops, and the disease was usually far more rapidly fatal. In these non-immune natives, tuberculosis closely resembled that of those young European children who succumb to their primary infection. The first stage of infection showed little in the way of symptoms, but the bacilli became strongly established in the lung. Sensitization developed rapidly with the production of antibodies against the protein of the bacillus. In chapter xv we said something about the increased responsiveness of adult tissues to harmful agents as compared with those of children. These natives, meeting the tubercle bacillus for the first time in adult life, developed an abnormally high degree of sensitization. If they were sent back to Africa soon after their primary infection, most of them recovered. In France, hard work, exposure and the strange environment eventually resulted in a recrudescence of activity in the lung. The original area of infection set free numerous tubercle bacilli, which were disseminated through the rest of the lung. In their highly sensitized state, the lung cells responded violently, and instead of the chronic changes seen in a European consumptive, these natives died of what was really an acute tuberculous pneumonia.

In South Africa cases of tuberculosis in Africans employed in the gold mines of the Witwatersrand tend to be of the same general type. Twenty years ago the mortality from tuberculosis in mine workers was about five per 1000 per annum. But for the modern developments in treating tuberculosis, we can be reasonably certain that industrialization in South Africa would have subjected the Africans to the process of 'weeding out' those stocks with an inheritable susceptibility to tuberculosis. Amongst the American Indians this process seems to have been accomplished, and after three generations of intense infection and high mortality they now appear to be only a little more susceptible than Europeans living under comparable conditions. The native population of Mauritius has been exposed to tuberculosis for a much longer period than either of the races we have mentioned. Study of their history seems to indicate that it takes something over a hundred years after its first contact with tuberculosis for a race to develop a resistance against the disease equivalent to that of a European population. The process of childhood immunization plays a vital part, but it cannot be fully effective until the more susceptible strains in the population have been eliminated by a very direct form of natural selection.

The precipitate fall in deaths from tuberculosis in the last dozen years is primarily due to the development of effective drug treatment of the disease. Improvements in living standards and in cleanliness continued to play a part and the success of drug therapy had a number of secondary effects that have further improved the situation. In the first place surgery of the lung now became relatively safe and could often greatly speed recovery. With the recognition that tuberculosis could be cured almost with certainty, plus the development of ways of reducing the financial burden of hospitalization, patients became willing and neven eager to sbmit to treatment. One of the results in Australia at least has been that despite the tremendous fall in mortality there are still nearly as many notified cases of infection. In the old days most of these would never have been found.

By 1960 the drug treatment of tuberculosis had become fairly standardized. Three drugs were used, two simple synthetic compounds, para-aminosalicylic acid (PAS) and isoniazide, and the antiobiotic streptomycin. Isoniazide and streptomycin when first tested showed dramatically favourable initial results but very soon organisms resistant to the drug being used appeared, often with a relapse in the patient's condition. The difficulty has been overcome by always using more than one of the drugs at any given time. The reason for this is easy to see if we accept the fact that resistance arises by mutation. To simplify conditions we can assume that whenever we have a population of a million bacilli one will have mutated to become resistant to streptomycin (S) and one to be resistant to isoniazide (I). We assume also that there are a million bacilli in the patient when he is treated. If he is given drug S all the bacilli are killed except for the one S-resistant mutant. This multiplies despite the drug and eventually we have a new population of a million S-resistant organisms. Amongst these will be the random mutant that is also I-reisstant and if we now change to drug I we may soon find that the patient is infected with doubly resistant bacilli. On the other hand, if we hit with both S and I together there will only be a chance of one in a million million that a spontaneously occurring doubly resistant mutant will be present.

Prevention of tuberculosis by immunization has had a rather controversial history, but in 1960 very widespread use was made of BCG vaccination. The method was introduced in 1922 by the French bacteriologist Calmette as a means of protecting infants born into tuberculous families. The BCG strain of tubercle bacillus is a variant which has lost all power of producing disease on injection into animals, but still has a considerable immunizing power against infection with a virulent culture. Calmette himself gave the vaccine in the form of a living BCG culture by mouth, but this method is now never used in English-speaking countries. The French results over the period 1922–36 appeared to show a great saving of life amongst vaccinated infants, but statisticians elsewhere were very sceptical of the validity of the control series used. Interest in the use of BCG was only awakened in England and America when the wartime experience of the Scandinavian countries became known in 1946. Here very valuable results were claimed from injection of BCG culture into the skin. In several controlled trials there has been a clearcut advantage on the side of the immunized, and in many countries there is now widespread immunization of young people with BCG. In almost all countries specially vulnerable groups like hospital nurses and medical students are routinely immunized. In areas where tuberculosis rates have fallen to a low figure and where public health authorities are keen to see that every case has early treatment, BCG vaccination tends to be resisted. In such areas it can be claimed that the benefit so far proved is not sufficient to balance the difficulties introduced by the fact that vaccination with BCG provokes a positive tuberculin test. This test has been of great value in the past in assessing the activity of tuberculosis in the community and in detecting cases. Once any considerable proportion of people have an artificially induced positive reaction the test becomes valueless and it is impossible to continue detailed epidemiological work. Even its strongest supporters would probably agree that BCG is only a temporary measure to help accelerate the rate of process of eliminating the tubercle bacillus from the community.

The same can be said of the use of mass radiography in case-finding. If everyone with 'open TB' were segregated from the community till he was non-infectious, tuberculosis would disappear within a decade or two. Mass radiography is the most effective available weapon for this purpose. The aim is to obtain a miniature X-ray picture of the chest of every adult in the community once a year. Few people have tubercle bacilli in their sputum without some evidence of trouble being visible in the radiograph of their chests. There are many practical difficulties, but experience in handling the method is steadily growing, and where it is socially and economically possible to provide effective treatment for all persons found to be excreting bacilli, the results are bound to have an important beneficial effect.

Overall the prospect for tuberculosis elimination is promising. Given continuing improvement of living standards, peace, and enthusiasm for the public health, the tubercle bacillus might be extinct by A.D. 2000.

CHAPTER XXII

PLAGUE

For many centuries plague has been the example *par excellence* of the dangerous pestilence. The symptoms are characteristic enough to make it easy to recognize the disease from classical or medieval descriptions, and we can be sure that the two greatest European pestilences, the plague of Justinian's reign (A.D. 542) and the Black Death of 1348, were both the result of the spread of the plague bacillus. Just at the end of the nineteenth century another great plague epidemic arose in Asia, and in India the deaths from plague rose to over a million per annum in 1904. Since then there has been a fairly steady diminution in the annual number of deaths and since 1945 plague has been of little significance as a public health problem in most parts of the world.

From our ecological point of view, it is one of the most interesting of all infectious diseases. Normally, it is not a disease of human beings at all. The great plagues of history were biologically unimportant accidents, the result of human entanglement with a self-contained triangular interaction of rodent, flea and plague bacillus.

Perhaps it would be better to omit the word triangular. Modern opinion is tending to stress the large number of different rodents that may be involved and the different roles they may play in the maintenance and spread of plague. In all probability the steppes and plains of north and central Asia are the homeland of plague. There it seems to need for its indefinite persistence an association of several rodent species and their fleas. In any area where plague bacilli are to persist indefinitely, there must be a species of relatively high resistance to infection which can serve as a carrier of the bacillus for many months. Alongside the resistant species there must also be a more highly susceptible rodent in which periodic epidemics will ensure a wide redistribution of the bacillus in the area. The marmots, susliks and tarbagans of Siberia and Mongolia are well known to be subject to recurrent acute outbreaks of plague and as such are dangerous to man. The long-term persistence of infection, however, depends on their association with resistant but infectible rodents of the gerbille and vole types. Irrespective of the rodent host, infection is spread from animal to animal by fleas. In an infected animal the bacteria are present in the blood and pass into the flea's stomach with its meal. Here, under suitable conditions, the plague bacilli multiply, often sufficiently to interfere seriously with the flea's blood-sucking mechanism. If the flea has in the meantime passed over to an uninfected animal and starts to feed, the blood is not swallowed cleanly, but is regurgitated, mixed with some of the plague bacilli which are obstructing the flea's gullet. The bacilli can then enter the body through the skin puncture made by the flea, and so infect the new host. During the winter, when no detectable cases occur, the germ probably survives in the tissues of mildly infected rodents and sometimes in fleas.

We are completely ignorant about the antecedents of the plague of Justinian, but enough is known about the Black Death of 1348 to reconstruct the probable way in which it developed. Probably one of the most important determining factors was the spread to Europe in the thirteenth century of the black rat (*Mus rattus*). This was originally a native of India, and appears to have reached Europe with returning Crusaders. It rapidly replaced indigenous rats and flourished in and around human habitations. Also, each rat supported a colony of fleas, fleas of a species which had not the exclusive tastes of some such parasites, but were equally ready to feed on rat or man. So conditions were made favourable for the spread of plague when it should arrive. There are several independent sources which locate the origin of the Black Death in southern Russia, and we may be reasonably certain that it was derived ultimately from the natural plague of burrowing rodents somewhere between the Volga and the Don. Probably it was contracted from these rodents by rats and passed to human beings from them. One account says that Italian traders were besieged in a small port on the Crimea for three years until plague broke out amongst their Tartar enemies and caused the siege to be raised, but not before it had been introduced into the town. The Italians returned by ship to Genoa in 1347, carrying the plague with them. Plague broke out in virulent form in Genoa soon after their arrival, and since it is stated that none aboard the ship had shown signs of plague, we can feel fairly confident that it was in rats and their fleas that the infection travelled to Europe. As the Black Death developed its activity, it is almost certain that transmission by flea from rat to man was very largely displaced by man to man transmission, either by way of fleas, or directly when the disease took on the pneumonic form. There is distinct evidence that in the winter 1347–8 the pneumonic form was dominant, while in the summer following nearly all victims contracted the bubonic form.

To understand the differences between the two forms, it will be necessary to make a little digression on the pathology of plague infection. When a flea introduces the bacilli beneath the skin, most of them are transported to the nearest lymph glands and filtered out there. They are not killed, but multiply, causing inflammation and enlargement of the gland. In a mild case the infection may go no further, but in the severer forms the bacilli enter the blood and pass to other parts of the body. The lymph glands first infected, usually in armpit or groin, however will in all but the most rapidly fatal cases show swelling and inflammation. There is a hot painful lump, usually discoloured red or purplish. This is the bubo which gives the name bubonic plague to the disease. When the plague bacillus gets into the blood, it will naturally pass to the lungs, and may lodge there, producing pneumonia. In certain circumstances, a patient with plague pneumonia may infect others by droplet infection, the germ being transferred directly to the lungs of these new hosts. Here it may produce a primary pneumonia in its turn capable of infecting others. This is the probable way in which an epidemic of pneumonic plague develops. It is the most deadly epidemic disease to which man is subject, but fortunately it appears capable of developing only under certain special conditions.

The Black Death burnt itself out after killing something of the order of one-fourth of the population of England, and for some reason concentrating on adult males. There are figures in regard to the deaths amongst the clergy and amongst the tenants of certain manors which indicate that almost two-thirds of these classes died, but the incidence was certainly much less heavy on women and children. In two parishes mentioned by Creighton, deaths from plague showed sixty-three men to fifteen women in one, fifty-four to fourteen in the other, and there are distinct suggestions that children also escaped lightly.

There was a lull for a few years, but England and Europe were thoroughly contaminated with plague, and fairly frequent outbursts occurred for nearly three centuries. The infection amongst the rats probably never completely died out, and every few years a flare-up of the disease amongst the rodents would be followed by a human epidemic. This went on in England until 1665, the year of the Great Plague. Then after the worst pestilence since the Black Death, the disease disappeared completely from England, until a small outbreak occurred in Essex in 1909. Almost the same thing happened in France in 1720, when Marseilles and the south of France experienced a final disastrous epidemic of plague. It is by no means certain why the long visitation of plague in Europe ended so abruptly, but it is highly probable that one important factor was the replacement of the black rat by the brown or sewer rat. Just as the black rat invaded Europe from India five centuries earlier, so at the beginning of the eighteenth century brown rats began to stream from their original home somewhere in central Asia toward western Europe. Great hordes swam the Volga in 1727, and in 1730 they had established themselves in England. The black rat was very largely displaced from Europe by the newcomer, but continued to be the common ship rat. The brown rat is an objectionable creature, but is not so dangerous a transmitter of plague as the rodent it replaced. It does not frequent dwelling houses so much, and its predominant fleas do not bite man so readily as those of the black rat.

Whatever the cause, plague certainly died out from Europe in the seventeenth and eighteenth centuries, and in the world in general it was very unimportant until 1896. Then an epidemic at Hong Kong marked the beginning of another great phase of plague activity which has not yet ceased. In 1899 it spread to Bombay, and in a few years became one of the most important causes of death in northern and western India. Ship rats and their fleas carried it to every port of consequence in the world, and in many countries it took root, in other words established itself as a parasite of the local rodent population, usually the rats of the waterfront. From these, human outbreaks took their origin.

During the first epidemic at Hong Kong, Kitasato, a Japanese bacteriologist, discovered the plague bacillus. This was the first successful step toward the scientific understanding and sanitary control of plague. During the first ten years of the new pandemic very active research was carried out, and at the end of that period the relation of the rat and its fleas to the disease was well understood and the necessary measures to stamp out, or at least to prevent entry, of plague could be clearly envisaged. It was clearly necessary to attack the rat by every possible method, and above all to prevent the movement of rats from infected to uninfected regions. Measures were devised to clear ships of rats by fumigation, to prevent their movements to and from ships in harbour, and to make grain stores and other warehouses along the waterfronts as nearly rat-proof as possible. Most port authorities kept up a steady campaign of rat destruction with periodic bacteriological surveys to determine whether plague infection was present in the animals. Such measures have been progressively improved and nowadays much more stress is laid on rat-proofing ships and wharf buildings by proper construction, than on destruction of rats. Most authorities now believe that plague is never again likely to cross the oceans. The steamships that spread plague around the world in 1896–1904 have been replaced by ships in which rats cannot exist. In several countries, however, plague imported from Asia at that time found the appropriate association of rodents that has allowed it to persist indefinitely since.

The story of plague in South Africa is particularly interesting. Like the rest of the world, its ports were infected from India during the period 1899–1905, and plague became prevalent amongst the rats. Other rodents with a range including both town and country were also infected, and plague spread slowly in these. About 1914 it reached sandy country in which gerbilles (a species of larger burrowing rodents) were numerous. Amongst these the infection spread very rapidly, and by 1935 enormous areas of country were potentially infected. Even within twenty years, plague amongst the gerbilles of South Africa seems to have taken on the status of a relatively well-balanced persistent infection. When seasons are good, the gerbilles multiply rapidly, but as soon as their numbers reach a certain level the plague bacillus spreads more easily, and an epidemic breaks out amongst the rodents. Their numbers are then rapidly reduced, but it is during the period of widespread disease in the animals that human infections are liable to take place. In South Africa there is a curious little zoological complication to the story at this stage. The gerbille is a creature of the veldt, and avoids human habitations, so the chance of human infections being derived from sick gerbilles is remote. Another rodent, the multimammate mouse, acts as an intermediary. This mouse takes the place of the common domestic mouse in

South African houses, building nests in the walls and living on household odds and ends, but on occasion it roves further afield. In the bush it frequently enters gerbille burrows, where it is liable to attach to itself fleas from an animal sick or dead with plague. These are brought back to the house, and hence human infection may occur.

Much the same state of affairs had developed in California, which, like so many other parts of the world, was infected with plague about 1900. The waterside rats as usual formed the first reservoir of the disease, and California has the credit of organizing the first thoroughgoing campaign against rats as a means of checking plague. On the whole, the antirat measures were successful, but it was disconcerting to find after some years that plague was widespread amongst the ground squirrels. American epidemiologists are still uncertain whether plague reached the ground squirrels from the imported San Francisco outbreak or whether it had been present unnoticed in the rodents from time immemorial. Whatever its origin, there is no doubt that plague finds as congenial a home amongst these American rodents as it does amongst the marmots and tarbagans of central Asia. There are the usual fluctuations in activity from year to year, but on the whole the area involved spreads progressively. The ground squirrels live mostly remote from human habitations, and relatively few human cases can be traced to them. It is rather alarming, however, to find that two small epidemics of the very dangerous pneumonic form have been traced to infection from ground squirrels. For some reason, there seems to be a tendency for plague contracted from burrowing wild rodents to take the pneumonic form, while infection derived from rats is almost always bubonic. In modern times the only great epidemics of pneumonic plague have been in Mongolia and Manchuria, where the tarbagan is the important reservoir.

As with other bacterial diseases the advent of potent antibacterial drugs has greatly changed the outlook for the patient stricken with plague. There have been few opportunities for careful studies of treatment, but at least one Chinese physician with pneumonic plague has been cured by the combined use of streptomycin and sulphadiazine, and experimental work in animals suggests that this combination should be highly successful in practice.

The development of drugs and poisons selectively active against plague bacilli, fleas and rats, since the days of the Second World War, has completely changed the outlook on plague. If patients, even those with pneumonic plague, can be treated early with streptomycin or one of the tetracycline antibiotics, nearly all will recover. DDT powders in rat runways and in houses will greatly diminish flea populations, and poisoning campaigns with fluoracetate (1080) carried out with proper regard to the subtleties of rat behaviour can be extremely effective. No country with a reasonable standard of living and a competent public health service need fear a serious outbreak of plague.

On the other hand, plague is bound to persist in the wild rodents of the steppes, the veldt and the high plains of North America. Plague may also smoulder amongst domestic rats in parts of Asia with occasional small human outbreaks. Rat-proofing of ships and waterfront warehouses will probably be effective in stopping movement overseas from these residual foci. Only the complete disorganization of civilization could bring the plague bacillus back as a major threat to human life.

CHAPTER XXIII

CHOLERA

Asiatic cholera is the result of infection by a bacterium discovered by Koch in 1884 and called by him the comma bacillus. This organism, instead of having the usual cylindrical form of most bacilli, was distinctly curved into the shape of a comma. Later on, bacteriologists decided that such a shape was individual enough to demand a new name, and the organism is now always referred to as the cholera *vibrio*. The vibrios are swallowed in contaminated water or food and multiply enormously in the intestine. They do not invade the tissues to any extent, nor appear in the blood, but in the intestine they multiply as rapidly as they do in a bacteriologist's test-tube. None of the natural bacteria of the bowel contents has a chance against them. Irritant substances produced by the vibrios damage and inflame the lining of the intestine. Everywhere along its length the blood capillaries dilate and allow fluid to leak into the intestine, providing further pabulum for the vibrios. An intense diarrhoea is the result, and soon the whole contents of the bowel are replaced by thin watery fluid from the blood, in which the cholera vibrio multiplies unrestrainedly. Poisons produced by the vibrio probably play some part in causing the symptoms, but far more important is the loss of fluid from the blood. The patient dies from simple dehydration when the blood becomes too thick and viscous to be circulated efficiently. It is another example of the way the reaction of the body to infection may do more harm than good. Liberation of fluid into the intestine with resulting diarrhoea is a reasonable and effective way of getting rid of any irritant substances, bacterial or chemical, which may have lodged there. But if the irritant flourishes like the cholera vibrio in the outpoured fluid, the continued reaction is not only futile, but in about 75 per cent of untreated cases, fatal to the patient. If cholera patients can be treated in hospital it is possible to remedy this loss of fluid to a large extent by administering a suitable weak salt solution into the veins. In a bad case, gallons of such fluid may have to be used. If the dehydration can be countered in this way the body has a chance to cope with the infection, and in practice the mortality of cholera has been reduced from 70–80 per cent to about 20 per cent by such treatment.

The vibrio passes out of the body with the bowel discharges, and under natural insanitary conditions, wells and streams in an infected community will be inevitably polluted with the germ and provide the method for the spread of the disease. Water is the great vehicle for the diffusion of cholera, but uncooked food may also be contaminated.

The epidemiology of cholera is full of puzzles. In the first place, there is only one area where the disease can be called endemic, the lower basin of the Ganges and the adjacent low-lying country extending round to Burma. Here cholera has been present since time immemorial, and on every occasion that the disease has spread beyond India it has started from this region. The first world spread of cholera started in 1817, first involving almost the whole of India, and then spreading slowly along the caravan routes to Russia and western Europe. England was invaded in 1831 with approximately 50,000 deaths resulting throughout the British Isles. There were four other world-wide pandemics during the nineteenth century showing similar general characteristics, but it was noticeable that the two most recent ones were effectively kept out of the more highly civilized countries. Despite such repeated diffusion over most of the world, cholera has not become endemic anywhere outside of India and some parts of south-eastern Asia.

In the endemic area, cholera shows many of the characteristics of the endemic respiratory diseases of temperate climates. It has been frequently stated that the danger of cholera is far greater for persons visiting such endemic regions as Calcutta and Rangoon than for the permanent residents. As in other examples, the relative insusceptibility of residents is explicable only as the result of previous infection by the germ, either as a typical attack or in subclinical fashion. The evidence of subclinical infection in the past can also be seen in the age-incidence of attacks. Endemic areas show a high incidence in children under ten, while in areas distant from India epidemics of cholera strike adults more severely than children. In one epidemic in Assam, 44 per cent of the patients were aged ten years or less, while in the Glasgow epidemic of 1832 less than 6 per cent were in this age group.

Like most endemic diseases, the incidence of cholera varies with the season. In Calcutta cases occur all the year round, but are concentrated in the hot months of February to May before the rainy season begins. It is reasonable to ascribe this to the relatively limited supplies of water at this time, and hence their greater liability to heavy contaminations by the vibrio. With the rainy season, the wells and 'tanks' are replenished, and most of the contaminated ground water washed away. However, in some other parts of India the wet season and the cholera season coincide, and again we must only confess ignorance of the reason.

There is no doubt that cholera is an anomalous disease which in its classical form produces symptoms unlike those of any other infection. Its epidemiology is puzzling and has never been fully explained. When the first edition of this book was written it seemed likely that a new interpretation of cholera was in the making, based on the assumption that cholera bacteriophages played an important part in the natural history of the disease. The war intervened, cholera remained important, but research shifted to strictly practical matters of control and treatment. The problem of treating cholera has been solved but, as far as I can ascertain, nothing significant has been written about cholera bacteriophages since 1936.

Yet even if the practical problems have been solved, there is much of interest in the story of the earlier work. It is a story that has simply vanished from the text-books, but it may still be true and it provides a particularly interesting commentary on the process of scientific discovery.

In our chapter on viruses, we said something of bacteriophages, the viruses which live at the expense of bacteria, invading and multiplying within them and in the process dissolving and destroying them. Now it has been shown that in the intestinal contents of patients who are convalescent from cholera there are bacteriophages (cholera phages) which can dissolve the cholera vibrio. The discoverer of bacteriophages, d'Herelle, put forward the revolutionary hypothesis that it was the presence of this cholera phage and not the patient's development of immunity to the vibrio, which was responsible for his recovery. He found that all those patients who recovered had an active phage in their intestinal contents, and that those who had no phage died. Here was a clear-cut statement which one would have thought would require only a few months' work to prove or disprove. Yet nearly forty years later we still do not know what part cholera phages play in determining the incidence of cholera.

The development of scientific knowledge is a slow process carried out by human minds which are no more perfect instruments of thought than are those of politicians and economists. Sometimes we find a first-rate medical discovery announced almost in its final form, and immediately accepted throughout the world. Koch's discovery of the tubercle bacillus is perhaps the classical example. Much more often we find a definite sequence of events: first the announcement of the discoverer that such and such is the cause of some disease, or that this or that drug or serum cures it with regularity. The results claimed are, in the light of later knowledge, nearly always exaggerated by the author's enthusiasm for his discovery. Exceptions are not mentioned or are explained away. Then if the discovery or claim is important enough to attract wide attention, a period of muddle begins. Enthusiasts rush into print confirming the new discovery, particularly when it is some method of clinical treatment. Sceptics try to repeat the discoverer's observations, often without taking care to use his exact methods, and with their eyes wide open to find exceptions have no difficulty in showing that things are by no means so straightforward as they were claimed to be. Other workers in the field become interested in applying the new idea along lines suggested by their own previous work, and a whole crop of secondary ideas arises, often very difficult to fit in with the original discovery. At this stage the outsider, who knows the subject only from reading the literature about it, becomes completely confused and exasperated. But the work goes on. More critical minds are brought to bear on the problem, and further revealing discoveries are made. At last the real significance of the discovery is established, and ten or fifteen years from its announcement it has become the orthodox teaching of the text-books. Sometimes, however, the work does not go on. The problem for one reason or another loses its importance or its interest and the papers that have been written on the subject remain unread with their contradictions and controversies unresolved. That has been the fate of the work on cholera bacteriophages. In 1960 nothing more is known about the relation of bacteriophages to cholera than we knew in 1936.

It may still be worthwhile to tell the story almost in the same words as in previous editions. Let us look first at the facts which were held to indicate that cholera phages played a part in assisting the recovery of patients and in determining the incidence of cholera. We have mentioned that phages are frequently found in the faeces of patients convalescent from cholera. They are also not uncommon in contaminated water or in the faeces of normal individuals. From all such sources at least twelve distinct varieties of phage have been isolated in India, all capable of actively dissolving the cholera vibrio. Phages, like the viruses causing disease of man or animals, do not arise spontaneously. All these types must have been living at the expense either of cholera vibrios or of vibrios nearly related to these. From what we have said of the interaction between living organisms and their parasites it would be almost inconceivable that under certain conditions the interaction between phages and vibrio should not swing violently against the vibrio. Experiments in test-tubes have shown that a bacteriophage flourishes best if the bacterium at whose expense it lives is multiplying actively in some fluid mixture like the nutrient broth of the bacteriological laboratory. If, on the other hand, the bacteria are multiplying more slowly in the tissues of an infected host or in artificially prepared tissue cultures, they are almost unaffected by the same phages. Cholera provides a uniquely favourable opportunity for the activity of phage from this point of view. In the bowel the vibrios are multiplying rapidly in what is the closest approach in nature to the bacteriologist's pure culture in broth. They should be highly susceptible to the action of any active bacteriophage introduced amongst them. d'Herelle's statement that they were so susceptible was very largely supported by the result of a large-scale experiment in Calcutta where alternate cases of cholera were treated with and without cholera phage. All received, in addition, the standard hospital treatment for the disease. Analysis of the results showed that for cases of cholera produced by typical vibrios the death-rate was reduced by phage administration from 20 to 8 per cent. That was a definite reduction, but not so striking as would have been expected if d'Herelle's claims were correct. Some other writers found even less effect of phage on mortality.

When cholera broke out twenty or thirty years ago in outlying parts of India, there was no opportunity for hospital treatment; patients lived and died in their own homes and only the simplest forms of treatment were possible. In one such outbreak the mortality amongst those untreated was 76 per cent, amongst those treated by cholera phage 34 per cent. It seemed likely from these results that phage might on occasion swing the balance in favour of recovery, but other factors were obviously important as well.

If the presence of bacteriophages influenced recovery from cholera, it would be logical to assume that they would play an important part in the epidemiological behaviour of the disease. d'Herelle in fact claimed that an epidemic of cholera could arise only by the introduction of the vibrio into a community where cholera phages were absent or of insufficient activity. As the epidemic developed, there were increasing opportunities for phages to live on the vibrios and to develop a higher virulence. Soon any water contaminated by vibrios would be bound to contain phages as well. Then according to d'Herelle the cholera epidemic should disappear. On this view cholera would never break out in Bengal if adequate amounts of active bacteriophages were always present in the water supply of the community. One large-scale attempt was made to test this hypothesis in India. In 1929 it was decided to select one administrative district in Assam in which cholera epidemics had occurred with considerable regularity at two-yearly intervals. This was to be used as the experimental area in which bacteriophage should be widely distributed. There were several other districts of similar size and physical character in the province which could serve as 'controls'. If the distribution of bacteriophage diminished the spread of cholera, its effect should be made visible by a significantly lower incidence of the disease in the chosen area than in the other districts. In the experimental district, Nowgong, arrangements were made that a supply of cholera phage should be available in every village and town. It was the duty of the headman of the village and of minor officials in each small section of the larger towns to see that everyone who had any symptoms of diarrhoea was given at once a dose of cholera phage, not so much as treatment for the diarrhoea as to ensure that there was always a certain amount of active phage present in the environment. The results in the experimental area were striking, and by all the available statistical criteria indicated that this distribution of cholera phage had been responsible for a great diminution in the number of deaths.

There was a complete absence of cholera epidemics in Nowgong from 1929 up to the end of 1936. A few small groups of infections occurred in some villages, but no epidemics developed from these. Unfortunately, experience elsewhere has

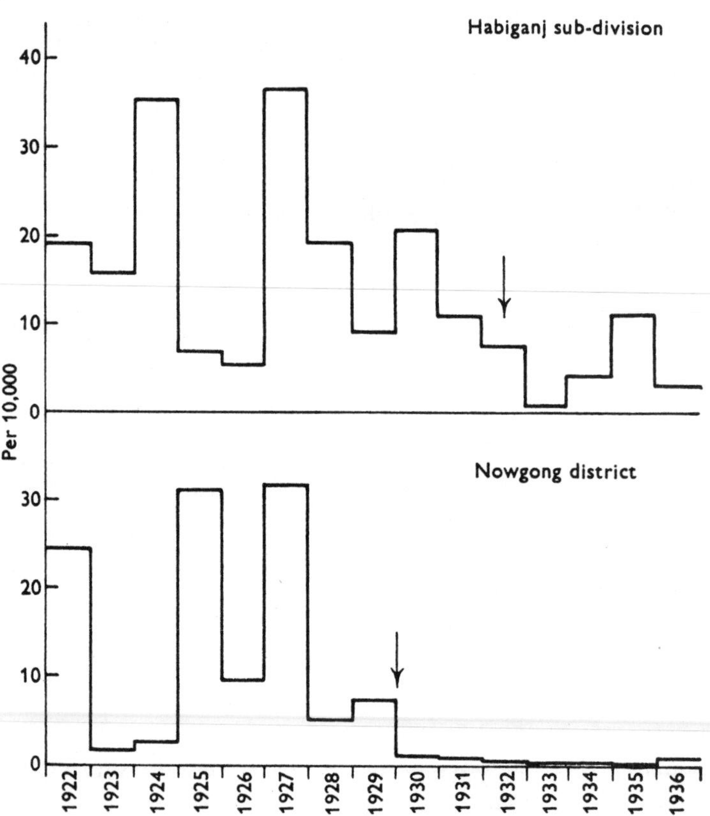

Fig. 14. The influence of cholera phage on the incidence of cholera in two Indian districts. The death-rates from cholera are shown for the district of Nowgong, where phage-distribution was commenced at the end of 1929, and for the subdivision of Habiganj in the same province, where it was commenced three years later.

not been so happy. In 1932, another district, Habiganj, was taken over as a second experimental area, and cholera phage was equally widely distributed. In this district there has been a much less significant effect on the incidence of cholera. Epidemics were of much the same extent and severity as in the 'control' districts of Assam. The verdict in 1936 was 'not proven' and so it remains today.

Cholera is only a public health problem where sanitary conditions are deplorable. It will vanish as soon as rural water supplies and latrines in the endemic areas of Asia are brought up to acceptable standards. There has been no significant spread of cholera to western countries for thirty-five years, although in 1947 Egypt was reached. No authority today would advocate any approach to the prevention of cholera that did not rely primarily on good environmental sanitation. Rightly or wrongly the use of bacteriophage is dead. Immunization with cholera vaccine is still a standard measure in India and all travellers to Asia are immunized as a routine. Few epidemiologists I think would say anything more definite than to suggest that we have no adequate reason to discontinue the practice. In the past there were trials in which immunized groups fared better than unimmunized groups and these results must be given some weight. Most of us, I think, would regard vaccination against cholera as a relic of the past which should be critically surveyed and reassessed in the light of modern ideas. One of the great new fields for immunological study is the part played by the intestinal tract in handling so effectively its own problem of defence. In normal life we have several ounces by weight and perhaps 10^{13}–10^{14} by number of potentially dangerous bacteria in our bowels. In cholera that population is almost wholly replaced by a single dangerous species with enzymes which can damage the cells lining the intestine but with little or no power to invade the tissues. Largely because there is no animal which can serve as an experimental model of the cholera patient, we have almost no knowledge of the finer aspects of the pathology and immunology of cholera. Nor has there been any serious attempt to find what might well have been the most promising approach to prevention, a living attenuated strain of vibrio that could be given by mouth and induce immunity where it was needed.

Cholera as a human problem would rapidly vanish if the endemic areas of Asia are brought up to a Western standard of sanitation and nutrition. A previously healthy individual admitted early to hospital will almost certainly make a rapid recovery under present-day treatment. It is perhaps foolish to feel that it is a pity that when cholera flourished no one was moved to bring finality to the problem of the intertwined natural history of the cholera vibrios and their parasites the cholera phages or to elucidate the fascinating problems of immunity to a purely intestinal disease.

CHAPTER XXIV

MALARIA

If we take as our standard of importance the greatest harm to the greatest number, then there is no question that malaria is the most important of all infectious diseases. All over the tropical and subtropical zones, wherever there were aggregations of people, there malaria flourished. In India it was calculated that in 1930 about a hundred million people were infected with the parasite responsible, and that about two million deaths per annum were directly due to malaria. The influence of the disease extends far beyond its obvious activities as a cause of death and serious illness. It was the great devitalizer of the tropics—much of the backwardness of the Indian peasant has been ascribed to malaria—and it was the main agent of infantile mortality all through history till the end of the Second World War.

With the development of effective methods for mosquito control during the 1940–5 period, it almost suddenly became possible to envisage the elimination of malaria from the world. In 1960 so much progress had been made that the World Health Organization could proclaim the elimination of malaria as one of its practical objectives. Whether the world's political wisdom will be adequate to handle the problems associated with the resulting tremendous increase in the numbers and potential vigour of the tropical and subtropical countries, is more than doubtful. By the Hippocratic oath and by the traditional morality of every country and every age, the medical scientist and the doctor must save every human life he can. All we can do as human ecologists is to underline the implications of overpopulation and press as hard as we can for a sane and realistic approach to the necessity of birth control in all countries and in all religious and ideological groups.

Once again it seems likely that the incidence of malaria is going to play, as it has in the past, a major part in human history. There is good reason to believe that malaria played a major part in the decline and fall of the Roman Empire, of Greece, and of the ancient civilization and power of Ceylon. If we knew more of the evolution and spread of malaria, we might well find that it played an even more important part in the shaping of human evolution and destiny. Whatever its early history, by the time of European sea-power, malaria was rife over the whole of the continental tropical and sub-tropical belts. Even twenty years ago the idea of its elimination was unthinkable. Man, mosquito and malarial parasites seemed to have reached a balanced interaction involving millions of square miles of territory and hundreds of millions of human beings. To disturb that equilibrium significantly appeared to be impossible. Today we are almost, but not completely, confident that a reasonable expenditure of intelligence, effort and money can remove malaria from any part of the globe. The doubt arose in 1960 when it was discovered that the monkeys of south-east Asia were carriers of a malarial parasite indistinguishable from one of the human types and proved to be capable of producing typical malaria in men experimentally infected via mosquitoes from the monkeys. No one knows yet quite how important this finding is but it has damped our optimism considerably.

Most readers will have a sufficient general knowledge of the nature of the symptoms of malaria—recurring attacks of severe fever, with intervals of two or three days during which symptoms are absent—to allow us to take them for granted. We must, however, say something about the three closely related species of microorganism which are responsible for the disease. They are protozoa, that is, minute animal organisms, with a rather complicated life history, part of which is spent in human beings, part in mosquitoes of one particular genus, *Anopheles*. It is natural to start with the mosquito bite by which a few tiny parasites rather smaller than most bacteria are inoculated from the insect's salivary glands into the blood. Within an hour these are swept out of the blood, finding lodgement in cells of the liver. Here the parasite finds suitable conditions for multiplication and each gives rise to a mass of close-packed germs that distend the cell eventually to breaking point. About twelve days after the mosquito bite the malarial parasites pass from the disrupted liver cells into the blood and the blood cycle that gives rise to the typical symptoms of malaria is initiated. The liberated parasites are small specks of protoplasm that attach themselves to and enter the substance of the red blood cells. Within the cell each invading germ feeds on the cell substance and grows almost as large as the cell. Then the parasite rapidly divides into twenty or more small pieces, each with its tiny living nucleus, and when the remnants of the cell break down, these pieces are liberated into the blood fluid. Then the cycle is repeated, each little descendant parasite enters a fresh cell and in the space of two or three days goes through its period of growth and division. When a large number of parasites are simultaneously liberated along with poisonous products of their growth, the body's response is the sharp attack of shivering and fever which is the chief symptom of malaria. These attacks continue for a time which varies greatly, according to the virulence of the strain of malaria, the general health of the patient, whether he has had previous attacks, what treatment he receives, and so forth. If he does not die, a substantial degree of immunity develops, fixed phagocytes, aided by antibodies in the blood, destroy most of the parasites, but in untreated persons small numbers remain in the blood for a considerable time. As immunity develops, a new phase of the parasite appears in the blood. These are sexually differentiated, and their function is to infect any mosquito of the right species which bites the patient at this stage. In the mosquito's intestine, the male and female forms unite, and from their fusion a new brood of parasites develop. These invade the wall of the intestine and grow into little nodules swarming with tiny needle-shaped germs. When the nodules break down, these germs pass to the salivary glands of the mosquito, and after a period of from ten to twenty days has elapsed since it became infected, the mosquito becomes capable of passing on its infection to another human being.

An important feature of this cycle is the necessity for each stage to be passed through in the appropriate order. The needle-shaped sporozoite from the mosquito cannot enter the red cell, neither can the liver form nor the primary form that develops in the red cell (merozoite) infect the mosquito. Even more important, from the practical point of view, is the fact that the different stages are unequally susceptible to the action of antimalarial drugs. Each of the three major species of malarial parasite, *Plasmodium vivax, Pl. falciparum* and *Pl. malariae,* has its own points of difference in detail, but there is nothing to be gained by attempting to describe these nor is it necessary to mention one or possibly two other species which on very rare occasions are found to be related to human malaria.

Malaria was a military problem of the utmost importance in the Pacific War of 1941–5, and great advances in its practical control were made during that period. Something must be said about the new methods of control, but for the most part we shall be concerned with the natural history of malaria as it existed, or still continues to exist, in regions where no serious attempt to interfere with its incidence is made. In the great majority of endemic areas the two main clinical forms of malaria, benign tertian due to *Pl. vivax* and malignant tertian due to *Pl. falciparum,* occur together. There are important differences in symptoms and in their response to drugs, but it is legitimate to deal with all types together when discussing the general problem and refer to the complex of infections simply as malaria.

Let us first take a population of natives in some heavily infected region, northern Ceylon, Nyasaland or certain parts of Central America. Conditions are suitable for the breeding of large numbers of *Anopheles* mosquitoes, and there is a fairly concentrated resident human population. Infants are infected at an early age, and throughout their lives will be subjected to repeated reinfections. Very many will die during infancy and childhood, some directly from malaria, others from a combination of other infections with the weakening influence of chronic malaria. Those who survive must have perforce acquired a considerable degree of immunity. As we have already mentioned, immunity to malaria is largely associated with the activity of fixed phagocytes, and one of the results of repeated childhood infections is a great enlargement of the spleen. Essentially this is an effort on the body's part to provide a sufficient supply of fixed phagocytes to carry out all the necessary destruction of malaria parasites. In practice, the degree to which the children's spleens are enlarged in a native community provides a useful index as to how intense malarial infection is in the region. The adults, provided they are adequately nourished, remain substantially immune—infection by an unusually active strain may provoke definite symptoms, but serious results are likely only when there is some failure of food supply. It is of interest that in heavily malarious African regions, although there is an appalling infantile death-rate, the adult well-nourished natives are very healthy. In India, where pressure of population on the means of subsistence is greater, chronic malarial ill-health is much more frequent in the adults.

There are many parts of the tropics where malaria is by no means as universal as in the regions we have described. The right mosquitoes are present, but the factors which make them dangerous are only intermittently present. A very good example of the way epidemics of malaria may affect a tropical population is provided by the story of the Ceylon epidemic of 1934–5. This is said to be the greatest malaria epidemic since accurate records have been available, causing 80,000 deaths amongst two or three million cases.

Ceylon can be divided into a dry northern area, which is highly malarious and relatively sparsely populated, and a large well-watered south-western area, thickly populated and relatively free from malaria in normal years. In 1934 the south-west monsoon and its associated rains completely failed to appear. Crops failed, rivers ceased to flow and became mere chains of waterholes—the climatic conditions approached those of the northern half of the island. The malaria-carrying mosquito of Ceylon breeds in pools of clear water exposed to sunlight, not in overgrown swamps or ricefields nor in flowing streams. With the partial drought, conditions in the south were ideal for its multiplication in the pools along river courses. There was a plague of mosquitoes, and the population was badly undernourished from failure of crops. The conditions made a serious outbreak inevitable, and in October 1934 malaria spread almost everywhere, striking whole villages at once. It was not abnormally fatal—only 3 per cent of patients with symptoms died, but it affected about half the total population. In the northern part of Ceylon there was no abnormal incidence of malaria—conditions remained as before.

In this example, we have a combination of three main factors which favour malarial prevalence. First, unusually suitable conditions for the multiplication of *Anopheles* mosquitoes, secondly, a human population, most of whom were not immune as a result of repeated previous attacks—it had been five years since the last serious prevalence of malaria in the region—and thirdly, a population whose resistance had been weakened by undernourishment.

Although malaria is pre-eminently a tropical disease, it was once very prevalent in England and until recently in certain coastal districts of the Netherlands. In the Mediterranean region malaria is dwindling rapidly, Sardinia and Cyprus have been cleared and there are probably only minor pockets left in Italy and Greece. The recent stages in this process of eliminating malaria from the Mediterranean have been the result of deliberate action but it is more difficult to understand why malaria had so largely disappeared from Europe before the new methods became available. Climatic and social factors have almost certainly been involved. In Italy there have been centuries in which the country was almost completely free from disease and long periods when malaria was rampant throughout the country. It may be significant that during the three ages of Italian political and intellectual importance, the first centuries A.D., the Renaissance and the present time, were all periods of low malarial activity. Such alternations probably depended on changes in the mosquito species or races, and particularly on changes in their habits. One of the most interesting and before the days of DDT one of the most important phases of malaria research concerns itself with the detailed ecology of the various species of *Anopheles*. There are many parts of the world where there are *Anopheles* mosquitoes, but malaria does not spread, even when cases are introduced from the tropics. Sometimes this is because local farming conditions make it much easier for mosquitoes to feed on cattle than on human beings. Sometimes more subtle factors are involved. In Holland, it has been found that there are two structurally similar races of *A. maculipennis*. Although almost indistinguishable in appearance, they have different habits, and while one race transmits malaria, the other does not. The harmful race spends its larval stage in the brackish water of coastal lagoons, the other prefers fresh water. In winter, the former (malaria-transmitting) race spends its time near the ceilings of warm farmhouses and continues to feed on human blood during the winter, incidentally transmitting malaria during the process. The other (harmless) race spends the winter in cold outhouses and the like, and hibernates. As exemplifying the difficulties of research on malaria, we may mention that in Holland, while most infections are transmitted by mosquito bite received in this way during winter, the attack of malaria does not occur until the following summer. This very long 'incubation period' has also been observed after experimental infections in man made during research on the treatment of brain syphilis by malarial infection. Such a long delay is probably a function of both the low environmental temperature and of the relatively low virulence of the malarial strain. Ecological work of this sort in Europe will probably allow the remaining foci of infection to be cleaned up without great difficulty.

One of the most impressive examples of anti-malarial work in recent years was in Brazil, where the introduction in 1931 and spread over thousands of square miles of a dangerous African mosquito was followed by a catastrophic outbreak of malaria in 1938. By this time effective methods of dealing with the breeding places of the mosquito had been developed, and an intensive two years' campaign, even without the new insecticides eliminated *A. gambiae* from the whole infested region. Similar success was achieved when this same mosquito spread into Egypt and caused a severe epidemic of malaria in 1942.

In many ways malaria is one of the easiest diseases to control. Until 1960 it was generally accepted that the only vertebrate reservoir of human malaria was man. The important reservoir from which mosquitoes drew their infection was the blood of native children recovered from their early infections but carrying large numbers of the infectious sexually mature forms in the blood. Even though we know that monkeys can be a reservoir in Malaya and chimpanzees in Africa, this is probably relatively unimportant. In the absence of a human reservoir, there would be only occasional cases of malaria in jungle workers and further spread could easily be checked.

The second helpful aspect is that each type of Anopheline mosquito has its own type of breeding place and does not readily adopt a different mode of life. At the human level we can prevent persons being bitten by malaria-carrying mosquitoes through such means as efficient screening of doors and windows. We can kill mosquitoes in the houses by leaving a fine residual deposit of DDT on walls and ceilings where mosquitoes rest in the daytime. By appropriate dosage with drugs like paludrine and chloroquin infected persons can be kept non-infective for any mosquitoes that bite them. Even without any attempt to reduce the number of mosquitoes the effective use of such measures could eliminate malaria. In practice, however, the control of mosquitoes is even more effective and practicable. Close study of the ecology of each important disease-carrying species will always indicate the type of action that will be most effective in diminishing its numbers. The attack will usually be on the larval stage and this can be pressed in a dozen different ways. The larvae can be suffocated by an oil film on the surface of the water, poisoned by DDT or Paris green or eaten by small fish. Breeding places may be drained or altered in one way or another to make them unsuitable for mosquito larvae of the significant species.

It is now too late to question whether rapid and complete eradication of malaria will be in the best interests of the peace and economic wellbeing of the world. The die has been cast and every country now demands that malaria be rooted out from its territory. The impact of diminishing malaria on vital statistics is evident everywhere. Mauritius offers a particularly striking example. Between 1945 and 1948 the two malarial mosquitoes were eliminated; birth-rates increased sharply from about 35 to 45, infant mortality fell from 150 to 80, and general mortality from 26 to 12 per 1000. Population from around 420,000 in 1945 has soared to over 600,000 in 1958. With an area of only 720 square miles, Mauritius has a desperate problem ahead but it is the same problem that the rest of the world must face not so very much later, if birth control fails to catch up with the surge of fertility and health that has been released by the removal of infectious disease—and particularly of malaria.

CHAPTER XXV

YELLOW FEVER

As Greenwood has pointed out, the name of each important disease has its own emotional colour, not necessarily very closely equivalent to the real importance of the disease. One has only to run over in one's mind the names 'plague', 'leprosy' and 'influenza' to realize this. Perhaps of them all yellow fever is the most vividly coloured by associations. There has been something grimly romantic about its story from its first appearance, when it seemed to rise like a miasma from the overcrowded stinking holds of the slave ships in Barbados in 1647.

For two and a half centuries, yellow fever held possession of the Spanish Main, slaying English, Spanish and Carib, soldier, buccaneer and merchant alike, but strangely sparing the negro slaves. In time there grew up a local population in the West Indies which seemed to be immune to its attacks but almost every newcomer had to face its peril. At times yellow fever spread widely over all subtropical North and South America, on several occasions causing severe epidemics in the southern United States. On the other side of the Atlantic was the west coast of Africa, the home alike of yellow fever and of the slaves with whom it had travelled to America. Here also the disease, hardly noticed by the native inhabitants, played havoc amongst Europeans and, with malaria and dysentery, was responsible for the evil reputation of the country as the white man's grave. From the west coast it spread northward at irregular intervals, reaching the Mediterranean countries more than once. Portugal suffered particularly severely about 100 years ago.

The same flavour of grim romance hangs round the story of the unravelling of its problems by modern science. The work of the American Army Commission, which showed how the disease could be prevented, has often been described. It was a heroic business. At that time no animal was known to be susceptible to the disease, and all experiments had to be carried out on human volunteers. They tried to work with milder strains of the disease, and most of the volunteers came through safely, but three paid the final penalty. The Commission proved three things conclusively: first, that yellow fever was carried by one particular type of mosquito (*Aedes aegypti*); secondly, that the patient's blood could infect the mosquito only during the first three or four days of illness; and thirdly, that the mosquito was not capable of infecting other human beings until ten or twelve days after its feeding on yellow fever blood. This knowledge was sufficient to show how to eliminate yellow fever from any city or town. The task was made simpler by the habits of the mosquito involved. It is a house-haunting mosquito that seldom flies away from any dwelling where it has once fed. By eliminating the breeding places of the mosquitoes, by shielding yellow fever patients from their bites, and by rigid measures to destroy at once all mosquitoes in any dwelling where a patient had become infected, yellow fever could be eliminated. In practice, yellow fever is the easiest of all diseases to deal with by public health measures, and its elimination from the West Indies and the more accessible regions of Central America was accomplished in an extraordinarily short space of time. All this was done without any knowledge as to the nature of the germ responsible for the disease.

This was discovered only in 1929. Yellow fever had shown increased activity on the west coast of Africa, and a group of American and English scientists, financed by the Rockefeller Foundation, undertook a study of the outbreak. Their first task was to seek an animal which was susceptible to the disease and for the first time the Indian rhesus monkey was tested. It proved highly susceptible, and with this discovery it became possible to use animals instead of human volunteers for yellow fever experiments. There was still danger enough in the work, however, and Stokes, the English member of the group, died of the disease just after their great discovery was made. It was soon found that the disease was due to a filterable virus, not to a spirochaete or to a bacterium, both of which types of microorganism had been incriminated by other investigators. Noguchi, a famous Japanese bacteriologist at the Rockefeller Institute, had some years previously announced that a spirochaete was the cause of yellow fever. The new work seemed to undermine his conclusions completely, and Noguchi also came to West Africa to retest his theories. It is one of the great ironies of science that both Noguchi and his collaborator died of yellow fever soon after they had started their investigations in the Gold Coast.

The West African period, 1927–30, was the end of the heroic days of yellow fever investigation. Nowadays all workers with the virus have been artificially immunized, and are as resistant to the disease as a West African negro. Yellow fever research is now no more dangerous to those who undertake it than any other branch of scientific investigation. With the discovery that the disease was due to a virus capable of infecting monkeys, the Rockefeller Foundation initiated a large-scale international investigation of yellow fever. Soon after this was begun a method of producing the disease in mice was discovered, and with this cheap and convenient animal available, work on an even larger scale became possible. Since 1931, when this extension of laboratory work became possible, all the major problems of yellow fever have been solved in principle, and great steps taken towards its control.

We may first briefly recapitulate what was said in an earlier chapter about the processes of infection, recovery and immunity in yellow fever. The virus is injected into the blood by the bite of an infected mosquito and sets up an infection primarily in the liver. The virus multiplies enormously, and at the height of the disease a single drop of blood contains many millions of virus particles. This flood of foreign material in the blood provides a very urgent stimulus to the antibody-producing mechanism, and if the patient is to recover, antibody appears within three or four days from the beginning of the fever. This is not enough at first to get rid of the virus from the blood, but it is sufficient to prevent infection of any yellow fever mosquito which may bite the patient. When recovery is complete, the blood contains large amounts of antibody, and this persists in only very slowly diminishing amount throughout the life of the person. Second attacks of yellow fever are practically unheard of. If an individual has once been infected with the yellow fever virus his blood will contain antibody that can be recognized by a simple laboratory test requiring the inoculation of half a dozen mice. As soon as this mouse test had been devised large-scale surveys were undertaken over most of the world to determine where people were being infected with yellow fever. It was soon found that in addition to people who knew that they had had yellow fever a great many others possessed antibody in their blood who had certainly never had a recognizable attack of the disease. All the 'positive' bloods, however, came from two well-defined regions: tropical Africa south of the Sahara; Central America and the Amazon basin in South America. Largely as a result of these surveys there emerged an understanding of what, from our point of view, are two of the most interesting features of yellow fever, the frequent occurrence of infection without symptoms and the existence of jungle yellow fever.

Experience in Cuba, Panama and the coastal cities of Brazil had shown that it was easy enough to rid such areas of classical yellow fever by concentrating an attack on the *Aedes* mosquito. The growing hope that the disease could be finally eradicated from the world, however, received a check when in 1932 there occurred a disconcerting epidemic in a country district of Brazil where no *Aedes* mosquitoes were concerned. In the next year or two isolated cases or small epidemics of what came to be called 'jungle yellow fever' were detected in widely separated parts of tropical America. The same virus is involved but the epidemiology of jungle yellow fever is wholly different from that of the classical disease of tropical ports. The virus is maintained in a cycle involving jungle monkeys, marmosets and howler monkeys particularly, and mosquitoes that feed on the animals of the tree-tops. A very similar situation occurs in the rain-forests of central Africa. In both countries there is an inexhaustible reservoir of yellow fever unrelated to human habitations and not amenable to attempts at eradication. The jungle disease in South America most commonly affects timber cutters and others working in the forests, but if someone infected in the jungle falls ill in a town where there are *Aedes* mosquitoes an epidemic may be initiated there. In Africa the most puzzling feature of yellow fever is the vast extent of country in which antibodies indicating past infection are very common but the clinical disease extremely rare or unknown. It seems that the negro races have some innate resistance to the virus, but possibly more important is the relative insusceptibility of children. As in so many other diseases, first infection in childhood is usually a mild fever with no distinguishing features which lays down a lasting immunity. Through all its history yellow fever has spared those born in the regions of its greatest prevalence. It is significant that the only recent great epidemic of yellow fever in Africa, the 1943 epidemic in the Nubian mountains, occurred in a region just at the edge of the area in which the disease is endemic.

The second phase of yellow fever control has been to devise means of protecting people from infection by jungle mosquitoes and of ensuring that no secondary epidemics spread by *Aedes* can develop. The first requirement is knowledge of the local situation. Are people being infected with the virus are some dying of yellow fever without a definite diagnosis being made? Tests of blood, particularly of samples taken from children, will usually supply the needed information as to the prevalence of the virus. In South America very valuable information is obtained by the use of the viscerotome. This is a specially designed instrument by which an unskilled orderly can take a specimen of liver from the body of any person dying of a short-lasting illness. If death was from yellow fever, changes in the liver will be visible on appropriate examination under the microscope.

In any area where the disease is endemic the essential control measures are first to immunize the population and secondly to eradicate *Aedes* mosquitoes from the district. In the early days, it was found adequate to reduce the number of mosquitoes to say 1 per cent of their normal abundance. That would soon stop any further cases of yellow fever and in the absence of any jungle reservoir of the virus it did not seem to matter much if the mosquitoes gradually regained their former numbers. With new methods of dealing with mosquito breeding, the present-day aim is nothing less than the elimination of *Aedes* from the two Americas. At the end of 1949 Bolivia was free of the mosquito as well as more than 90 per cent of the vast area of Brazil.

Modern methods of immunization against yellow fever make use of a strain of living virus called 17D which, on injection under the skin, gives a wholly symptomless immunizing infection. The principle is quite similar to Jenner's vaccination against smallpox: in fact, there is a very practical method used in French Colonial Africa by which natives are vaccinated simultaneously against smallpox and yellow fever with a mixture of vaccine lymph and attenuated yellow fever virus. It was found early in the experimental study of yellow fever that virus grown in the mouse brain and passed repeatedly from mouse to mouse gradually lost its power to produce the fatal liver disease in monkeys. By transfer through tissue cultures and then growth in chick embryos the virus became even less virulent and in this way the immunizing strain 17D was produced. The vaccine was progressively improved, and its use has been gradually extended to larger and larger groups of people. The complication of 'serum jaundice' that marred its wide-scale use by the American Army in 1942 has already been mentioned. That difficulty has long since been eliminated, and the vaccine is used very extensively in infected areas—something like seven million people in South America had been immunized by the end of 1949. By international agreement yellow fever immunization is now compulsory for all persons travelling through the endemic regions of Africa and America.

It seems appropriate that the last disease to be discussed should be the one which provides the outstanding example of the successful application of the ecological approach to infectious disease that has been the central theme running through this book. The story of yellow fever is an illuminating example of the effectiveness of biological research when it is supported by adequate finance, skilled direction and the goodwill of peoples and governments. It is significant that by far the greatest share in the planning and support of the work was taken by the International Health Division of the Rockefeller Foundation. For this achievement alone the Foundation might well claim to be the most effective organization yet designed for the well-being of mankind. If its growing interest in the problems of psychology and human conflict, of population levels and social organization, can lead to similarly effective study and control in those fields we may be able to hope a little more confidently for the future of civilization. Nowhere else can one see power, whether political or monetary, so effectively linked to the methods of science and directed not to the increase or maintenance of power but to human welfare.

In a wholly different direction we can point to all the incidental results that have emerged from the medical, ecological and social studies that have been primarily concerned with the prevention of yellow fever. They are specially noteworthy in the way success in dealing with so important a disease brought the power of the ecological approach to the notice of all biological scientists. One might almost say that it was this success which made ecology respectable. The work, too, opened a new world of the viruses carried by mosquitoes, particularly in the tropics. There are now more than sixty named varieties of these Arborviruses, many of which are rather closely related to yellow fever virus. The first to be isolated was that subsequently called Murray Valley encephalitis virus, in Australia in 1918, but all the others came after the isolation of yellow fever virus in 1928. Most were actually obtained as by-products of the search for yellow fever virus in Africa and tropical America. Some are responsible for important human diseases like dengue, and some types of encephalitis, others are still 'viruses in search of a disease'. Perhaps the chief significance of the group will be to offer clues to the general nature of virus evolution and perhaps hints as to how new virus diseases of man may appear in the future.

EPILOGUE

CHAPTER XXVI

NEW DISEASES AND THE OUTLOOK FOR THE FUTURE

In 1961 the broad outlines of the picture of infectious disease are fairly clear. In the first place it is evident that many of the important diseases of the past can be eliminated with relative ease by simple applications of hygienic measures. The organisms of typhoid fever, cholera and dysentery, we can suspect, are rather crudely adapted parasites which can only find opportunity to flourish when there is gross opportunity for contamination of food with faecal matter. Plague and typhus vanish when rats are kept under control and people are taught how to rid themselves of lice. There are specialized and effective ways of dealing with another group of diseases not amenable to simple hygienic control. Immunization is highly effective against smallpox, diphtheria, poliomyelitis and yellow fever. Prophylaxis or early treatment, after exposure, with penicillin, atebrin or other drugs has made it possible to prevent or minimize infection with the two important venereal diseases as well as with malaria, scrub typhus and a number of rarer conditions. Where disease is conveyed by an insect carrier and the process of transmission is clearly understood it is virtually always possible to eliminate the disease. Since the end of the war in 1945 indigenous malaria has been banished from continental United States, from Sardinia and from Cyprus, while the threat to Egypt from the spread of the most dangerous malaria-carrier in Africa (*Anopheles gambiae*) has been removed.

Neither malaria nor yellow fever will vanish overnight, but both have lost their terrors, probably for ever.

One might almost say that a new ecological situation has

been reached for major communities in which technical facilities and social discipline are not destroyed by war or other disaster. The essence of that situation seems to be that only those microorganisms of disease will survive which find it possible to infect healthy human beings in the minute amounts that can be transferred from infected to susceptible individuals under civilized conditions. In technical terms the microorganisms must be able to infect intact mucous surfaces in minimal dose. There are two main possibilities of transfer, by droplet infection from the mouth and nose and by the transfer in one way or another of minute amounts of faecal material. It has been usual in recent years to suggest that the disappearance of cholera, typhoid fever and dysentery means that the intestinal route of infection is no longer of any importance. Studies on the prevalence of thread worms in children, on poliomyelitis and the Coxsackie viruses and on mild dysentery due to the Sonne bacillus, make it clear that this opinion must be modified. Minor faecal contamination, particularly on children's fingers, is widespread and a very important potential factor in epidemic disease.

What must be recognized is that different types of pathogenic organism differ greatly in the ease with which they can initiate infection. This is quite a different quality from their virulence which is essentially their capacity to produce damage once infection has been initiated. Every professional bacteriologist knows that if he uses normal precautions he will be very unlucky if he suffers a laboratory infection from typhoid, diphtheria or tubercle bacilli. Yet despite the use of exactly the same precautions if he works with the organisms responsible for Q fever, Malta fever or tularaemia he is almost certain to become infected within a few months. If we had enough information we could probably express the difference in the form that if one living organism of typhoid fever is taken into the body the chance of its initiating infection is 1 in 1000 but if one Q fever *Rickettsia* lodges in the lung there is 1 chance in 3 that it initiates infection. The numbers are of course pure guesses, but the ratio between the two may be nearly correct.

The diseases which we may have to face in the future will be those that are capable of initiating infection in minimal dose. And since bacterial infections are, with unimportant exceptions, amenable to treatment with one or other of the new drugs our real problems are likely to be concerned with virus diseases. It is only within the virus diseases that nature is likely to engender any novelty in infectious disease. 'New diseases' in the past have nearly always been virus diseases. Almost certainly the English Sweats of the Tudor period was due to a virus, so was the 'Spanish' influenza of 1918–19 and the encephalitis lethargica that was first noted in Roumania in 1917 and had virtually disappeared by 1930. And we must not forget that poliomyelitis is a new disease that never produced epidemics before 1890.

In the future we can feel certain that respiratory infections will persist, mostly trivial but playing their part as in the past in causing deaths amongst the old in winter. In some years influenza will be more severe than in others and it is unlikely that methods of immunization will ever be able to keep quite in step with its changing antigenic character. What has been, may be again. In 1957, as we have seen, a new pandemic of influenza moved over the whole world. It caused many deaths but these were to be measured in thousands instead of millions and on the whole the episode gave us confidence that we need not greatly fear that any pandemic as lethal as that of 1918 will arise in the future. A few years ago I wondered whether deliberate work on the genetics of influenza virus in the laboratories might not be able to produce a virus intrinsically lethal for man. A careful comparison of the 1918 and 1957 pandemics has made me more optimistic. Nature, working with 2600 million susceptible subjects, has far greater opportunities to sort out lethal variants should they arise. In the present-day world, I doubt whether anything worse than 1957 is going to arise from natural processes nor do I think that any attempt to devise a hypervirulent strain of influenza virus as a weapon of war would ever be successful.

In the decade of the 1950's between twenty and thirty new viruses responsible for respiratory infection in man were identified. Amongst them variation and selection are constantly at work and it is possible, even probable, that one new virus capable of producing symptoms emerges each year. It is equally possible that some well-known microorganism will develop unsuspected virulence and ease of transmission. So far no man-to-man transmission of infections due to *Rickettsiae* or the psittacosis-like viruses has been observed as an epidemic phenomenon. But two episodes may be mentioned to show how narrow may be the line that keeps some strains from becoming the source of spreading epidemics. In Louisiana a hunter went down with a severe fever almost certainly contracted from some bird or animal. From him there started a chain of infection involving nurses, doctors, patients and visitors that in all involved nineteen people, eight of whom died. The virus was found to be closely related to that of psittacosis. In a London hospital a man died of an unexpected pneumonia; a fortnight later a nurse who had looked after the body and two pathologists who performed a post-mortem examination came down with Q fever. Both the germs in question have a bad reputation in laboratories and both can certainly infect human beings when inhaled in very small numbers. Probably the reason that they do not give rise to infectious disease in the ordinary sense is that the organisms do not reach the saliva except when the patient is extremely sick. Under such circumstances only sick-bed attendants will run the risk of infection. A strain of either of these organisms only needs to change slightly so that infectious material can pass to the saliva while the patient is not too sick to go about his business, and a new infectious disease would be born.

Measles, mumps, chickenpox and german measles seem to be very old-established and stable diseases that are not likely to change much in character either for better or for worse.

There is little to suggest either that much would be gained by trying to prevent them or that any effective and practicable method of preventing them is likely to be developed. The problem of poliomyelitis in communites with a rising standard of living and of hygiene has already been discussed. The discovery that there are at least thirty viruses of the same general quality as polio virus, which may be present at one time or another in the human intestine, provides a possible source of new diseases affecting the nervous and muscular systems. There is already evidence that a variety of minor infectious diseases can be produced by some types of these primarily intestinal viruses. One of these has been known for a long time as Bornholm disease—it was first observed on the Danish island of that name. The symptoms are predominantly of muscular pain and tenderness, particularly in the region of the diaphragm. The condition usually subsides in a day or two but the early symptoms are often so marked that a diagnosis of acute appendicitis may be made and the patient subjected to an unnecessary operation. Amongst the others there are several diseases with fever and rash of the same general quality as the common childhood diseases. There is a type of sore throat with numerous small blisters round the pharynx and several sorts of fever with signs of irritation at the surface of the brain—meningo-encephalitis. In general all these are trivial conditions, but it might only need a minor mutation of one or other to produce a disease as disturbing, say, as the English Sweats. Similar possibilities hold that one of these anonymous intestinal viruses may one day emerge as a fourth type of polio virus. In 1957 Russian virologists isolated a virus from three cases of typical polio and, since it could produce paralysis on injection into monkeys and was unrelated to the three standard types, they quite legitimately labelled it Poliovirus Type IV. This is not necessarily modified by the fact that subsequently it was shown that this virus had been known for some time as Coxsackie A7. It is even rather likely that when the whole world's children are satisfactorily vaccinated against Polioviruses I, II and III, we shall observe that a high proportion of the few cases of polio that appear will be identified as due to one of the anonymous but already known viruses.

Every general statement about the future of infectious disease must carry the implicit qualification that it is made on the assumption that no new world war occurs. With the menace of atomic and biological war already facing us the future may well see a renaissance of infectious disease in new and perhaps uncontrollable forms. War is part of the human social tradition and no realistic consideration of the future of disease can afford to neglect its possible influence. In a hundred years of military history we start in the days of the Crimea when infection was the main cause of wastage in armies and when wounds were fatal for the most part because of subsequent infection in hospital. The advances of preventive medicine and surgery in the second half of the nineteenth century were incorporated into military hygiene and the care of the wounded, and in many ways the experience of war has helped to stimulate discovery and application in these fields. The mosquito transmission of yellow fever was discovered by United States Army doctors seeking the answer to the main military problem of a campaign in Cuba. Typhoid fever in the South African War stimulated Almroth Wright to the introduction of typhoid vaccination. The war of 1914–18 showed great improvements in health services, and in the Second World War deaths from infectious disease and from wound infection were reduced to a small fraction of the number killed by direct enemy action. In any third world war it is hard to believe that we shall not see the converse results of eighty years of study of the processes of infection by pathogenic microorganisms. As in every other field, the advance of knowledge merely places in the hands of men with power more effective means of obtaining what they desire. The more we know about the nature of virulence, the significance of immunological reactions, the mechanisms of variation and recombination in microorganisms and the mode of action of antibacterial drugs, the more effectively we can prevent or cure infectious disease if we desire to do so. But we can also use this increasing knowledge in ways never dreamt of in nature to fashion sooner or later a potent weapon of mass destruction.

It is no secret that active research on the military use of disease-producing bacteria has been in progress since early in the Second World War. Much of the work done in British and American laboratories has provided results of great interest to bacteriologists generally and has been openly published in the technical journals. Other countries have not admitted the existence of bacteriological warfare research within their boundaries but obviously every military group in the world must be deeply concerned with the topic in one way or another. The published papers indicate that the anthrax bacillus and botulinus toxin were being closely studied in 1945–6, while some attention was also being paid to the organisms of tularaemia and psittacosis. Any experienced bacteriologist will know that there would be great technical difficulties in producing and using dangerous bacteria in war, but he would also realize that most of the difficulties are only technical ones. How far workers in military establishments for micro-biological warfare have succeeded in overcoming these technical difficulties will probably not be known to the public until a micro-biological weapon is used in actual war. It would be futile to attempt any guesses as to the species of organism now being studied or the methods being developed for their dissemination. There are many different possibilities that can be imagined, but the essence of the matter is that it is physically possible to produce in a room a thin mist of bacteria so that any animal that takes a few breaths in that room will die unless it is treated subsequently with an appropriate drug. To produce similar conditions over the large volume of air within and around an enemy city is physically possible and in view of past experience it would be foolish to count on moral, psychological, technical, industrial and military difficulties stopping the achievement of that possibility. The one certainty is that every year the technical difficulties will diminish.

A ton of anthrax spores would contain about 10^{18} individual spores. If these could be uniformly distributed in a volume of air six or seven miles across and extending 300 feet upwards from the ground each litre of air (about one deep breath) would contain about a hundred thousand spores. There are a number of microorganisms which induce fatal infection when less than ten individual organisms are introduced into a susceptible experimental animal. Those calculations in one sense are fantastically misleading. Nothing approaching such uniformity of distribution could be produced under the most ideal conditions. But they do suggest that even the very inefficient distribution over a city of the amount of bacteria that could be carried in a single aeroplane might produce a startlingly large toll of illness and death.

It is a platitude nowadays to agree that a third world war may mean the end of civilization and the untimely death by direct and indirect means of hundreds of millions of human beings.

Public discussion has been concerned almost wholly with the use of atomic weapons and particularly with the H-bomb as the major weapon of destruction and extermination. In 1961 there was a general feeling that a phase of effective mutual deterrence had been reached that might at least postpone the outbreak of nuclear war until other countries than U.S.A. and U.S.S.R. had accumulated the necessary weapons. Limited wars to be fought with 'conventional' arms are envisaged as likely to go on indefinitely, but very little public discussion has taken place about the 'intermediate' mass weapons of bacteriological and chemical warfare.

It may be that the extreme reticence of military and political leaders to mention such weapons offers a grain of hope. The claim by North Koreans that biological warfare was being used against them in 1951–2 was probably baseless, but it had a very significant effect on public opinion in Asia and perhaps had an unconscious influence on Western thought. War is a traditional method of human behaviour but the use of poisons and microbes is not part of the tradition. There has always been war and wars have always up to the present been fought according to a traditional pattern constantly evolving but never showing any sharp discontinuity. There has always been a hierarchy of leadership and the inculcation of loyalty and discipline. Weapons have evolved continuously from axe and spear to sword and arrow, crossbow and catapult gave way to firearms, the horse and the war-canoe to battleship, tank and bombing plane. Ball and shrapnel were replaced by high explosive and the proximity fuse, and now the atomic bomb and the intercontinental ballistic missile brings the tradition up to date.

But the use of biological warfare is an absolute novelty, a complete break in the tradition of war as an extension of personal combat. As Vannevar Bush has pointed out, there is bound to be an intense resistance on the part of the statesmen and generals to the use of such a method, not necessarily from any moral feelings but simply because of the intrinsic human resistance to any violent break with an existing social pattern. Yet if world war comes again the possession and effective use by one side of a weapon that the other lacks will be likely to turn the balance. The fact that on both sides of our divided world responsible men must be thinking out the implications of biological warfare offers a remote and slender hope. It is simply that the men with power will be forced to think of the human species in biological terms.

Anyone who has spent his whole professional life in the study of infectious disease in man can hardly avoid applying the ecological approach that has proved so successful in his own field of study to other aspects of the human situation. It is possible and within the necessary limits scientifically legitimate to look at man simply as a mammalian species subject to the same conditions as other mammals. Essentially this has been the attitude to infectious disease that has been adopted throughout all the preceding chapters. The same ecological approach can obviously be applied to the pressing problems of population and food supply, and there is a growing interest in the possibility of an objective biological approach to many of the basic occasions of human conflict.

From a biologist's viewpoint history is an account of the increase and decrease of human populations and of their movements from one part of the world to another. The rest is mere incident. If this is true the dominating factor in human history is something that hardly ever appears in the books, the level of infant mortality at different times and places. In all unsophisticated populations the birth-rate runs at about fifty per 1000 per annum. If the expectation of life is taken as that of modern western democracies, sixty to sixty-five years, such a birth-rate will double the population every twenty-five to thirty years. In the past, infectious disease and limited food supply saw to it that mortality, especially infantile mortality, kept nearly in step with the birth-rate. The main political problems of the present and the immediate future spring from the fact that in many parts of the world the prevention of infectious disease has allowed population growth up to or beyond the means of subsistence. There are many other human problems of the same general quality, ecological problems concerned with the necessity that a species must reach an equilibrium with its environment. One way or another, means must be found by which the population of a given region does not increase beyond the level that the region in question can support from its continuing resources. An equally important corollary is that the irreplaceable resources of the world must be conserved until effective substitutes are in sight that do not deplete capital resources. Conservation is sound ecology.

Most of the ostensible and some of the real causes of war lie in this field of interaction between population levels and natural resources whether for food production or for the provision of raw material for industry. A broad ecological approach is the only answer.

The other side to human conflict is, as we all know, 'human nature', selfishness, aggression and desire for power on the one hand, loyalty to individuals, groups or ideas on the other. These things may seem to lie right outside of the province of science, but one of the most interesting developments of modern biology, the comparative study of animal behaviour, is making it clear that 'human nature' is by no means confined to human beings. It is not too much to say that all the basic elements of human conflict are visible in animal behaviour. Anyone who reads the scientific literature, now fairly extensive, on 'peck-orders' in fowls and corresponding hierarchies of dominance in other vertebrates, will certainly begin to look at human problems from a rather different angle. This is no place to discuss the findings of comparative psychology, but perhaps one observation from the fowl-yard should be quoted. It is simply that altruistic behaviour is never observed except where domination is complete. That is a principle which, appropriately refined to human circumstance, is applicable to most of the situations which keep men awake in the small hours of the morning.

There is only one justification for the intrusion of such ideas on human conflict into a discussion on the natural history of infectious disease. Not so long ago it would have been inconceivable that anyone should even attempt to describe disease in terms based on scientific observation and experiment. Even as late as 1880 the most learned historian of disease in England, Creighton, flatly refused to believe in the micro-organismal theory of infectious disease. Today every individual who can read a newspaper has a crude but practically useful background knowledge of bacteriology. The housewife preserves fruit by heat sterilization, insists on pasteurized milk and accepts a ritual of boiling the baby's bottle. The soldier accepts his innumerable immunizing injections as a matter of course and is liable to be over-confident that a timely 'shot' of penicillin will eliminate any risk of venereal disease. The essentials have filtered down from the research laboratories through medical practitioners and the press until they have been incorporated reasonably effectively into the social pattern of our times.

Similarly, a working knowledge of the bases of nutrition is available to everyone, and as a result our children are the best nourished and probably the healthiest since civilization began.

Fever, famine and war are the three traditional scourges of mankind, and the method which has banished the first two is the only one which conceivably could banish the third. An objective scientific sociology drawing its fundamental ideas from the *experimental* study of animal behaviour and analysing social phenomena in the light of these ideas is in the making. All the techniques of modern statistics are being applied in an attempt to extract from observations on human phenomena conclusions as valid as could be looked for if controlled experiment were possible. It is probable indeed that there is already available sufficient factual material to allow a clear picture of the problems of human conflict to be given at the biological level. There must be some way in which an account of that material can be given which is acceptable at the intellectual level to all intelligent people. Some day someone will write a natural history of human conflict built up from a solid experimental basis of work on comparative behaviour in birds and animals and adequate objective non-political surveys and analyses of actual human behaviour. Books of that type could be written with the same biological approach and the same objective honesty as can be found now in a dozen different popular or semi-popular accounts of other aspects of the human situation. Perhaps the diffusion of such ideas would do more than anything else to develop an atmosphere within which a peaceful development of civilization might be possible.

The control of infectious disease marks the greatest human success yet achieved in the control of our environment to our own benefit. The success as we have seen is virtually complete. There is still great scope for the application of available knowledge in countries which have not reached a Western standard of hygiene. In the process many local problems will have to be solved before administrative action can be successful in applying accepted principles for the elimination of disease, but basically new methods and materials will not be needed. Research in microbiology at the fundamental level can do little more than help in a slow asymptotic approach to perfection in the prevention and control of infection. Nevertheless, at the present time research in the fundamental biology of microorganisms is more active and productive than ever before. Not one-thousandth part of this activity is consciously directed toward the use of microorganisms in war, but it is a disturbing thought that if this flood of new knowledge is to have any important impact on human affairs it will not be by the prevention and cure of infectious disease. If it is to emerge from the laboratories and the libraries into the main current of human activities it must be in some new direction. It may be that biochemical studies will lead to a vast increase in the use of microorganisms for the synthesis of substances that are outside of the province of the organic chemist. Yeasts and bacteria can synthesize protein from simple materials more rapidly than the green plant or the farm animal, and an important source of protein for an over-populated world may be found thereby. The new science of microbial genetics offers promise in that direction, but when applied to pathogenic microorganisms it has at least equal potentialities for the production of organisms which will kill as required. In Australia the virus of myxomatosis between 1951 and 1959 brought the rabbit pest down to a controllable level before biological processes made its further use almost ineffective. In the first two years, its power to kill the rabbit without harm to any other species was demonstrated with fantastic success. Other possibilities for the elaboration of new uses of microbiological knowledge to human benefit must arise from time to time. But as long as the possibility of the irresponsible use of power persists, we cannot escape the conviction that the steady advance of experimental microbiology will progressively increase the likelihood that effective biological weapons of mass destruction, sabotage and assassination can be produced.

This is a situation that must be faced. While war is possible, the development of microbiological weapons will go on and if they are perfected they will be used as seems expedient when war occurs. Apart from the fact that they represent a break in the traditional techniques of warfare there is no reason to consider them more inhuman than any other method of killing. Every legitimate argument against their use in war is equally an argument against the whole institution of war.

It cannot be too urgently stated that the advance of science is allowing the development of wholly unnatural modes of human domination and mass destruction—unnatural in the sense that they represent conditions never encountered in the course of human evolution. In the physical field no mammal before the last sixty years was ever exposed to penetrating radiation. Nor, except in small experiments in recent years had any mammalian species to face the impact of a pathogenic microorganism that had not evolved and been able to survive by natural processes. Perhaps in another field something equally unnatural is emerging in the new techniques of forced public confession and 'brain washing'. Somehow the use for human domination of nuclear reactions, artificially virulent and artificially disseminated microorganisms and control of thought and behaviour by unnatural methods, whether pharmacological or psychological, must be prevented. Unless this can be done the whole biological and social background to the human species is in danger of complete disorganization of a type so apart from any previous experience that nothing less than a new process of evolution will be needed before a healthy civilization again becomes possible.

Despite every discouragement, we must look forward to a continuation of the process of controlling the irresponsible use of all the sources of social power that has been the greatest contribution of the Anglo-Saxon peoples to civilization. Until that process reaches the stage where one world authority can compel the disarmament of any group that might forcibly challenge its ability to maintain peace, research on the military development of microbiological weapons will inevitably go on. In the process there will be interesting scientific developments which will be applicable to preventive medicine, particularly in regard to protection against the use of such weapons by the enemy. But these benefits will bear much the same relation to the killing power of the eventual weapon as the present use of radioactive isotopes in medicine bears to the proven lethality of the atomic bomb.

So we come to a strange and gloomy ending of this account of the natural history of infectious disease. Science having freed a large portion of the human race from every type of pestilence, and being potentially capable of doing it equally effectively for the rest, now stands poised to create new more lethal and more uncontrollable plagues than ever sprang from nature. The one star of hope in the gloom is that biological science, along with its development of this sinister power, is just as definitely pointing the way by which human conflict can be understood and, if we desire it fervently enough, controlled.

INDEX